D1074844

INTRODUCTION TO
RUMANIAN LITERATURE

Other books published in conjunction with
the Cultural Exchange Program between the
United States and Rumania:

EVENING TALES by Mihail Sadoveanu

TALES OF WAR by Mihail Sadoveanu

THE MUD-HUT DWELLERS by Mihail Sadoveanu

INTRODUCTION TO RUMANIAN LITERATURE

Edited by Jacob Steinberg

Foreword by Demostene Botez

TWAYNE PUBLISHERS, INC.
New York

Library of Congress Catalog Card Number: 66-16111

Manufactured in the United States of America

Printed by Profile Press, New York

Table of Contents

(Because this anthology is intended for the general reader who is not familiar with Rumanian accents, they have been omitted.)

Editor's Note

The editor is indebted to the critic* who observed in the course of a review of Romanian** titles which included *Evening Tales* and *Tales of War* by Mihail Sadoveanu: "These books . . . show strikingly how a country's history may be made more plainly intelligible to an outsider through its literature than when the approach . . . is limited to statistics and factual details. . . ." If a writer—even one so highly regarded and in tune with his countrymen as Sadoveanu—could provide such satisfactory insights, how much more valuable is a collection of representative writings by many pens? Mr. Demostene Botez, a veteran observer of the Romanian literary scene, points out in his Foreword that it requires no "searching analysis to gather from these pages the specific national features of the Romanian people as they emerge from the portrayal of the passions and thoughts of the heroes of these varied writings." It would appear then that this anthology may be recommended as a pleasurable and reliable way of getting acquainted with a people and their concerns.

Introduction to Rumanian Literature is the fourth of a series of books that have been published in conjunction with the cultural exchange program between the United States and Romania. In all instances the publisher made a selection from a wide choice of titles available to him in largely rough translation. It is gratifying to note critical approbation of the books that have appeared thus far. The present volume of prose selections will be followed by a similarly representative collection of poetry and drama and by translations of the individual works of leading Romanian writers.

The compilation is also part of the publisher's world literature program, one of the goals being the introduction of foreign writers of merit to American readers. The first steps of this program have already been taken and consist of a series of critical biographies—appreciations that assess the contribution of the world's leading writers, both past and present. More than twenty national literatures are being evaluated in this way. Some indication of the scope of the undertaking, in which both foreign and

---

* Aileen Pippett in *Saturday Review*, August 4, 1962.

** The spelling "Romania" rather than "Rumania" has recently been designated the preferred form. The anthology proper uses the older spelling, which could not be changed at this late date.

American scholars are participating, may be noted in the fact that the series devoted to American writers alone has already celebrated the publication of its 100th volume. Whenever representative writings of the authors surveyed are not generally available, it is the intention of the publisher to provide them in English translation, either in anthology form or as individual volumes. It is hoped that in this way a measure of international good will and understanding will result.

"The passions and thoughts of the heroes of these varied writings," to quote Mr. Botez again, will strike a familiar note with any American reader. He too knows from first-hand experience the heartbreak and the humor, for example, of three generations living in one household. His own matriarchs rule with as heavy a hand. The battles of the generations and the sexes, the impulse to tenderness, the dedication to social service, the heroism, the ugly and the beautiful—to catalogue but a bit of the varied literary landscape herein presented—are all part of the American scene. Indeed, one of the conclusions that emerges from a reading of this collection is that literature is preeminently a common ground, demonstrating how truly universal is the human condition. "Slice the bread of humanity as you will, the substance is the same," says the world of letters.

Preparations for this volume began in 1963 and involved editorial discussions both here and abroad. For meetings in Bucharest which permitted a frank and friendly exchange of views, the editor is indebted to arrangements made by Dr. Ovidiu Popescu of the Romanian Embassy in Washington. To Mr. Ion Blaga, Director of Editura Meridiane and his associates, with whom the editor discussed his views, and to Messrs. Dumitru Tranca, Virgil Craciun, Constantin Maciuca, and Ion Banuta, publishing dignitaries, the editor wishes to express appreciation for making his stay in Romania so memorable an experience.

There remains the pleasure of voicing the editor's appreciation to Professors Adrian Jaffe and Ralph M. Aderman, who, while Fulbright professors at the University of Bucharest, spent freely of their time and energies to further this project. They are not, however, responsible for the contents. This responsibility remains the editor's. Without the professional and personal participation of Romanian editors and translators working under the direction of Mr. Dan Baran, editor-in-chief of Editura Meridiane, Bucharest, this volume could not have been published. They supplied the translations and the biographical introductions to each selection. The editor wishes to record his gratitude to Mr. Baran and his associates for their many kindnesses.

Foreword

The American reader of this book will discover a distant shore washed by the foamy waters of the Black Sea and will learn something of the life of the people living in this land. For this is the first and foremost asset and aim of a foreign literature.

This volume contains sketches, short stories, and excerpts from novels written in the span of less than a century, ranging from Creanga's *Recollections from Childhood* and including the works of the youngest prose writers of our days.

These selections, each with its own vision of life, reflect in artistic form landscapes, characters, and customs bearing the specific traits of the life led by the Romanian people, a people settled along the northern bank of the Danube and astride the ranges of the Carpathians. The universal significance of their contribution resides in the authenticity of the life they have endeavored to render.

The literary genres have been selected to give a graphic and wide-ranging picture of the original features of a nation, to render the complexity of the people's way of life, their thoughts, feelings, and aspirations. The subject matter of each of these works is rich in national realities, being the expression of the soul of the Romanian people and the mirror of their concepts of life.

The reader needs no searching analysis to gather from these pages the specific national features of the Romanian people as they emerge from the portrayal of the passions and thoughts of the heroes of these varied writings. All the works collected in this anthology are pervaded by this distinctive national spirit; and yet two names stand out—that of Ion Creanga and Mihail Sadoveanu—as the writers who have rendered with the most colorful vividness the specific Romanian ethos.

Typical fragments of life, horizontal or vertical cross-sections of the pattern of living of the Romanian people, these pages will aid the American reader to obtain a limited, yet fair and revealing picture of this nation and land, perhaps entirely unknown to him before. His outlook will thus have been enriched by the revelation of new facets, new characters, and a new experience.

The first thing a reader is entitled to demand of any literature is that it afford pleasure and knowledge. In his incursion into world literature, the reader will this time meet the gift of a newcomer, a work new and original.

The present book is for us an initial stage in the development of the world-wide interchange of knowledge and literary values; a fraction of the artistic creation of the Romanian people thus becomes known, adding the specific national genius of our country to the fund of world literature, which is, in sum, "the totality of the most outstanding national creations."

The translation of literary works from one language into another creates a spiritual space, a spiritual universe, in which the nations address each other through the voices of their poets and writers. Thus is paved the way to a dialogue between nations, a sharing of common riches and an exchange of gifts selected from the treasures of the mind.

In this way the gates of the golden-domed fane of world literature open to works originally written in languages of limited circulation. To gain the right of admission, however, these works must fulfil two conditions: they must contain a vivid testimony of the specific national genius and breathe at the same time the deepest humanism. For it is only this profound interest in human ideals and the portrayal of a genuine national culture, raised to highest artistic excellence, that can ensure the world-wide success of a literary writing. These two elements are the begetters of life and fancy, the pollen that guarantees literary efflorescence.

Romanian classical and contemporary prose, closely bound to the realities of national life, bears a profound national seal. Each of the writers reproduced in the present anthology mirrors, in his own way—through the coloring prism of his soul—the most typical and relevant features of the Romanian realities in their multifarious aspects.

The interest in human ideals and aspirations has likewise constituted the constant golden fund of Romanian literature, both classical and contemporary. Humanity is, as literary history has proved, more salient and powerful a trait in the literary heritage of nations with an adverse historical past. The history of the Romanian people is fraught with hardships and trials. Suffice to mention the 500 years of vassalage to Turkish rule. This life of struggle, adversity, and shattered aspirations found its echo in the oral folk legends and stories from which cultured literature gradually emerged.

This historically recent genesis has marked Romanian literature, in contrast to Western literary production, with an original stamp, a popular character, which at times may appear "exotic" but constantly breathes an air of freshness, sincerity, and strength of feeling. This coarse-grained, somewhat crude approach, with a direct artistic expression, stripped of the artifices of an art seeking forced originality, and free of what may be called "literaturism," is bound to rouse the attention and interest of the American reader.

The foreign reader, accustomed to stylized parks with mown and trimmed lawns, will here meet nature in its unadulterated rusticity. Though this volume of Romanian prose may be the first glimpse he has had of some original aspects of the past and present life of a nation in Eastern Europe, it will not be its "exoticism" that will retain his gaze, but the deep impression of naturalness, of genuine feeling, of man's undisguised response to the forces of life.

There is an element of "exoticism" conspicuous and arresting in Romanian prose, but this feature does not stem from the strangeness of surroundings or characters, but rather from the deep impression of true life and genuine experience rendered with utmost frankness. It is a literature drawn from life, often from its very core. Its keynote is spontaneity, simplicity, and straightforward, unvarnished portrayal of life.

The new offshoots of cultured literature have risen from the century-old roots of folklore, inheriting their vigor and power of endurance—just as in nature a grafted species survives and evolves thanks to the sap drained from its time-hardened stock.

This evolution from folklore is manifest in Romanian literature in its general atmosphere, in some of its artistic forms, and in its challenging spirit blended with humanity. In poetry, in particular, we can detect the thread of folklore weaving its way into cultured art, lending it its simple, unalloyed grace and sturdiness.

The Romanian classics, and to a lesser degree contemporary poets too, have drawn their themes from folklore, creating works of memorable value. The loftiest of Romanian poems, "Luccafarul" ("The Evening Star") written by Mihail Eminescu, the greatest lyrical poet of the Romanian people, is, in essence, a brilliant re-creation of a folk tale, enhanced with a symbolic universal significance, defining the destiny of a man of genius living in our world. The theme is akin to Lermontov's "Demon" and to Vigny's "Eloa."

The transition from folk to cultured literature and the inherent impact upon the latter has been a phenomenon common to the literary history of all nations. However, where the cultured literature is several centuries old, the traces of folk origin are barely detectable. Such is the case with most Western literatures.

The well of folklore in Western literature has gradually grown dry. And yet there is a popular heritage, evinced in the bias for "local color," stemming from folklore tradition. Few authors revealed—as Walt Whitman did—the deep bond uniting folk sources and "cultured," "elaborated" literature; most of them contented themselves merely to borrow their subjects and certain literary artifices from this traditional fountainhead.

From this folk origin—which has stamped Romanian literature with its dominant feature—have sprung forth its other specific traits. In the first place, its militant, national, and social character—a natural reaction of a people that suffered, for centuries on end, the oppression of a foreign inferior rule and of a political regime of flagrant social injustice. This literature—at the beginning anonymous and oral and in a later stage written—is the response of a nation struggling for its liberty and dignity. Such a literature always implied, and still does to this day, the writer's total participation in the life of the people. A literature bearing the characteristics of folklore origin might appear "exotic" to the American reader and its creative process may at times be difficult to appraise.

Situated in the Danube plain, the Romanian people in the course of their stormy history, in the days of the ancient invasions from the East and of later days of hardships, found shelter and safety either in the vast Baragan plain that Panait Istrati popularized throughout the world by his novel, *The Thistles of the Baragan,* or in the deep valleys of the Carpathian mountains. In all their moments of trial, nature was ever their kind and protective host. Even the outlaws—these "heyducks," romantic rebels against social injustice—hunted by the armed bands of the authorities found refuge in the same mountains and century-old forests which enveloped these fugitives in their folds of darkness and safety. This is the origin of the verse that recurs in folk poetry "Codrul frate cu romanul"—(The forest—the faithful brother of the Romanian . . .).

It is this aspect of the life of the Romanian that engendered his tender and all-pervading love of nature, so richly rendered in both folk and cultured Romanian literature. It is ever present in the verses of every Romanian poet and storyteller and plays a significant part in practically every novel. Naturally, folklore is the first to record the manifestations of this feeling (almost every folk verse contains the invocation "Frunza Verde"—Green leaf. . . .) while the ingenuity of the countryman led him to use the leaf as a musical instrument. This love for nature has been preserved to this day and is one of the dominant and specific features of Romanian cultured literature. Of all Romanian writers who have cherished this feeling, the one who sang the beauty of nature with unparalleled artistry and endowed it with a human, universal significance, linking the landscape of today with the vision of past ages and the beginning of biological life, is Mihail Sadoveanu—the great master of Romanian style and consummate poet of nature.

Nature, which was the constant guardian of the Romanian people, could not appear in Romanian literature as an indifferent, hostile force. On the contrary, in an inseparable symbiosis with man, nature participates, like a giant-like mythological being, in man's frame of mind and feeling; she welcomes him with light and birds' songs in his hours of joy and unleashes all the tempestuous forces of heaven in his hours of bane. The most beautiful and most profound folk ballad in Romanian literature, "Miorita," is worthy of study for its grandiose human vision.

Another characteristic feature of Romanian literature is a sense of balance. It results from man's awareness of his close bond with nature but also from the wisdom the Romanian people needed in order to be able to steer their course through the crags of their troubled history, surmounting the dangers with which they were confronted. A balanced judgment establishes the Romanian's relationship with nature, with people and with the world at large in every circumstance of his life—a profound earth-born sagacity. Hence the wealth of proverbs present in Romanian literature. Proverbs represent the unwritten code whereby the people pass judgment upon the world. The writers closest to the soul of the people convey their judgments in proverbs, just as the common man with his mind unadulterated, expresses his thoughts in sayings. In this respect Ion Creanga is undoubtedly the most representative. His proverbs reflect many of the distinctive traits of the Romanian people: irony, satire, humor, vividness of mind, ingenuity, intelligence, power of synthesis, and a forceful gift for pithy expression.

Although the foundation stones of Romanian literature were laid during the Romantic Age and many of the patterns of this literary current were adopted by the Romanian writers of those times, Romanian literature has avoided the verbal excesses of romanticism.

The great economic, social, and political changes that have taken place in the Socialist Republic of Romania have engendered a new literature consistent with its ideology and ideals, yet faithful to the heritage of classical literature with its specific national character. These transformations have stamped more clearly the essential features of Romanian literature. National independence and social liberation of the people have created a new climate in which the people reflect no longer, as in the past, their opposition to and protest against a social order based upon oppression, but their enthusiasm to share in building a new life. It is this novel climate that has bestowed upon contemporary Romanian literature its mark of optimism, confidence in the future and in the power of man. A tonic and spirited revolutionary, neo-romantic literature has thus come into being.

The American reader of this volume will discover in the works of the younger writers in this anthology the true sense of the new Romanian literature. He will thus be able to understand it by direct contact, more eloquently and truthfully than by any definition or passionate argument. He will also be able to assess the aesthetic value of these works, the lofty message they carry and, above all, their genuine humanity.

This is one more facet of Romanian literature linked with contemporary life. It is a picture, original and specific, of a socialist system displaying its achievements and enunciating its outlook on life and society. Even for those readers who do not favor such a social system, contemporary Romanian literature still affords a subject of interest, as it is able to provide true, unbiased insights. A literature inspired by these ideals offers the reader of any country in the world a new, authentic picture of life; it thereby makes an original contribution to the treasure store of world literature.

The humanistic trend in contemporary Romanian literature is organically linked with its social character.

Bearer of these two prerequisites—a specific national tradition and deep interest in human feelings and ideals—Romanian literature may rightly aspire to join the concert of world literature. Its artistic craftsmanship is called to smooth the path leading to the heart and soul of readers all over the world.

The universality of a literary work is dependent upon the linguistic possibility of world-wide dissemination. This can only be achieved by translations into foreign languages of wide circulation. Only in this new form can the autochthonous creation rouse an echo among the people of other countries, stimulate critical studies, define the peculiarity of its genius and be eventually incorporated in the commonwealth of world literature. In this respect, the present anthology is a modest token of the tribute paid by Romanian literature to world literature.

The universality of a national literature is also closely linked with the international contribution of that nation to the life and progress of the world community. The steadily increasing economic, political, and cultural contribution of Romania manifest in international conferences and congresses has roused the interest of many nations eager to gain a closer knowledge of the Romanian people.

Some of the names of the classical writers of Romania: Caragiale, Creanga, Eminescu, Sadoveanu, Rebreanu were known abroad also before—true, in restricted circles only. The international prestige of Romania, however, has today created the basis for a broader expansion of Romanian literature throughout the world. Today it is not only the works of reputed Romanian writers, accepted masters of our literature, that cross the country's borders; the creation of an ever increasing number of young writers accompany the works of their classical forerunners. . . .

We feel confident that Romanian literature has created works of genuine value, works that mirror the life of the Romanian people whose concepts of life and artistic vision are worthy of recognition.

* * *

The present anthology—an offering of the Romanian nation—cannot in its limited dimensions convey an all-embracing picture of the Romanian people nor a complete illustration of the potentialities of Romanian literature. Incomplete as it is, however, it contains in essence all the vital traits of the Romanian people.

We cherish the hope that this anthology will rouse the interest of the American reader for Romanian books, and that the other works of the authors of this collection and many more shall find their way onto the shelves of the private and public libraries in the United States.

This Foreword does not claim to be a survey of Romanian literature either; it is a brief letter of introduction presenting the Romanian people to the American reader.

The American reader, on laying down this book after having read its stories, will have the feeling that he has traveled to a distant country of which he was totally unaware and that he has gazed at landscapes and met people he had never seen before. Though no new Columbus, he will have discovered, however, crossing the Atlantic—eastwards this time—a land rich in beautiful scenery, with people leading lives fraught with struggles and victories and fired by ideals, people nurturing a true love for mankind and unbounded confidence in the power of man.

Should he succeed in discovering that, I shall be proud and happy.

DEMOSTENE BOTEZ
Member of the Academy of the Socialist Republic of Romania

Ion Creanga

(1837-1889)

In the gallery of Rumanian prose writers, Ion Creanga occupies a place as the foremost Rumanian storyteller and one of the great storytellers of world literature. He began his literary career late in life, prompted by Mihail Eminescu, to whom he was attached by a close bond of friendship.

Creanga is the author of tales ("The Mother with Three Daughters-in-Law" [1875], "The Goat and the Three Kids" [1875], "The Story of the Pig" [1876], "The Story of Stan Tryhard" [1877], "The Story of the White Moon" [1877], "Ivan Turbinca" [1878], and others) and of stories ("Old Nichifor Cotcarul" [1877], "Old Ion Roata and the Union" [1880]). His crowning work is his *Recollections from Childhood* (1880-82), in which, with poignant nostalgia, he evokes the village of his childhood, with its people and customs. As one of the fundamental works in Rumanian literature, *Recollections from Childhood* constitutes a monument of Rumanian lyrical and humorous prose—written with verve, optimism, and consummate artistic skill—blending caustic satire with the gayest vagaries of humor. A past master of the "oral" narrative style, Creanga enhances his stories with a wealth of proverbs, sayings, and images drawn from the inexhaustible fountain of folk wisdom. The characters created by Creanga in his stories are lifelike and genuine. Old Nichifor Cotcarul is the embodiment of the waggish, sharp-witted Moldavian peasant. Old Ion Roata represents the simple man with his thirst for justice, proud and bold in his revolt against boyar oppression. The same strong realistic vein also runs through his tales, the action of which is laid in the Rumanian countryside, while the personages and even the animals that populate his fictional world are live portraits of peasants of the Moldavian villages.

His delightful humor, the "orality" of his style, the sprightliness of his language, his fertile fantasy enriched with folklore, have led critics to label Ion Creanga the Rabelais of Rumanian literature. His works have been translated into numerous foreign languages.

Selections from *Recollections from Childhood*

I don't know how others may feel, but when I think of the place of my birth, of our home in Humulesti, of the fireplace pot to which mother used to tie a piece of string with balls of wool at the end of it so that cats played with them to distraction, of the whitewashed mantel of the fireplace, to which I used to cling when I first began to totter, of the stove on which I hid when we boys played hide-and-seek, and of other games and pastimes full of childish fun and charm, my heart even now seems to leap with joy. And Lord! how delightful it was then, for my parents as well as my brothers were all in good health and in the house there was plenty, and the boys and girls of the neighbors were always playing with us, and everything went as I wished, without a bit of unpleasantness, as if all the world were mine.

And I was as blithe as fine weather, and as carefree and wilful as the wind in a storm.

And sometimes when the sun was beginning to show itself from behind a cloud after a spell of rain, Mother, renowned for the wonders she could work, would say to me, smiling: "Go outside, fair-haired child, and smile at the sun; perhaps the weather will be fine again." And when I smiled the weather did change. . . .

You see, the sun knew full well whom he had to deal with, because I was my mother's son, and could indeed perform many great wonders: she could turn the black clouds away from our village and could send the hail elsewhere, by sticking a hatchet into the ground in front of our door; she could make the meat jelly with only two cow's feet, so that people crossed themselves in surprise; she would beat the ground, or the wall, or a piece of wood against which I had hurt my head, saying: "There! there!" and the pain would leave me at once. . . . When the burning embers spit in the stove (which, it was said, brings wind and nasty weather) or when the embers hissed (which means that someone is speaking ill of you) Mother used to scold them, there on the hearth, and beat them with the tongs so that the enemy might be defeated. And even more than this: whenever it seemed to her that I looked queer, she would at once prepare a remedy for me and, after spitting on her finger, scrape a bit of earth off the dusty sole of my boots, or, better, she would take some soot from the mouth of the stove, saying: "As the stove's mouth cannot be hurt by the evil eye so shall my child not be hurt by the evil eye!" and she would smear a speck of soot on my forehead so that nothing might injure her pet. . . . And she could do many other things too.

That's how my mother was at the time of my childhood, full of marvelous things, as far as I can remember; and I remember well, for it was her arms that rocked me while I was feeding at her sweet breast, and she cuddled me, babbling at her bosom and looking into her eyes lovingly! And I took my blood from her blood, and my flesh from her flesh, and from her I learned to talk. And wisdom I learned from God when the time came for a man to understand what is right and what is wrong.

But time slipped by with sweet delusions, and I grew up little by little; other thoughts continually crowded my mind and other joys awoke in my heart, and instead of becoming wise, I grew more mischievous all the time and my yearning was now boundless; how flighty and deceptive is man's thought, on whose wings an unceasing yearning carries him and gives him no peace until he goes down into the grave!

But woe betide the man who broods! You see, just as water can draw you down stealthily into the deep, from the gayest mood you can suddenly fall into painful sadness.

But come, let's rather talk about childhood, which alone is gay and innocent.

What does a child care, when his father and mother are thinking about life's worries, or are harassed by other anxious thoughts or what tomorrow may bring? The child, astride his stick, thinks he is riding the smartest of steeds, and races gladly along on it, beats it with his whip and reins it as if it were a real horse, and shouts at it with all his might, deafening you; and if he falls down he believes the horse has thrown him, and he vents his rage upon the stick with all the words he can find. . . .

That is how I was at that happy age, and I believe all children have been so, ever since this world and earth were made, whatever anyone may say.

When Mother was dead tired and lay down to rest a little during the day, that was just when we boys chose to make the house ring with our din. At night when Father returned from Dumesnicu forest, frozen stiff and covered with grime, we used to frighten him by pouncing upon his back in the dark. And tired as he was, he would catch us in turn as you do at blindman's buff, lift us up to the beams saying: "So high shall you grow!" and kiss us over and over again. And when the lamp was lit and Father had sat down to his supper we would pull the cats from the nook under the stove and from behind it, and shake them and worry them in front of him till they were out of breath and the poor cats could not escape our hands until they scratched us and spat at us.

"And you sit there looking on, man," said Mother, "and even encourage them! Ha-ha! served you right, naughty scoundrels that you are! No beast can live in this house because of your wickedness. Now then, just because I haven't given you a thrashing today, you worry those poor cats to death and rush at people like mad dogs. Pshaw! I tell you, you're overdoing it. I'll get down the rod from the beam at once and give you such a caning as'll make you smart!"

"Just leave them alone, wife, leave them. It's only that they're glad to see me back," said Father rocking us on his knees. "What do they care: there's firewood in the shed, plenty of bacon and heaps of flour in the garret; the cask is full of cheese, and enough sour-cabbage in the barrel, thank God! I only wish them healthy enough to eat all there is. Let them play now while they're young; their naughtiness will wear off as they get bigger and full of cares; they won't escape *that,* don't you fear. Moreover, don't you know there's a saying 'If he be a child he must play, if he be a horse he must pull, and if he be a priest he must read prayers . . .' "

"Of course, it's easy for you to talk, man," said Mother, "since you are not with them all day long, which is enough to turn one's hair grey. I wish the earth would swallow them up—may God forgive me for such a thought! If only the summer would come sooner that they might go and play outside, for I'm sick to death of them. They do any mischief that comes into their heads. When the church *toaca** is heard, your good and obedient Zahei rushes out and starts beating the *toaca* on the loom, making the walls shake and the windows crack. And the harum-scarum Ion takes the sheep bell and the fire tongs and makes such a din and hubbub as to deafen you; then they each put a rug on their backs and paper helmets on their heads and start singing 'Hallelujah!' and 'God have mercy, the priest goes a-fishing . . .' till it drives you out of the house. And this happens two or three times a day; I have a good mind to whip them blue, that's what they deserve!"

". . . Well now, woman, you ought to be pleased, being such a good church-woman—which is known far and wide—that the boys have made a church here, to please you, and you've got the church in your own house, far as it is. . . . Henceforth, boys, you ought to start having vigils and all the humbuggery you like, and maybe every day she'll give you honey-smeared "All-Saints" cross-buns and *coliva*** with walnuts in it."

"Where's your common sense, man? I was wondering why they're so good, the poor little mites! It's because you encourage them and side with them! Just look how they stand, all wide awake, staring fixedly at us, as if they intended to take our picture. Just try to ask them to do some work and you'll see how they shirk and sulk and what a fuss they make," said Mother. "Get to bed, boys! The night will soon be over; what do you care, as long as there's plenty of food under your noses. . . ."

And when we had all gone to bed, well, boys will be boys; we would start fighting one another and could not go to sleep for excite-

---

* Long iron or wooden plate on which the priest or the monk beats with one or two little hammers, calling people to church.

** Sweetmeats given as alms in memory of the dead, made of boiled wheat, sugar and ground nuts, ornamented with sugar, candies, and other sweets shaped like crosses.

ment, and poor Mother would have to box our ears soundly and take a strap to our backs. And Father, tired at times of so much noise, would say to Mother:

"Now, now, shut up! That'll do, you shrew! They're not old women to go to sleep at once!"

But Mother would give us a few more blows, harder ones, saying:

"There, that's in the bargain, you little devils! Am I not to get a bit of rest even at night, with all your carryings-on?"

And that was the only way poor Mother had of getting rid of us, poor soul! But do you think that put a stop to our naughtiness? It didn't! Next morning, we started anew. And again Mother would take the rod from the beam and again she would beat us, but do you think we cared a rap about it? . . . As they say:

The hide bad and tattered
Should either be left or battered.

And the ideas that came into our heads, and the things we did and plenty more! I can remember them all as though they were happening now.

Just try and remember things *now,* as you used to, Ion, and see if your memory is as good as it used to be.

At Christmas, when Father killed the pig and singed and scalded it and then wrapped it up quickly in straw to make it sweat, in order to get the hair off easier, I used to sit astride the straw-covered pig and make a tremendous racket knowing I would get the pig's tail to fry and the bladder to fill with grain, to blow up and rattle after it was dry; and woe betide Mother's ears until she broke it against my skull!

But to get on with my story! Once on St. Vasile's day, I decided with some of the village boys to go caroling with the "plough"* for I was a rather big boy now, alas. And on the eve I kept worrying

---

* On New Year's Eve and on New Year's Day the village boys used to go from house to house with a small plough (*plugusorul*) adorned with carols, while others went with a "bull" (*buhaiul*), an instrument contrived from a small cheese-cask covered on one end with a tanned sheepskin through the middle of which was drawn a thread of horse-hair; when they drew at this thread with their wet hands it produced a loud sound like the roaring of a bull. All these noises suggested different agricultural practices. The carols told about ancient scenes of field-labor, wishing abundant harvests to those to whose houses they went to recite or sing. One of the boys delivered a recitative and the others, in a choir, accompanied the cracking of the whip with loud shouts of "*hai, hai.*" Generally, the carol singers got money or eatables (apples, walnuts, cracknels, cakes, etc.).

my father all day long to make me also a "bull"** or at least a stock-whip to crack.

"Lord, I'll sure give you a 'whip,' I will," said Father after a while. "Don't you get enough to eat at my house? You want to be knocked about in the snow by those ne'er-do-wells? I'll have to take off your boots, on the spot!"

Seeing I had said the wrong thing, I sneaked out of the house with only the pig's bladder, lest Father should take my boots away and shame me before my pals. I don't know how it came about that none of the boys had a bell. My sheep bell was at home, but how could I go and fetch it? Finally, we did as best we could, and pinched a broken scythe from here and a bit of the iron belt of a yoke from there, a poker with a ring, and my pig's bladder, and at sundown we started going from house to house. We began with Father Oslobanu's house at the upper end of the village, meaning to go through the whole place. . . . But what do you think? The priest was chopping wood on the stump outside; and when he saw us lining up in front of the window and getting ready to carol, he began to swear at us:

"The fowls have hardly gone to roost and you've already begun? You wait a little, you scoundrels; I'll teach you!"

We took to our heels. But he rushed after us and whirr! hurled a piece of firewood after us, for he was a gruff and surly sort of a man, was Father Oslobanu. And we got such a fright that we ran back half-way through the village without having had time to recite

Mushrooms on the floor
Toadstools on the walls,
As many pot-bellied children
As the feathers on a cock

as carol singers do at houses where they get nothing.

"My! What a damned ill-tempered priest he is!" we said when we had gathered together, frozen and frightened. The fiend had almost lamed us. I wanted to see him carried on a bier to the church of Saint Dumitru below the fortress, where he holds services; it's clear the Devil had wheedled him into coming to our village and making his home here. God forbid our priests be like him, for one would never, never get a taste of good things from the church! And while we kept on wishing him well and grumbling about him and so on, dusk came on.

"*Now*, what's to be done? Let's go into this courtyard," said

** See *supra.*

Zaharia, the son of Gitlan; "We're wasting our time standing here in the middle of the road."

And we went to Vasile Anitei and stood before the window as usual. But it looked as if the Devil had bewitched us; one boy couldn't hit the scythe, he was so cold; another said his hands froze on the bolts; cousin Ion Mogorogea, with the poker under his arm, refused to recite the carol; I could have cried with vexation!

"*You* recite, Chiriac!" I said to Goian; "and we two, Zaharia, shall roar like the 'bull,' and the others shall shout: *hai! hai!*"

All of a sudden we began. And what do you think happened? The niggardly wife of Vasile Anitei ran after us with the burning fire-hook, as she had just been drawing the embers out of the oven where the cakes were baking.

"Goodness gracious! I wish fire'd burn you, I do," said she, all in a flurry. "What's all this din you're making? A curse on him who taught you!"

So then run, boys, quicker than from Father Oslobanu's. "Well, that was a fine beginning," we said, stopping at the crossroads in the middle of the village, near the church. "One or two more of these, and we shall be chased out of the village, like gipsies. We'd better go to bed."

And when we had agreed to go caroling again next year, swearing we'd go together all of us, we parted, all benumbed with cold, and starving; and everyone made for his home, for it was better so. And that is how things happened when we went caroling that year.

And what larks I had with the creaming of the milk! When Mother left milk to clobber, the very next day, no matter whether it was a fast day or a meat day, I began to lick the cream off the top; and I went on doing so every day until I came to the curds. And when Mother wanted to skim the cream in the jars, there was nothing left for her . . .

"Perhaps the vampires have stolen the best of the milk, Mother," I said, squatting, my tongue lolling out, on the ground near the jars.

"By God, if I ever catch that vampire when he's at it!" said Mother looking steadily at me, "then you'll see! The rod that's hanging from the beam will take such an interest in him that all the vampires in the world, male or female, shall not save him from me. . . . One can tell the vampire who ate the cream by his tongue. I've always loathed sly, gluttonous people, that I have, dearie. And let me tell you, God never helps him who steals anything, be it clothing or food or anything else."

"There now, she's hit the right nail on the head," said I to myself, for I was not quite so stupid as not to understand that much.

* * *

What a lot of trouble I had with old Chiorpec, the bootmaker, our neighbor! Or rather, to be honest, it was I who gave him trouble, for I was continually going to the man and worrying him to death to give me bits of strap to make a whip. And as often as not I would find old Chiorpec smearing boots with the best tar, which rendered the leather as soft as cotton. And seeing he could not get rid of me with kind words, he caught hold of my chin with his left hand while the right one dipped the brush into the tar pot and smeared my mouth with it, so that all the apprentices in the shop burst out laughing. And when he let go of me, I ran home to Mother, crying and spitting right and left.

"Look, Mother, what that devil of a Chiorpec has done to me!"

"Dear me! one would think I had taught him," said Mother with satisfaction. "I'll stand him a drink, I shall, truly, when I meet him, for you go and stick to a man like the mange and worry him out of his wits with your impudence, you vagabond!"

Whereupon, I would wash my mouth nicely and go about my business. . . . And no sooner had I forgotten my anger, than off I would run to old Chiorpec again to beg straps. And seeing me enter the door he would exclaim good-humoredly: "I say! welcome, sonny!" And he would smear me again, making a laughingstock of me; and again I would run home, weeping, spitting, and cursing him. So this was another source of trouble for Mother.

"Dear me! I wish winter would come so that I could send you to some school," said Mother, "and ask the schoolmaster to send me back your skin and bones only!"

* * *

Once, in summer, about the time of the Mosi,* I sneaked out of the house and, in broad daylight, went to Uncle Vasile, father's older brother, to steal some cherries; for it was only in his orchards and another two places in the village that you could find summer cherries which ripened just about Whitsunday. And I thought it over and over, wondering how I could manage so that they shouldn't catch me. First of all, I went into the man's house and pretended to be looking for Ion, to go swimming.

"Ion isn't at home," said Aunt Marioara. "He's gone with your uncle down under the fortress, to a cloth mill in Condreni, to fetch some cloaks."

I must tell you that at Humulesti boys used to spin as well as girls, women as well as men; and they used to make many bales of cloth, brown and black, which were sold by the yard or made into

* Saturday before Whitsunday, when alms are given for the dead.

cloaks. The stuff was bought either on the spot, by Armenian tradesmen—who came there specially from other towns—Focsani, Bacau, Roman, Tirgu-Frumos, and from other parts—or was sold at fairs all over the country. This is what they made a living on, mostly, the Humulesti peasants who were yeomen but had no land; and they traded in other things as well: cattle, horses, pigs, sheep, cheese, wool, oil, salt and maize flour; cloaks—long ones, short ones down to the knees, and others just to the waist; wide and narrow trousers, long shirts, plain and ornamented rugs, silk veils for women, and many other things that were taken to market for sale on Mondays, or on Thursdays to nunneries, as markets were rather out-of-the-way for nuns.

"Well, then farewell, Aunt Marioara," I said. "I'm sorry cousin Ion isn't at home, as I should have been mighty pleased to go for a swim with him . . ." But I thought to myself: "Well, haven't I hit it? It's fine their not being at home; and if they don't come soon, so much the better . . ."

The long and the short of it is that I kissed my aunt's hand and took my leave like a good boy; I went out of the house as if I were going to bathe; I crept stealthily as best I could and, all of a sudden, found myself in my aunt's cherry tree, picking cherries and stuffing them into my shirt bosom, green ones and ripe ones, just as I found them. And just as I was most eager and anxious to get the job done as quickly as possible, up came Aunt Marioara with a stick in her hand, right at foot of the cherry tree!

"So that's where you're having a bath, you devil!" said she glaring at me. "Get down, you thief, and I'll teach you!"

But how was I to get down, knowing what was in store for me? Seeing that I didn't and wouldn't come down, whirr! she threw two or three lumps of earth at me, but missed. Then she started climbing the tree, saying: "You wait a minute, you swine, and Marioara'll catch you, she will!" I then stepped quickly down onto a lower branch, and suddenly, hop! I jumped down in the middle of a hemp-field that stretched out on one side of the cherry tree; it was not ripe yet and waist-high. Crazy Aunt Marioara was after me, and I ran through the hemp like a hare with her at my heels, until we reached the fence at the end of the orchard, which I had not time enough to scramble over, so I ran back through the hemp just as quickly, and she still after me, to the cattle pen, which was difficult for me to jump, and the fence again, on both sides, and that shrew of an aunt wouldn't leave off chasing me for the world. She almost had me that time! And I ran and she ran, and I ran and she ran, until we laid all the hemp low; and to tell the truth, there were about ten or twelve square rods of good hemp all ruined. And when we had done this fine business, I don't know how my aunt got entangled in the hemp, or stumbled over something, but she fell down. Then I quickly turned on my heels, took two good jumps, and threw myself over the fence without even grazing it, and so put her off my track; then I went home and was very good for the rest of that day . . .

But towards evening up came Uncle Vasile with the mayor and the watchman, and calling my father to the gate, told him why they had come, asking him to come and estimate the cherries and the hemp—I'm sure Uncle Vasile was also a niggard and a skinflint like Aunt Marioara; they were well matched, as people say! Well, there's no use in me wagging my tongue: a man has a right to profit by his labor, hasn't he? The damage was done and the guilty had to pay. You know it's not the rich who have to pay but the guilty. And so my father paid the damage for me. And when he came back, after seeing how much damage I had caused, he gave me a good hiding, and said:

"There! I hope you've had enough cherries now! Henceforth you've lost all your credit with me, you wretch! How long am I going to pay for the mischief you make?"

And this was the story with the cherries; Mother's words came true, poor thing, and sooner than I thought: "God never helps him who goes about stealing." But what's the good of crying over spilt milk? And think how ashamed I was. How could I face Aunt Marioara and Uncle Vasile or cousin Ion or the village boys and girls? Specially on Sunday in church, and at the *hora** where it's so nice to stand and look on, or at the bathing place, in the Cierul Cucului, which is the trysting place of the lads and maidens who pine for each other all the week while busy at work!

Well, you see the news about my prank had spread like wildfire, so that I dared not face the people; and particularly now when a few pretty girls had grown up in our village, making my heart beat faster.

As they say:

"Well, Ion, are you fond of the girls?"

"Of course, I am . . ."

"And are *they* fond of you?"

"Of course I am of them . . ."

However, what was to be done? This would also pass; be thick-skinned and lie low, as I did for many other things that happened during my lifetime, not in a year or two all at a time, but in the course of several years, and one after the other, as your turn comes at the mill. I always tried to avoid getting into trouble, but it looked

---

* Folk ring-dance.

as if the Devil were egging me on and leading me into numberless scrapes.

And lo! directly after the affair with the cherries a new thing happened.

One morning my mother had great difficulty in rousing me from sleep, saying: "Get up, you sluggard, before the sun rises, else the hoopoe will 'hoopoo' you and spoil your whole day." This was how Mother used to threaten us with a hoopoe that for years had made its nest in a very old hollow lime tree, on the hill at Uncle Andrei's, Father's younger brother. And in the summer one heard nothing else but! "Hoo-poo-poo . . . Hoo-poo-poo!"—first thing in the morning and every day, and the village rang with it. As soon as I was up, Mother sent me out into the fields with food for some gipsies who were hoeing for us just then in the Valea Saca, near Topolita. And, setting off with the food, I heard the hoopoe:

"Hoo-poo-poo! Hoo-poo-poo! Hoo-poo-poo!"

Do you think I went about my work? No, not I. I stopped at the lime tree with the idea of catching the hoopoe, for I hated it; not so much because it brought me ill luck, as Mother said, but because she woke me up every day at unearthly hours on account of this bird. As soon as I reached the tree I put the food down on the footpath that led up the hill, and cautiously climbed up the lime tree that sent you off to sleep with the scent of its flowers. I stretched out my hands into the well-known hollow and, luck being on my side, I caught the hoopoe sitting on its eggs and said with satisfaction: "Shut up, sweetheart, I've got you now; you'll hoopoo the devil from now on!" But when I was about to pull out the hoopoe, I don't know how, I was startled at its crest of ruffled feathers—for I hadn't seen a hoopoe before—and I let it go again into the hollow. And as I stood wondering what to do, I thought it couldn't be a feathered serpent after all—I had heard that sometimes there are serpents hidden in the hollows of trees—so I took courage and reached out once more for the hoopoe . . . come what may . . . but the poor thing had crept away somewhere in the recesses of the hollow, for nowhere was I able to find it; it seemed to have been swallowed up. "Why! what a strange thing," said I, all in a rage, taking off my fur cap and hurling it into the mouth of the hollow; then down I slid, looked for a stone of the right size, climbed up the lime tree again with it, took away my fur cap, and in its place laid the stone, thinking to myself that the hoopoe would come out from somewhere by the time I returned from the fields. After this I slid down the tree and proceeded with the gipsies' meal . . . But though I walked fast, time had flown quickly, while I had been strolling about hither and thither, goodness knows where, dawdling or wasting time in my own endeavor to catch the hoopoe in the lime tree, whereas the gipsies—there's no doubt about it—must have been ravenously hungry waiting. As the old folk say: "When hungry, the gipsy sings, the boyar goes for a walk with his hands behind his back, and our peasant lights his pipe and grumbles to himself." And thus it was with our gipsies; they had started singing like mad in the fields, leaning on their hoes, eyes blurred with scanning the horizon to see where their food would come from. Then, towards midday, I put in an appearance, from behind a mound, now walking, now stopping, carrying the food all cold and dried up, not daring to approach the workers, hearing them humming tunes with such gusto. Then down came the black devils upon me, and I would have been nearly swallowed up by them had it not been for a young gipsy among them who came to my rescue.

"Hey! Stop that! Keep quiet! Why do you go for the boy? Have it out with the father, but not with him!"

At this the gipsies left me alone and fell upon the food, as silent as mice. So as I had gotten out of this scrape too, I took the bag with the dishes and started back for the village; again I stopped under the lime tree, climbed it, and, when I put my ear to the mouth of the hole, I heard something fluttering inside. Then carefully removing the stone, I thrust my hand in and drew out the hoopoe exhausted by the struggle. As for the eggs, when I tried to take them, they were all scrambled. After this I reached home, tied the hoopoe's leg with a string, and for a couple of days I hid it from Mother in the loft, among some rickety casks. And every little while I would go up to the hoopoe so that the whole household began to wonder why I went so often up to the loft. But on the following day, in came Aunt Mariuca, Uncle Andrei's wife, foaming with rage, and she started to pick a quarrel with Mother because of me.

"Did you ever hear the like, sister-in-law? Fancy, Ion stealing the hoopoe which for so many years has awakened us at daybreak in time to go to work!" said my aunt with grief. She was terribly upset and was almost crying while she said this, and then I realized that my aunt was quite right, for the hoopoe was the village clock. But Mother, poor soul, hadn't the slightest idea what it was all about.

"What do you mean, sister-in-law? If it's true, I'll thrash the life out of him for catching the poor bird in order to torture it. Now, I am glad you've told me; leave it to me, I shall give him a good shaking."

"No doubt about it, sister-in-law Smaranda," said my aunt, "for nothing escapes this naughty son of yours. No use in his denying it. I was told by people who saw him that Ion took it; I'll bet my life on it."

I was hiding in the storeroom and no sooner did I hear these words than I climbed into the loft, took the hoopoe from where it was, stole down from the eaves of the house, and made straight for the cattle market to sell it. For it happened to be Monday, a market day, and as I reached the fair, I began strutting up and down among the people, with the hoopoe in my hand, for wasn't I, too, in a way, a merchant's son? A foolish old man, dragging a heifer by a rope, asked me:

"Is that chicken for sale, my lad?"

"Yes, for sale, grandfather!"

"And how much do you want for it?"

"As much as you think it worth!"

"Come, give it to the old man, and he'll feel its weight!"

And as I put it into his hand, the surly old devil feigned to examine it for eggs, and gently undid the string from its leg; then he threw it up into the air, saying: "What a shame! I've let it go!" Whirr! went the hoopoe to the top of a shop and after taking a little rest, took its flight towards Humulesti and fie! left me flabbergasted, gazing after it with tears streaming down my cheeks! Then I gripped the old man by his coat, to make him pay for the bird.

"What's the idea? Do you think you can play with people's property? If you didn't mean to buy it, why did you let it go? You won't get rid of me, even if you gave me this heifer. Do you understand? I'm not joking." And I nearly came to blows with the old man and kicked up such a row that people gathered round us as at a show; and wasn't it a fair?

"D'ye know, you can stand up for yourself, my lad?" said the old man after a while, laughing. "What makes you so cocksure, my son? Well, I never! You wouldn't perchance wish to take my life for a mere bird, would you? I think you are looking for a thrashing, laddie, and you'll get it if you really want it. I could pull the hair off your head, until you'd cry for mercy, you little fool!"

"Let the lad alone," said one of our men from Humulesti. "He's the son of Stefan Apetrei, a man in our village, and you'll get into trouble with him over this."

"Well, well, God bless him, my good man; do you reckon we don't know each other, Stefan Apetrei and I?" asked the old man. "I just saw him a little while ago, walking through the market with a yardstick under his arm, trying to buy some peasant broadcloth, for such is his trade; and he's sure to be somewhere around, or in some shop drinking over a bargain, as is the custom. I am glad to know who you are, you brat. Wait a bit, I'll take you to your father and see whether it was he who sent you selling hoopoes, to bring disgrace upon the market!"

All might have gone well, but when I heard him speak of my

father, my mouth went dry. I managed to slip through the crowd and took to my heels towards Humulesti, looking back to make sure the old man was not going to catch up with me, for now—to confess the truth—I was eager to be rid of him. As the proverb says: "Let him go! *I'd* let him go, but, you see, *he* wouldn't." That's just what happened to me, and I was glad to have escaped with that much. "It would be a blessing if I could be as successful with Mother and Aunt Mariuca," thought I, with my heart beating like a hare's from fright and fatigue.

But when I got home, I discovered that Mother had gone to market too; and my brothers, terrified, told me about the great to-do with Uncle Andrei's wife, that she had roused the whole village over the hoopoe in the lime tree. She said we had taken it, and that had made Mother very angry. You know Aunt Mariuca was one of those who could make a drunk man sober. She was not a reasonable woman like Aunt Anghelita, Uncle Chiriac's wife. And as my brothers were telling me everything with some anxiety, what do you think we heard from the lime tree but:

"Hoo-poo-poo! Hoo-poo-poo! Hoo-poo-poo!"

My sister Catrina said then with astonishment:

"Listen, brother; God only knows how unjustly some people accuse a person when he is in the right!"

"That's so, sister." But inwardly I thought: "If you knew what the poor bird and I have gone through on each other's account, you'd be sorry for it!"

Zahei left us talking and went to the market for Mother and told her the good news about the hoopoe.

And the following day being Tuesday, Shrove Tuesday, during St. Peter's feast, Mother baked an oven full of *alivenci* and *poale in briu** and roasted some tender young chickens on the spit, after having rolled them in butter; she then sent for Aunt Mariuca, Uncle Andrei's wife, about noon, to come to us, and said to her kindly:

"Good gracious, sister-in-law, how people may quarrel about nothing at all, when they are made to believe what evil tongues say! Better come in, sister, please, and let us have a bite and drink a glass of wine to the good health of our husbands and:

May all bad things be washed away,
And all good things be gathered together;
May ill will between us cease,
May the fields be rid of weeds!

* Moldavian cheese pies.

If you were to fret over trifles, by God, the time would come when you'd go mad."

"You're right, dear sister-in-law," said Aunt Mariuca shrugging her shoulders in embarrassment when she sat down at the table. "One can't trust what people say."

Then we all began to eat. I do not know about the others, but as for me, feeling an empty stomach, I tried to eat enough to last me the whole day. No sooner had I got up from the table, than I showed a clean pair of heels, in a hurry for a swim, and when I bravely dived into the pool from a high bank, I happened to fall flat on my stomach and was so stunned with the pain that I really thought my belly had burst, yes, actually burst. When I got out of the water with great difficulty, dragging myself onto the bank and clasping my hands over my heart, the boys gathered around me in a cluster, and buried me in the sand and said the prayers for the dead as best they knew, and I was an hour in recovering my senses. Then I had a nice long swim until sunset, contriving to return home with the cows and tell Mother that our herdsman, having lost our cows from the cattle pen at midday, I myself had taken them grazing and that was the reason why I was so late. Mother, like a good Christian, believed it all to be the naked truth and, listening to the account I made of it, praised me for the good work I had done and gave me something to eat. I went for my food like a starving wolf, tried to look meek, laughing inwardly and marvelling at the cleverness of the lies I had concocted, till I almost came to half-believe them myself!

And so, man often deceives himself without realizing it, unless he learns to judge soundly. But turning things over in my head, I say, "All suffering buys experience."

One day, towards St. Eliah's Day, Mother had, as usual, lots of things to do: some peasant broadcloth had to be taken off the loom; the warp and woof for some more had to be set and more weaving done; a pile of cut-out peasant cloaks waited to be sewn; there were cards lying idle on the bench and no one to run them through; the spinning wheel was right in the middle of the house, and the heavy yarn not ready for the weft. As they say: "Don't sit idle, for your luck runs idle too." Cards of wool to be wound off the wheel, an unweaned baby in the cradle, and five or six little children waiting for someone to cook their food: there was plenty to do, indeed, and, no doubt about it, it had to be done in a hurry, for the Falticeni fair would soon open, which is quite an event. So Mother woke me earlier than usual, saying:

"Nica, Mother's pet, your father has gone reaping, as the oats are dropping to the ground, and I have such a lot to do, so, please, give up your loitering and stay near Mother, wind the bobbins, and rock the baby. I promise to bring you a hat with ribbon from Falticeni, and a little leather belt with a pocket, you know, all for yourself!"

"All right, Mother," I replied, but only I knew what was in my mind.

In sewing and embroidering of peasant cloaks, and especially at spinning, I could outdo the elder girls. On this account, naughty Mariuca, Savucu's daughter—who, to tell the truth, I did not dislike —often grew angry with me and would tease the life out of me and nicknamed me "Ion, the big spinner," the name of a gipsy from the village of Vinatori. But despite it, she was all the dearer to me, and we would sit and spin together in the shade of their walnut tree and such heaps of bobbins of wool would we do that Mother would kiss me when I showed them to her at night.

That's how boys and girls used to take their work to each other's houses, to make it more pleasurable; in the country, those gatherings were called evening bees, each person doing his own work. And how heartily I spun, always trying to beat Mariuca, and as the spindle whirled round and round, so did my heart whirl round for love of Mariuca, God be my witness. And I remember that one night at a work bee, while corn-husking, I snatched a mouse from Mariuca's bosom, which would have sent the poor girl into fits, had I not been there.

And then in summer, on holidays, how I would go with the lasses across the plain over the hillocks, and especially through the meadows and the oak groves so full of beauty, to gather osiers for making yellow dyes, marjoram for the painting of floral ornaments, balm mint and melilot to put among the clothes. As the song goes:

Turn me, O Lord, into a lime-flower posy,
And throw me among the lasses.

To make a long story short, where there were three, I was the fourth. But every time I heard I'd have to rock the baby, I don't know what came over me! I had the misfortune of being the eldest of my brothers. But what could I do when Mother begged me? On that particular day though, when she asked me, the sky was so clear, and it was so lovely and hot out of doors that one would like to bask in the sun like the hens. Seeing such weather, I dashed to the water, thinking nasty thoughts of Mother, no matter how dear she was to me and how overwhelmed by her duties. God knows it is the truth! For after a while, Mother, believing me to be in the orchard, came out and started shouting with all her might: "Ion, Ion, Ion!" But there was no Ion. Then, hearing no answer from anywhere, she left everything and came running after me to the pool, where she knew I was in the habit of going, and there she discovered me lying down full length, stark naked in the sand.

I remember the ritual very well. I would get to my feet, holding to my ears a pebble burning from the heat of the sun, with the grains of silver on it, and I would begin to jump, first on one leg, then on the other, would bend my head to the right, then to the left, reciting the words:

Golden fairy in the meadows,
Draw the water from my ear,
Ancient coins I'll have for thee,
Buckets I shall wash for thee!
And tambours shall I beat for thee!

After this I would throw the pebbles one by one into the deep pond where I bathed, one for the Lord and one for the Devil, giving equal shares to both of them; then I would throw some more to lock up the Devil at the bottom of the pond, so that water would gush from his mouth, and then I would dive into the pond, to catch the Devil by the leg, as has been our custom for ages. After this I would submerge three times in succession, once for the Father, once for the Son, and once for the Holy Ghost, and then once for Amen. Then I would gently pull myself sideways onto the shore of the pond like a huge fish and cast a sidelong glance at the water that played over the small pretty feet of some fair lasses bleaching cloth on the river farther up; I believe there never could have been a prettier picture!

Poor Mother saw all this, standing not far from me, behind a bank of sand, with arms crossed and terribly worried. But I could not see her for I was very busy. Half an hour must have elapsed while Mother waited there, and maybe three or four hours since I had run away from home, and I must have been starving for it was well past noontime. But I was in such a state of bliss that I quite forgot I was living in this world! At last, Mother, long-suffering though she was, lost her patience and tiptoed stealthily behind me, while I was looking at the lasses, as I told you, and carried off my clothes lying on the bank, leaving me stark naked in the pond, and saying to me angrily:

"You'll come home, my little vagrant, when you're overcome with hunger, and then I'll give you a piece of my tongue," and off she went.

Well, well! what are you going to do with yourself now, Ion? The girls who were bleaching cloth saw it all, nudged each other, and howled, making the sandy banks ring. I almost fainted with shame and was almost choked with vexation; all my former love had changed into a desire to wring their necks. But you know the saying: "Can you stop the wind, the water, or men's tongues?" And so I let these girls laugh till their mouths stretched from ear to ear, and, seizing a moment when they bent down to put the linen into the water to bleach, I dashed out of the pond and rushed off, and tore so fast along the sandy bank that the stones I kicked bounced as high as my head. And on and on I ran, without ever looking back, until I came to the lanes leading into the road that went to our home. I did not follow the road; I was afraid I'd meet someone; but I leaped into Costache's garden and, bending down, crept through the corn; then along a lane; from the lane into Trasnea's garden and again through the corn; and just as I was leaving the garden, I realized that Trasnea's dogs would be after me and tear me to pieces. What was I to do? I heard people say that if you didn't want dogs to bite you but to leave you alone, when you saw them rushing at you, you should throw yourself onto the ground and lie very still, letting them bark at you as much as they liked, for they bay and bay and after a while they leave you and go off. And it's true, and that's how I escaped from Trasnea's dogs, when I had the ill luck to meet them, and they me. I thank my lucky star that that spiteful monster, Trasnea, who bore me a grudge since he caught me in his garden stealing his big apples and his summer pears, did not catch me or he would have thrashed me to death. In my present miserable condition it would have been the end of me. At last, when Trasnea's dogs had abandoned me, I sprang into a cross-road, then into our own garden, and I was so happy that I felt in seventh heaven. Now I walked without hiding through the corn till I came right up to the courtyard, looked through the fence, and saw Mother bustling about, sometimes in the house, sometimes outside. I felt very sorry for her, but was also very sorry for my belly, so empty after such a long time in the water. As the saying goes: "I pity thee, but my heart is breaking with pity for me." Unable to bear the pangs of hunger any longer, I started whimpering humbly through the fence: "Mother, dear, here I am." I immediately jumped into the courtyard, went up to Mother, in the fine state I was in, seized her hand by force, kissed it, and said whimperingly: "Mother, beat me, kill me, hang me, do what you like with me, only give me something to eat, for I am starving!" You know that "nakedness beats about the bush, but hunger goes straight to the goal." So Mother, kind-hearted as mothers are, looked sadly at me and said with a sigh:

"*That's* a nice thing for you, a big grown-up fellow, to be wandering about the road in such a state, and just at a time like this, leaving me without a scrap of help! Come and have something to eat, but let me tell you that I'm fed up with you; perhaps if you behave very well after this, I may feel for you again as I used to, but I'm not sure, no! I'm not."

So the long and the short of it was that I swore I'd never again do what I had done. I behaved very well and never disobeyed her wishes either by deed or word, for a gentle word works miracles. At my work I was as industrious as could be; I would tidy up and dust the house like a grown-up girl, so that Mother didn't need to worry when she went out anywhere. Then one day she kissed me and said kindly:

"May God grant you a wealth of days, little Ion, Mother's pet, and give you all His richest gifts if you behave as I see you have been doing for some time now."

I began to cry then and there, and my joy was real. Never before had I felt such remorse in my heart. Had Mother beaten me with all the slats of the village fences, had she driven me from the house like a stranger, even then I should not have felt so humiliated in front of her as I did then when she treated me gently. And you needn't think I didn't keep my word from that Thursday on for a long time, for I am like that, patient and true to my word in my own manner. Not that I wish to boast, for self-praise is false. To tell the truth, when I was asleep I did not ask for food; when I got up, I didn't wait for others to get it for me, and when there was work to be done I sneaked away from the house. Then I had other good traits: when people treated me roughly, they would get but little out of me; when they treated me gently they wouldn't get even that much; but when they left me to my devices I would perform some dear little prank such as even St. Nastasia, the Deliverer from Poison, couldn't do with all her cunning. The saying goes: "A fool can throw a stone into a pool, but ten wise men cannot fetch it out."

After all, why so much ado about nothing? Well, in this world, I have been only a lump of earth with eyes, a piece of animated clay from Humulesti, and I didn't manage to become good looking by the time I was twenty, or sensible by the time I was thirty, or rich by the time I was forty. But I have never been as poor as this year, as last year, or as I have ever been at any time since I came into the world.

* * *

Ion Luca Caragiale

(1852-1912)

Ion Luca Caragiale is the foremost author in Rumanian literature of comedies of manners and character sketches (*A Stormy Night* [1878], *Master Leonida Versus Reaction* [1879], *Carnival Scenes* [1885]). His most famous dramatic creation is *A Lost Letter* (1884), a virulent satirical comedy depicting the corrupt political customs of his time. He is also the author of a psychological drama, *The Bane* (1890), the heroine of which, Anca—"a female Hamlet"—is the personification of vengeance.

Caragiale is one of the most brilliant creators of types in Rumanian literature. His plays are remarkable for vividness of plot, masterly sense of composition, and dramatic force. His writings include numerous volumes of prose, short stories, sketches, tales, and essays. The picture of the life and morals of Rumanian society at the end of the 19th century, sketched by Caragiale in his dramatic works, is enhanced and completed by his prose. Liberal demagogy (in "Boborul," "Tempora," "The Rumanian Tenant Farmer," "Telegrams"), false patriotism ("The Reward for Patriotic Sacrifice," "The *Green* Rumanians"), the boastful and shallow philistinism of the petty bourgeois ("Moments"), the arrogance and cosmopolitanism of so-called "High Society" ("High-Life,"), schools and education (the sketches "The Pedagogue of the New School," "Mr. Goe," "A Call," "The Chain of Indulgences"), are all scored by his caustic critical pen.

The keynote of Caragiale's creation is its genuine popular character, its subtle wit, and precise and profound psychological analysis. He raised Rumanian comedy and humorous sketches to the heights of the great satirical masterpieces of world literature. His chief works have been translated into more than twenty-five languages.

Minjoala's Inn

"A quarter of an hour to Minjoala's inn . . . from there to the village of Popestii de Sus a league—at a moderate amble, an hour and a half. . . . My horse is good . . . feed him at the inn and give him a rest for three quarters of an hour . . . he'll do it. So a quarter of an hour and three quarters make an hour, with another hour and a half to Popestii two and a half hours. . . . Now it's just turned seven: by ten o'clock at the latest I'll be at Polcovnic Iordache's. . . . A bit late, true; I should have left earlier . . . but, never mind. . . . He's expecting me. . . ."

Thus turning things over in my mind, I saw in the distance, within gun range, lights blazing from Minjoala's inn—yes, it was still called that, though it was the inn of Minjoala's wife now, for her husband had died some five years before. . . . A fine woman! It's hard to say how she'd done it, for the inn had come very close to being sold at auction when her husband was alive, whereas now she'd paid her debts, repaired the outhouses, built another stable—a stone one—and, people say, she must also have put a tidy sum by. Some suspect her of having found a treasure . . . and others of using magic. Once, indeed, her inn was nearly robbed. The burglars had actually broken down the door. The strongest, as big as a bull, had raised his axe and, as he struck with all his might, he had dropped to the ground. The others wanted to help him up, but he was dead. His brother tried to speak, but he couldn't say a word—he'd been struck dumb. There were four of them with the dead one. They hoisted the dead man on his brother's shoulders and then the other two took hold of his legs to get him away from the place and bury him somewhere. As they were going out of the inn yard, the woman started yelling at the window: "Thieves! Thieves!" she cried, and right before them was the county chief with a party of men and four mounted gendarmes . . . "Who's there?" the chief shouted. Two thieves ran for their lives but the dumb man remained with his dead brother on his shoulders. And what a to-do at the inquiry! Everybody thought the dumb man could speak. Who could believe he wasn't pretending? Well, they beat him to pulp to make him recover his speech, but it was no good. No one since then has dreamed of robbing the inn.

By the time I had gone over all these things, I was there. A number of carts had turned into the inn yard—some were taking timber down into the valley, others carting corn up into the hills. It was a cold, autumn evening. The carters warmed themselves around fires. That was why so much light could be seen from afar. An ostler took charge of my horse. I entered the inn; there were a whole lot of people there, causing a pretty good uproar, while in a corner two gipsies half asleep—one with a lute and the other with a *cobza**—were playing a drowsy Oltenian song. I was cold and hungry; the damp had got into my bones.

"Where's the landlady?" I asked the youngster behind the bar.

"At the oven."

"It must be warmer there!" I said, going through a passage into the kitchen.

How clean that kitchen was . . . and there the vapor did not rise from sheepskin coats, boots, and soaked raw-skin sandals—as it did

* A kind of guitar.

at the bar—but from freshly baked bread. The woman was there seeing to the baking.

"Greetings to you, Mistress Marghioala!"

"Welcome, Mr. Fanica."

"Is there anything left for me to eat, I wonder?"

"For a decent man like you, even at midnight."

And so saying, Mistress Marghioala dismissed an old hag that was about to lay the table in her room, after which she went over to the open hearth and said:

"Here, take what you like."

Mistress Marghioala was handsome, stalwart and large-eyed—that I knew. But never had I known her (and I had known her a long while, for in my father's time I had gone to Minjoala's inn time and again as a child, the inn being on the way to the fair) no, never had I known her to look so attractive. . . . I was young, smart, and with plenty of cheek—there was perhaps less smartness than cheek about me. I went up to her from the left, and, as she leaned over the hearth, I put my arm round her waist, my hand touching her right arm, as hard as stone, and in so doing the devil prompted me to pinch her.

"Have you nothing better to do?" the woman said, looking askance at me.

To mend matters, I said:

"What eyes you've got, Mistress Marghioala!"

"No, don't try getting round me. Better tell me what you want to eat."

"Well, I'll have . . . I'll have . . . what you give me . . ."

"Really!"

I went on with a sigh:

"What eyes you've got, Mistress Marghioala!"

"Now, what if your future father-in-law should hear you?"

"What father-in-law? How do you happen to know about him?"

"Ah! so you think if you put your head in the sand nobody sees what you do? Aren't you going to Polcovnic* Iordache's to become engaged to his elder daughter? . . . Now, now, don't look at me like that; go into the next room and have your dinner."

Many a clean, restful room have I seen in my time, but none like that one. . . . The bed there! And the walls and ceiling! And the little curtains! All was as white as milk. And the lampshade and all those things crocheted with fairylike fingers. . . . And it was as warm there as under the wing of a mother hen. . . . And there was a fragrance of apple and quince in the room.

I was about to sit down at table and, after a habit of childhood,

* Colonel.

to look towards the east and say a prayer. I carefully scanned the walls all round—no icon. Mistress Marghioala asked:

"What are you looking for?"

"The icons," I said. "Where d'you keep 'em?"

"To blazes with the icons!" she answered. "They're no good except to breed woodworms and bugs."

A clean woman. . . . I sat down to my dinner, crossing myself according to the customs of old, when suddenly there was a howl. I had evidently put my hobnailed boot down on the old tomcat under the table. Mistress Marghioala got up quickly and opened the door wide, the angry cat rushed out, and a chill blast rushed in and blew out the lamp. Looking for the matches somewhere or other, we came breast to breast in the dark. . . . Game as I was I took hold of her and began kissing her. Mistress Marghioala was reluctant at first, then less so—her cheeks were burning, her lips were cold, and the peachlike down near her ear was abristle. Finally the maidservant came in with a tray of food and a candle. We must have been a long time looking for the matches, for the lamp chimney was quite cold. We lit the lamp again.

The food was good. New bread, roast duck and cabbage, fried pork sausages, and what wine! And all this with Turkish coffee, laughter and talk—Well done, Mistress Marghioala! After the coffee she turned to the old woman:

"Have half a bottle of Muscat brought up."

What wine! I reclined comfortably on the bed for a smoke to accompany the last sips of the amber draught from the glass, and looked through the cigarette smoke at Mistress Marghioala, who sat on the chair in front of me, rolling cigarettes for me. I said again:

"What bright eyes you have, Mistress Marghioala! D'you know what?"

"What?"

"If you don't mind, I'd like another coffee, though not so sweet as the last . . ."

At this there was more laughter. When the maid came in with the coffee, she said:

"You sit talking here, mistress, and don't pay attention to what's going on outside."

"Well, what's going on outside?"

"A wind is blowing from the hills . . . a fearful wind."

I jumped up with a start and looked at the clock; nearly a quarter to eleven. Instead of half an hour I had been two and a half hours at the inn. That's how it is when you indulge in talking . . .

"Have someone take my horse out, will you?"

"Who's to do that? The men have gone to sleep."

"Then I'll see to him myself."

"They're casting spells at Polcovnic Iordache's to get you over," said Mistress Marghioala, bursting into laughter as she waylaid me at the door.

I gently pushed her aside and went out on the veranda. The weather was fearful indeed. The carters' fires had died down; man and animal, huddled together, were sleeping quietly on the cornstalks spread on the ground, while on high the wind was howling madly.

"A terribly high wind," said Mistress Marghioala, shivering as she held my hand tightly. "Don't be a fool; why should you leave in such weather? Stop here overnight and leave tomorrow in daylight."

"Impossible . . . "

I drew my hand away sharply and went into the stables. With great difficulty I woke up one of the men and routed out my horse. I tightened the saddle girths, led him to the steps, then went into the inn room to say good night to my hostess. The woman was sitting thoughtfully on the bed, my fur cap in her hand, turning it round and round.

"How much do I owe you?"

"You can pay me on your way back," answered the landlady looking deep into the inside of the cap.

Then she rose, and held it out to me. I took it and shoved it on my head a little to one side. Looking straight into the woman's eyes, which held a very strange gleam, I said:

"I kiss your eyes, Mistress Marghioala!"

"I wish you a safe journey!"

I swung into the saddle; the old maidservant opened the gate for me and I rode out with my left hand resting on the horse's rump. I turned my head: above the tall fence the open door could be seen, and in the opening the white shadow of the woman with her hand held above her arched eyebrows. I went at a canter, whistling a song as if for my pleasure until, turning the corner of the fence to get on to the road, the figure in the doorway was hidden from my sight. I said: "Gee-up! Now for the road!" And I crossed myself. It was then that I distinctly heard the door slamming and a tomcat squealing. My hostess knew I could no longer see her and had gone back to the warmth of the room, probably catching the tomcat in the door. Darned tomcat! always getting entangled in people's legs!

I had been on the road for some time. The wind was raging wildly, almost blowing me from the saddle. Clouds followed one another in quick succession, as if driven by the fear of some punishment from above—some downhill, others, above them, uphill, drawing for long moments a curtain, sometimes thick, sometimes thinner, across the faded light of the moon's last quarter. The cold went through me; I felt my thighs and arms freezing. Riding with bowed head to keep the wind from taking away my breath, I felt a pain at the back of my neck, on the forehead and at my temples, while a hot feeling ran through me and a thumping sounded in my ears. "I've drunk too much," I thought, pushing my cap to the back of my head and raising my forehead to the sky. But the whirling clouds made me giddy, and I had a burning feeling under my left ribs. I drank in the cold wind, but a pain shot through my chest. I dropped my chin. The cap seemed to squeeze my head like a vise; I took it off and put it on the saddle bow. I was ill. It had not been wise to leave the inn. At Polcovnic Iordache's everybody would be asleep by now. They probably had waited some time for me, but had finally thought I would never be such a fool as to take to the road in weather like this. I spurred on my horse, who reeled as if he, too, had had a drop too much.

Then the wind subsided a little. The air felt as if it were going to rain. The light was misty; then it started drizzling—a thin, stinging drizzle. . . . I put on my cap again and suddenly the blood came rushing to my head. The horse was tired to death. I urged him with the whip; the animal took a few hasty steps forward, then snorted and stopped as if he had come against an unexpected obstacle. I tried to see what it was. A few steps ahead of the horse I could see a small figure jumping and skipping. An animal! What was I to do? Was it some savage creature? Too small for that . . . I grasped my pistol; it was then that I distinctly heard a kid. I urged on the horse as much as I could; he veered round and started going back. After a few steps he came to a standstill and again snorted . . . again the kid! I stopped the horse, turned him the other way, struck him several times, drew the bit tight. He took a few more steps. There was the kid again. The clouds had thinned; I could see very well now. It was a small black kid, now skipping forward, now turning back: it threw up its hoofs, then rose on its hind legs, darted on, its chin resting on its breast and its forehead high, ready for an attack. And it took unbelievably high jumps and bleated and played all manner of tricks. I dismounted; the horse simply refused to go on. I took him by the halter, crouched down, and called to the kid, holding out my hand as if I had some food for it. The kid came frisking. The horse snorted crazily and tried to break away. He forced me down to my knees, but I held him tight. The kid came up to me; it was black and very sweet, and tamely allowed me to pick it up. I put it in my right-hand knapsack, on some clothes. In the meantime, the horse was shaking and shivering in all his joints as if caught by the fever of death.

I mounted him and he dashed forward as if gone crazy.

For a long time he galloped straight ahead, jumping over holes and hillocks and logs without my being able to do anything. Where was he going? And while galloping—I could have broken my neck any moment—my whole body frozen, my head burning as if on fire, I could only think of the good bed I had so foolishly left behind. Why had I done so? Mistress Marghioala would surely have given me her room or she wouldn't have asked me to stay. The kid shifted about in the knapsack to find a comfortable position. I turned to look at it; it looked at me with a clever look, its head stuck out of the knapsack. It put me in mind of another pair of eyes. . . . What a fool I had been! The horse stumbled; I pulled him up in disgust; he made as if to start on his way again but dropped to his knees in exhaustion. Suddenly, in a break between the clouds, a sliver of moon, turned a bit on its side, could be seen. The sight was like a blow struck right between the eyes. The moon was right in front of me. . . . Then there were two moons in the sky. I was going uphill, so the moon should have been behind me! And I quickly turned round to see the real one . . . I had lost my way and was going downhill. . . . Where could I be? I looked ahead. There was a cornfield with the stalks still uncut, and behind me were wide fields. I made the sign of the cross, at the same time pressing the horse angrily between my numb thighs to make him rise. I felt a jerk on my right leg . . . then heard a squeal. . . . Had I crushed the kid? When I put my hand into the knapsack, it was empty. I had lost the kid on the way. The horse got to his feet, shaking his head as if to shake out a hornet; he rose on his hind legs, drew to one side, and threw me; then he set out at a gallop across the field as if maddened, and was lost in the dark. As I was rising, I heard a rustle among the cornstalks and a man's voice quite near saying clearly:

"Come on, kid. Curse you! You damned devilish thing!"

"Who's there?" I shouted.

"A decent man!"

"But who?"

"Gheorghe!"

"Gheorghe who?"

"Natrut . . . Gheorghe Natrut, watchman of the cornfields."

"Why don't you come over here?"

"I will."

In the cornstalks a man's shadowy form appeared.

"Gheorghe, my good man, where might we be? I've lost my way in the storm."

"Where do you want to go?"

"To Popestii de Sus."

"I see. To Polcovnic Iordache's."

"Well, yes."

"Then, you haven't lost your way. There's still a goodly way to go for you're only in Haculesti."

"Haculesti?" I said joyfully. "Then I'm near Minjoala's inn."

"There it is; we're behind the stables."

"Come and show me the way; I don't want to break my neck just now."

I had been wandering about for some four hours.

I took a few steps and there I was at the gate. There was a light in the window of Mistress Marghioala's room and a shadow moving across the curtains. Who knows what wayfarer, wiser than myself, was now enjoying that clean bed. Very likely there was nothing for me but a bench by the ovens. I was lucky enough. As soon as I knocked, the old maidservant hurried to open the door for me. As I was about to enter, I stumbled on something soft on the threshold. The kid . . . the very same! It had been the landlady's kid! It entered the room too and quietly went to sleep under the bed.

I didn't know what to think. Was the woman sure I would come back? Or had she got up early? . . . The bed was made.

"Mistress Marghioala!" that was all I could say. And wishing to thank God for saving my life, I raised my right hand to my forehead.

Mistress Marghioala took hold of my hand, and dragging it down, she took me forcefully in her arms.

I seem to see that room to this day . . .

The bed there! And the little curtains . . . And the walls and ceiling! All as white as milk. And the lampshade and all those things crocheted with fairylike fingers. . . . And it was as warm there as under the wing of a mother hen. . . . And there was a fragrance of apple and quince about.

I would have stayed a long time at Minjoala's inn had not Polcovnic Iordache—my father-in-law, peace be with him!—come to drag me out of it with much ado. I ran away from his place, and returned to the inn three times before I finally became engaged, until the old man, who wanted me for a son-in-law willy-nilly, had me bound hand and foot by his men and took me to a little monastery up in the mountains where I had forty days of fasting, prayers and genuflections. When I came out of it I was penitent; I became engaged and married.

Much later, one clear winter night, while I was having a chat with my father-in-law, a jug of wine between us, as is the custom in the countryside, we learned from a steward who was returning from town with his shopping that there had been a big fire at Haculesti at dawn and Minjoala's inn had burned down to the ground, burying poor Mistress Marghioala, now an old woman, under a heap of live embers.

"At long last she's gone to the fire where she belongs!" said my father-in-law with a laugh.

And he asked me to tell him the story I have just told you and which I had told him I don't know how many times. Polcovnic Iordache insisted that Mistress Marghioala had bewitched my cap and that the kid and tomcat were one and the same. . . .

"Don't you believe it," I said.

"It was the devil, I tell you."

"It might have been," I said. "But if that is so, then the devil sometimes leads you on to good things too . . ."

"He takes you to good things to give you a taste of them and then he alone knows where he drives you . . ."

"But how do *you* know?"

"That's none of your business," said the old man. "That's a horse of another color."

Mihail Sadoveanu

(1880-1961)

Mihail Sadoveanu is, along with I. L. Caragiale, Ion Creanga, and Liviu Rebreanu, among the greatest writers in Rumanian literature. His extraordinary output (his works number over a hundred volumes) includes tales, short stories, and novels.

Mihail Sadoveanu is a consummate and highly original storyteller, the creator of an expressive, inimitable language, stemming, like Creanga's, from the spoken language of the people. Unlike Creanga, however, who realistically reproduces the common man's speech, Sadoveanu writes a stylized version of the spoken language enriched by a deep and festive tone. Sadoveanu's universe is as vast as his work, both in space and in time. His writings embrace a wide span of Rumanian history, ranging from the 15th century to the present day. Every aspect of the life of the Rumanian people is painted on his vast canvas: peace and war, love and death, cities and countryside—all are brought to life with unequalled literary skill. No writer in Rumanian literature had ever before pierced so deeply into the soul of the common man, peasant, or townsman, nor sensed with more intense feeling the relationship between man and nature. No writer has ever rendered so broad a picture of the historical development and the moral virtues of the Rumanian people as Sadoveanu has in his stories and novels, which, through their masterly style and deep humanity, have attained world-wide recognition. Frequently compared to the great Russian prose writers for his realistic approach, Sadoveanu has also been called the Homer of Rumanian literature.

Excerpt from *The Hatchet*

The people who live in the shadow of the pines are strange people: quick-tempered and fickle like the waters and the weather, enduring with fortitude both hardships and the stress of fearful winter weather, yet radiant in their joy under the August heat. Eager for love and drink, they preserve their traditions that date back from the beginning of the world; wary of other peoples and of the men of the plain, they return to their lairs like the forest beasts. Above all, they face the sun with hearts quickening to the delights of song and friendship; hearts, in their wild pulsation, that might be pieces of the sun itself.

That was what Nechifor Lipan was like. And that's why others besides Mos Pricop bade Vitoria a kind welcome on her journey.

At Borca, they came upon a christening. People came out to meet them, took hold of the horses' halters, and led them into a courtyard. With flushed faces, they took pleasure in treating the wayfarers to their goodly fare. Vitoria was forced to dismount and enter the house to see the young mother, under whose pillow she slipped a little bag of sugar lumps, while on the forehead of the newborn babe she placed a twenty-lei banknote. She raised her glass to the godfathers, kissed the hand of the priest, and to those who wanted to hear, told them that she was in trouble on account of a debt which she could not recover and added she was spending her last penny to get through to Dorna in this winter weather. She didn't even know how she would reach Brosteni. Luckily she had some friends here from whom she might borrow money. This would enable her to reach the place where her business called her.

The priest greatly wondered at such heartless, nay, scarcely human folk.

"It grieves us," he said, "to admit such things, but we must confess that there are among us mountain people rascally fellows who trespass upon men's rights, taking their money without any thought of returning it. Grasping as wolves, some of our people are," and here His Reverence sighed. "God must have laid a curse on them. Why else should they cheat people with sly schemes or turn highwaymen, and surprising the husbandman in the road, strike him upon the head with an axe and rob him of his goods." Then, in a brighter vein, His Reverence proceeded: "The mountain people are either such as we, delighting in joy and song and prepared to win entrance to Paradise, or fiendish ogres. But those are few who, holding hands, will go down to the Evil One in hell. Beyond them, seeking entrance to the one place or the other, there are none! Our people don't do things by halves!"

"That was my misfortune, to meet with people who will go down to hell," Vitoria said, secretly amused at her slyness.

At Cruci she came upon a wedding procession.

The sledges carrying the wedding guests glided swiftly over the ice of the Bistrita. The bride and bridesmaids had flowers in their hair, while the married women wore only short, furred coats over their peasant skirts. The men fired their pistols at the fir trees to scare away winter before its proper time, and as soon as they caught sight of the strangers on the upper road, youths who were specially appointed to invite the guests spurred to meet them, the ornaments on their horses' ears waving in the wind. They held out their flasks of liquor and raised their pistols: either they would drink in honor of the lordly bridegroom and his most worthy bride or be killed on the spot.

The wedding procession wound its way along the high road, while Vitoria accepted the flask and wished the bride joy. Her face took on a pleasant look and her tongue wagged merrily, though it might have been more fitting had she shown displeasure, for was she not on her way to Dorna, to confront her rascally debtors?

"I am from the high Tarcau," she told them, "the wife of one Nechifor Lipan, who has passed through here before and who may have drunk with you at a wedding, as I do now. On my way I met with a christening. It would have been more fitting had I seen the wedding first and the christening afterwards, but sometimes things are the other way about, which is no great matter considering everything comes from God. Then there's the change of calendar that makes me wonder. It seems it has changed in accordance with the new orders issued by the authorities and explained by the village crier, who in our parts comes beating a drum to announce the news. And when all was explained, we found we were thirteen days older by counting the days, the feasts and the periods of fasting after the fashion of popery. By the law we should be in Lent, while you celebrate weddings as if we were still at Shrovetide."

"Ho, ho!" the sponsors shouted, standing up in the sledge. "You that come from the Tarcau seem not to know that we desire to be—and protest we are—younger by thirteen days, and that we stand for the old calendar which the Lord God gave Adam at the beginning of the world. How could we have it otherwise and not compel our priest to be with us? But he, poor man, does as we tell him willingly, and if others like to side with the Germans or the Jews, we cannot help it. The fire that never goes out will consume them in the next world."

"Have no care," the woman of the mountains answered. "Those on the Tarcau stand by the old law. But what I would have you tell me, if you can, is whether any of you has seen a man from our parts, riding a black horse with a star on its forehead—a man with a brown fur cap."

None of the wedding guests could say they had seen him except one woman who seemed vaguely to remember such a man. The wedding procession continued on its way, gliding merrily along the frozen Bistrita.

Riding at a slow amble, Vitoria wore a look of deep dejection, and she gave her troubled thoughts expression in the few words she spoke to her son Gheorghita. She said she did not mind being delayed by one thing or the other, for it was better she should mix with people as opportunity offered, that she might observe and try to find out the things she wanted to know. She was learning, she said, how to fend for herself in the world as the need arose. It was better to be in the open with friends than in the dark with unknown enemies. When there were many people about, less notice was taken of you and you could watch them more easily. When there were many, it was as if you were alone with your troubles. When there were few, they pierced you with their eyes and laid you bare.

Gheorghita did not understand everything but he felt that it was all as it should be.

Nechifor, then, seemed to have ridden this way without misadventure.

"Maybe nothing untoward will happen to us either, and we'll reach the sheepfolds safely. We'll see, too, what kind of country Dorna is and what sort of mountain is Mount Rarau."

And, indeed, they went on their way without hindrance, halting always at suitable places. As they neared the country of the Dornas, Vitoria inhaled the air and felt a fragrance in her nostrils. A mild breeze wafted from the west, which would gradually melt the snow. However, she was insensible to any influence from without; a burning fever within consumed and stifled her. She was convinced that henceforward her life would be fashioned after a different pattern.

The Dornas consisted of innumerable brooks, little fir-clad mountains, hillocks, and rural settlements. Every clan had its own settlement. These people were clean and handsome, and Vitoria took delight in them. She saw them having fun at the taverns and noted with what passion and joy they danced, as if the end of the world were near. No, there had been no fair, nor any sheep sold in this settlement, nor at Sarul-Dornei, nor at Dorna Cindrenilor, as far as the merrymakers knew. But there had been a great fair at Vatra-Dornei last autumn, where many sheep were sold.

Vitoria's spirits drooped and she looked about her with tired eyes. Well, she would have to go to Vatra-Dornei in her quest for her debtors.

"Come, Gheorghita, take a morsel of food on horseback so as not to delay here. And we'll give the horses their barley when we stop. I myself have had no peace or sleep since yesterday, and can take neither food nor drink. It is as though I had reached God's seat of judgment and had to kneel."

As they set out towards Vatra-Dornei the sun shone brightly from the east, melting the snow. Little rivulets flowed everywhere. There were places in the beaten snow where the horses' hoofs clattered noisily, as if they were crossing a bridge. Dazzled winter was retreating from the valleys, the mists mounting sunward.

For some time a tall, lanky fellow, his short sheepskin coat slung across one shoulder, with boots of Russian leather and a stick with which he amused himself by tracing lines in the snow, had been accompanying them; walking almost level with them at the horses' pace. Now, suddenly, he quickened his step and came up to the woman.

He asked her where she was coming from and, in particular, where she intended to put up.

"I have come a long way, my good man, and shall stop only at Vatra-Dornei."

"Have you business there?"

"I have some debtors."

"And have you no wish to ask me where I go and what I am after?"

"I will ask you if you wish."

He was a merry man it seemed and, grinning under his moustache and unwinding like a thread from a reel, he stretched up towards Vitoria and whispered something into her ear, something that the young man behind was not to hear. The woman struck the horse over its neck with the end of the reins and bound forward, turning at the same time to Gheorghita saying:

"Strike him with the hatchet."

Both her young son and the stranger were filled with awe at her voice, so dry and full of venom. Gheorghita seized the hatchet. The man cleared the ditch and struck out for a path skirting an abrupt slope. He laughed to himself, wondering at the woman. Surely, she was from another world. The women in our parts, he thought, are more friendly; they use cutting words, not a hatchet. The truth was that Lipan's wife, herself, felt that she had entered another world. She threw a glance sideways at the departing man, a glance full of hatred! Then she put her horse to the trot.

Without anyone showing her, she recognized from what she had heard the Pietrele Doamnei and the Rarau mountains to the east. It was from those icy solitudes that the shepherds had come with the sheep, to meet Nechifor Lipan.

They entered Vatra-Dornei. Vitoria asked a shopkeeper who had taken his wares, leather and ironmongery, out into the sunshine, which was the street where the fair was being held. The shopkeeper pointed to the right. The woman turned her horse in that direction, her cloudy eyes set hard.

They pulled up at an inn near by. And here, leaving their things in a room and without either eating or resting, they went to an office to which the innkeeper had directed them, and where they found a clerk wearing a cap. He seemed to be a German, judging from his speech.

"*Bitte,* what can I do for you?" he asked them, raising his hand to his cap.

"We would beg of you, sir, to look up in your books the sale of some sheep last autumn," the woman answered with a beating heart.

"That can be done, and without much cost."

"We're ready to pay. The man who sent us to you said we were to give you enough for a pint of beer."

"If he said so, I won't grumble. Now let me see; what month did you say?"

"November."

"Yes. Here it is. November, the first Sunday, Gheorghe Adamachi and Vasile Ursachi sold three hundred sheep to Nechifor Lipan."

Vitoria gave a cry, "That's it!"

She was breathing hard and her eyes opened wide as she looked at the German.

"*Bitte,* what is it?" he asked anxiously.

"Nothing, except that Nechifor Lipan is my husband."

"All right, then, there's nothing to be frightened about. No, please, you don't owe me anything," he added, waving off the money offered him. "I had a drink at the time to celebrate the bargain, and that is enough. It was the largest number of sheep sold hereabouts. Yes! Your husband was here, closed the bargain, counted out his money, and asked for a receipt. There were other customers, too, but no more sheep. Two poor, honest husbandmen asked him to sell them some of the sheep. He drank with them and promised he would. They agreed on one hundred head, and your husband asked only a small profit; he was very generous. I liked him and felt friendly towards him; but what are you crying about?"

Vitoria had collapsed upon a chest and was sobbing, her head between her hands.

"Will you sit on this chair, please?" the man asked kindly.

But she refused to get up from her lowly place.

"Will you not tell me what is the matter?"

She told him, speaking hurriedly and wiping her eyes with her coat sleeves. After buying the sheep, Lipan had not returned home and no one had heard from him since.

"That cannot be."

"Oh, yes, it can. That is why I've come all the way here, following in his tracks."

"But I cannot understand. I was present when they separated the hundred sheep. They all went towards the valley: the sheep and the dogs and the asses and the shepherds employed by Gheorghe Adamachi and Vasile Ursachi, to help take them to the place where they were to winter. Then, when the dust raised by the sheep had settled, they too mounted their horses and set off."

"Who set off?"

"My friend Lipan and the other mountain people I have spoken about."

"But which mountain people, oh, which? And where were they from?"

"That I don't know. They had dealings together. They probably knew one another. They had the musicians play for them, and drank and embraced, after which they followed the sheep. I bade him farewell: 'I hope to see you soon,' I said. It is true; I have not met him since."

The old man passed his fingers over his short-cropped moustache and the back of his palm along his clean-shaven chin and looked up at the ceiling, seeking to find an answer to his puzzle. There was nothing there but a lamp with a smoky globe.

"It's very strange!" he said shaking his head. "So he didn't come home?"

Vitoria shrugged her shoulders, hurt by the question.

"Possibly he is wintering with the sheep."

"If so, why hasn't he sent a letter? Why haven't I had news from him?" the woman cried in her sorrow.

"How can I know that? I'm not to blame in this matter," the German said, throwing up his hands. "To my thinking, if nothing untoward has happened to him, he'll return home of his own accord."

Vitoria glared at him.

"I do not understand what you mean."

"If nothing untoward has happened to him," the old man repeated in a lower voice.

Gheorghita understood what the clerk meant although his mother did not seem to; yet he dared not interfere to make things clearer. Looking sideways at her, he suddenly realized that she had long suspected such a thing; not only suspected, but knew. And that was why they were here, at Vatra-Dornei.

"What's to be done now?" the clerk asked with strange humility.

Vitoria swayed gently from side to side, her hands clasping her temples. She had closed her eyes. She opened them at last and looked around, and the old man, in wonder, saw her smile. He did not understand what was going on in her mind.

"I'll be following in the tracks of those sheep," she explained. "You say they went towards the valley?"

"Yes, *bitte*."

"Towards the valley, to winter there?"

"Yes, *bitte*. As far as I could make out, they went along the bank of the Neagra."

"With God's help I'll pick up their scent."

"H'm, well, yes, you might," the little old man said, but when left to himself he greatly wondered at such a strange woman.

When Lipan's wife returned towards the valley bad weather set in. The wind changed its course and began to blow from the north. There was an end to the thaw and the light grew behind the enshrouding mist. With a cold breath behind them the two travellers rode on silently, as if exploring a new land under a thin, unending canopy of cloud. They had seen it only the day before, but could not recognize it now, in its new aspect.

The horses, newly shod by Mos Pricop, clattered over frozen, uneven land. The roads and paths were deserted. The windows of the taverns displayed their brightly colored drinks in bottles—but to little avail: they all looked empty and desolate. Their gloom would be short-lived, however, for the glorious triumph of the sun could not be delayed for long.

Everywhere, there was a feeling of expectation. When the mountain waters started to flow towards the valleys, they would bring a new message with them. At any rate that was the way Vitoria looked upon this changed world.

As they entered the last of the Dorna villages, they came upon an inn on its outskirts, as is usual in those parts. They dismounted and left their horses standing near each other, without securing them and without giving them their feed.

From behind the bar a woman rose, trying to smother a yawn with her hand. Vitoria asked for a jug of wine and three glasses. The landlady set a third glass with the other two. They spoke little at first and then only about the weather and fodder. But, although sleepy, the owner (a woman and the mistress of an inn, besides) did not fail to put the usual questions.

"From where have you come?"

"From Vatra-Dornei."

"And where might you be going?"

"Down towards the valley."

For a moment Vitoria hesitated, adding quickly:

"I'm collecting a debt."

"Is that so?"

"Yes. I have money owing me for some sheep, which passed through here to a wintering place last autumn around the time of St. Gabriel's Day."

"Oh!" the woman said carelessly.

"They didn't halt here by any chance, I suppose?"

"Oh! They might have."

"I'm interested in a flock of three hundred, with three owners on horseback, one riding a black horse."

"I don't remember. They may have passed through here when I was away from home, visiting a married girl of mine who lives at the far end of the Sar Valley."

"But your husband, isn't he here? He may know about them." "No, he's visiting our daughter now, in his turn. And I think enough has been said over a glass of wine," the mistress of the inn added sourly.

As they were mounting their horses again, Vitoria observed in a voice loud enough for the woman inside the inn to hear:

"It seems that this is no halting place."

"Then what is it?" the mistress of the inn asked sharply, putting her head out of the door.

"Just a place to look at and pass by," Lipan's wife said, pressing her lips tightly.

The mistress of the inn felt the thrust and was stung by it. She came out on the threshold, uttering sharp words. But Vitoria, as if she had not heard, did not even turn round, although anger was at work in her breast. She wished this first enemy she had run into dead and buried under her very eyes.

Without exchanging a word, the two rode on to the other end of the village. Again, the woman reined in her horse.

"Do we stop here to talk again?" Gheorghita asked doubtfully.

"Yes. What am I to do? Isn't that my job?"

Here was a wide courtyard, full of scraps left behind by the many people that had halted there. The innkeeper, a thin, swarthy man with grey hair and keen eyes, looked in no way sullen.

"Back so soon?" he asked. "Why, I saw you pass this way only yesterday."

Vitoria looked at him attentively; then spoke in a complaining voice.

"What can we do, my good man? My affairs are all in a muddle. But I can see that you'll remember things, if I ask you."

"Ask on and we'll find out what you want to know. Here's the wine you ordered and the glasses, too. But I give the questioner the right to drink first. If I can be of use to you, then I'll drink after."

"Now, don't speak that way with me, my good man," Vitoria said kindly. "May the Almighty keep you from troubles such as mine."

"But if you don't tell me what your troubles are, how can I be of use to you?"

The woman spoke, then, about the three hundred sheep and the three men on horseback.

The man remembered them very well and the woman's face brightened. Some time towards the feast of Archangels Michael and Gabriel, a flock such as the woman described had pastured a little lower down the valley. And, as the shepherds neared the inn, the owners—there were three—had caught up with them. Yes, one of them, wearing a brown fur cap, had been mounted on a black horse with a star on its forehead. He it was who had ordered the brandy for the shepherds, and another pint for himself and his two companions. As Father Vasile was there too, he had invited His Reverence to have a glass with them. Father Vasile had not objected, for he saw they were honest folk, and the innkeeper had placed a chair for him at the travelers' table. Then quite soon, after another pint, the man with the brown fur cap had taken it into his head to have His Reverence read a service for him and sprinkle the sheep with holy water.

"Which I liked him for," the man went on. "And Father Vasile sent for his red stole, his prayer book, and the other things he needed. He blessed the flock, praying that it should reach the wintering place in safety and increase in the spring. And the man with the brown cap took money from his belt and paid handsomely and Father Vasile was greatly pleased. Then, much later, they rose and called for their horses."

"Who was it gave the order?"

"Again, the man with the brown cap. He owned two-thirds of the sheep; the other two only one-third. I heard them speak about where they should winter. The others said the sheep would fare well. But I forgot to tell you that before mounting, the fellow with the brown cap remembered something else. He asked me for a piece of bread and gave it to his dog. I liked him for that, too. They paid their reckoning generously and were gone."

"You say the friends were honest people?" "Aye, they were honest folk. One of them was of a small build and swarthy, like myself. The other was burlier and laughed a lot and loudly. He had a harelip, and enjoyed his drink. Didn't speak much. Just laughed and drank. The man with the fur cap was clever with his words."

"The man with the brown fur cap?"

"That's right."

"Yes, I know," Vitoria said with a sigh. "It's on his account that I've come this way."

"So he's your husband?"

"Yes, he's my husband."

"And now you're after him?"

"What am I to do? If he doesn't come back to me, I have to chase him."

"You should look for him where he stayed longest . . ." the innkeeper said and smiled.

Vitoria shook her head returning the smile, the semblance of a smile, trying to suppress the pang that gave her no rest. She looked for her kerchief thrust in her bosom, where her money was tied, took from it and paid for the wine.

When they were mounted again, Gheorghita saluted the publican.

"Fare you well, Mr. Macovei, and good luck to you!"

"A pleasant journey and may you retrieve your money."

"Now, how is it you know his name is Macovei?" the woman muttered to her son.

"How can I help knowing, for it's written on the sign above his door. See there, Dumitru Macovei."

"Yes! you are clever and have schooling. I alone am stupid."

The young fellow was silent. Sometimes he found it hard to look his mother in the face.

The woman felt a great restlessness in her heart but also a great power surging up. Seemingly, God had been pleased with her prayer to Saint Ann, and had given her the first light in this matter, and the first good advice; and she pledged herself to light candles and bring gifts to the Bistrita monastery. The wind that blew behind them drove them towards the valley. She noticed Gheorghita's fatigue and hunger, but pretended not to see.

They rode on as fast as they could towards Paltinis, thence to Dirmoxa, and after that to Brosteni, only calling a halt when Vitoria saw that their horses were tired out. Her own eyes were burning, though her son's were dull and listless. The horses fed contentedly on the barley, their muzzles deep in the bags that hung over their heads; they shook, snorted, and waited to drink.

The young man, these days, was sleeping less than usual. His face was drawn.

"It suits you better," his mother assured him with a malicious smile.

"Will there be an end to all this some time?" Gheorghita asked.

"My darling scholar," the woman retorted, "I can see that your wisdom comes from books and the written word, though it would be better if it came from your own head. Eat your fill and gain strength, not so much for your own sake as for the sake of the hatchet."

"Mother, there is something I don't understand," Gheorghita said. "Why do we go about on this quest and not leave the job to those who are paid to do it? The country has an administration, and its police and judges."

Vitoria answered contemptuously: "What have I to do with

them? I have to attend to my troubles. Do as I tell you."

"I'll do as you tell me," Gheorghita answered, "but shall we find what we are after?"

"What we're after?"

"Shall we find Father?"

"We'll find him, never fear."

And indeed they picked up his scent at every landmark; that is, at every inn. Sometimes it seemed to disappear, but it was found again a little farther on. At places where they came across scatter-brained publicans nothing could be discovered about the events that had taken place fourteen weeks before—as if a gesture, a look, a word had been forgotten and buried forever. Such people have no better memory than a stone accidentally touched in passing. But, later, the brown fur cap showed up again; a living memory in another man's mind. At yet another place, the brown cap was an indistinct image, but the harelipped fellow who spoke little, laughed much, and drank heavily appeared again. The third man semed to be like a shadow. He passed, too, but neither his face nor character left a mark. She found enlightening words at the big inn at Brosteni. The sheep had passed through the village towards the mouth of the river Neagra, Bistrita way, raising clouds of dust. A paunchy shepherd had mounted a little ass to save his strength. From the knapsack hanging on the back of another ass, three tiny puppies had peeped out on the world, while the old bitch trotted by their side. The children had gathered at the edge of the road to see the sight. Then had come three mounted fellows. They had stopped at the inn without dismounting and had called for a pot of wine. A young lad had served them, and the innkeeper had come out on to the threshold. He was an old, civil-spoken German.

"Good wine this," the horseman with the brown fur cap had said to his companions, "well kept and cold. I tell you this old German is a very father to wayfarers."

The old man remembered the words and repeated them to Vitoria and Gheorghita.

And the woman took pleasure in listening to them and pondered deeply, looking before her into the distance.

She picked up the tracks of the three horsemen again at Borca where the flock had turned to the left, away from the waters of the Bistrita. So, Vitoria once again crossed into unknown land, where villages and mountains had strange names. She halted in a village, Sabasa, and found that the sheep and the horsemen had been there. She went on up a winding path cut in the rock, through lonely places, vultures hovering above. Here was a wilderness of ice and snow, and the wind was like a powerful, living presence: she felt as if she could have leaned against it. From the summit the prospect opened out onto wide, sunlit expanses leading down to the waters of the Moldova. And the mountain, with its winding path and stone bridges spanning the precipices, was called Stinisoara. A young lad, the son of the innkeeper at Sabasa, whom they had taken as a guide, provided Vitoria with this information.

When they reached the peak, they rested their horses under the shelter of a high bank beneath the cross which they call the Talians' Cross, listening in silence to the wind that howled in the precipices and to the agitated rustle of the pines. Nechifor Lipan must have bent his steps towards those glints of sun on the waters of the Moldova, Vitoria thought. He must have stopped here and gazed into the distance.

They descended at a swifter pace along the beaten track, crossing rivulets that were still frozen, though the weather was milder now; only stopping on the far side of the village of Suha, where the valleys begin.

"Mr. Iorgu Vasiliu keeps the inn," the little fellow of Sabasa explained. "You will stay there, and I shall go back. Father enjoined me to be home by nightfall."

"Give my thanks to your father," Vitoria answered. "With God's help we may stop with him again, and I may be less worried then than now. Here is the money I promised you, Neculaies. And remember me to your mother, and tell her that we went onwards and came down to the waters of the Moldova and to the borough of Falticeni. From here it seems we have to proceed as far as the Pruth in the Botosani county."

Returning thanks, Neculaies parted with them, making for home uphill on his fat mare without a saddle, nothing under him but a woolly, long-napped rug. He wore a sheepskin coat tied round his waist with a rope and a big fur cap on his head.

Gheorghita looked at his departing back and laughed.

Vitoria soon reached the inn of Iorgu Vasiliu where they were to rest and get something to eat.

Iorgu Vasiliu seemed a sedate man, for he wore glasses and kept writing things down in a big register. He was bald, which, for the woman of the mountain, was proof that he had much learning. With his short, thick hands he adjusted his blue apron over his paunch, which made her conclude that he was a man with an inclination for orderliness as well as for writing. On either side of the wooden shelves, crammed with jugs in serried rows, there were other shelves and drawers packed with all the good things of the earth.

From a vat he took out a fine herring for Vitoria, holding it by its tail as if his fingers were a delicate pair of tongs. He placed it carefully on a sheet of paper on a clean, well-scrubbed table. Then he brought a warm loaf of bread. And from a small cask he filled two big glasses with foaming beer.

"Beer is a good thing when one is tired and hungry," the woman thought. Gheorghita, not used to the drink, took a sip and pushed it aside, for it seemed to him that it was bitter.

Iorgu Vasiliu walked about softly in his felt slippers and gave civil answers to all her questions. They were alone, without other customers. The sun shot oblique rays on to the windows. It was about one o'clock in the afternoon and it seemed to Vitoria that the wind had subsided. When she had made certain of this, she felt worried. Yet she returned to her duty.

She skillfully brought the conversation round to her concerns, making use of the experience she had gained.

Having determined the year and month of the event and weighing carefully the notes in his register, the innkeeper thought things over for a long time, and then recalled precisely what had been asked of him: on such a day and in such a month sheep had indeed passed through there.

"So that's all right; we will go on our way," Gheorghita thought.

But Vitoria was not satisfied with this answer. She wanted to know everything about the owners of the sheep. Naturally, the sheep had passed first, with the shepherds, the dog and the asses; after which the owners had come up.

"That's right," Mr. Vasiliu agreed after much thought. "The owners came after the sheep."

"The flock and the shepherds stopped here, and the shepherds waited for the owners."

"No," Mr. Vasiliu said, with a shake of his head. "The shepherds grabbed a loaf as they passed and went on their way."

"And the owners of the sheep arrived later, on horseback, is that it?"

"Exactly! They arrived later, as you say, on horseback. And the two dismounted and I served them a light meal, as you yourself are having: a herring, bread, and beer. The herrings are good here. I first stocked them a long time ago, when some Italians were working high up the mountains, building bridges and the road."

"There weren't two of them," Vitoria said quietly. "There were three."

"No, no! There were only two."

Vitoria blinked, trying to pierce the darkness that welled up within her. Iorgu Vasiliu repeated his statement. The woman of the mountain stood there thinking, waiting for the darkness within her to disperse.

She realized, then, that the wind had in fact subsided. It was blowing, now, only down in the valley and could no longer be heard. The sign was obvious. She could not proceed on her way. She must retrace her steps. She never for a moment thought that Nechifor might be one of the two men. He had not come as far as here; nothing of him, no living spark of his was about this place.

"So there were two of them now?" she asked quietly, warily. "One a big man with a harelip and the other a smallish, swarthy fellow?"

"Yes," Mr. Vasiliu agreed. "That's what they were like: men I'd come across before, from places down in the valley. The one with the harelip is called Iepure. No, it's the other way round: the small fellow is called Iepure. They followed in the sheep's tracks."

"And do you know whether they're back?"

"They must be, for they only took their sheep to winter somewhere. The other fellow is called Calistrat Bogza."

"Which of the men?"

"The one with the harelip. There were only the pair of them, I tell you, and I even know their names. What makes you think they were three?"

"Well, it's what I heard tell," the woman muttered, her eyes half closed. "But now I realize there were only two, as you say."

The darkness was beginning to lift. There had been three men at Sabasa, but at Suha, on the other side of the Stinisoara mountain, Nechifor Lipan had not shown himself. Had he risen above his enemies or been laid low by them? Here, between Sabasa and Suha, she had to seek for the truth. It didn't seem to be so difficult either, for Calistrat Bogza and his companion could be found at their homes in the valley to the right or to the left. In the first place, she had to learn from them if Lipan had survived or had gone drifting down some stream, a lifeless corpse. . . .

God must have preserved his tracks. It was her duty to turn back and find them. Saint Ann had given her a sign, checking the wind and altering its course.

And this was not the only sign. Others soon appeared.

The door at the end of the room opened. Through the small, round window in that door, which the head of a man of average height might reach, a keen eye had looked several times. This eye, together with its companion, set in a rubicund face that terminated in a body overflowing at the breast and hips, now appeared in the shadows. Mr. Iorgu Vasiliu withdrew as far as he could to make room for the richly gathered, swelling petticoats of his wife. The woman of the mountains immediately realized that she must be careful in handling this woman who was so white and large, who wore red stockings and leather-soled slippers that clattered lightly as she walked.

"Yes, you remember everything so well," she addressed her husband, seating herself on a chair, "but I wonder at your leaving out the name of one of the men. Are you sure you didn't put it down in your register?"

"No, I have only Bogza in my books. The other one, I know, is called Iepure."

"No, no," the innkeeper's wife answered. "Iepure (Hare) is Bogza's nickname, because his upper teeth show between his cleft lip; the other one they call Ilie Cutui, as everybody knows. Don't we know them? Don't they live down in the valley at Doi Meri?"

"Yes, I suppose you're right, wife," the innkeeper answered, showing his admiration for the woman's perspicacity in a broad smile.

"I am most thankful to the lady for her explanations," Vitoria said, with a humbleness that greatly astonished Gheorghita.

Seating herself more comfortably on the chair, Mr. Vasiliu's wife let her double chin sink onto her breast.

"Are you after a debt? One of these people owes you money, perhaps? It's very likely, for they've swollen and spread themselves like frogs in a pond. I'm a little related to Bogza's wife. She's grown very uppish these days and won't even call on me. 'What's the matter with you, Ileana?' I say to her, 'Have you forgotten the ways you used to tread and your friend's faces?' 'No,' she says 'but there's no time for such things now; I'm so busy, you see.' When you hear her talk thus, no wonder you're vexed. No time for such things! When she's always visiting the mayor's wife or the priest's lady. Does she owe you money for the sheep they bought last autumn?"

Vitoria stared at her in silence. Then she spoke slowly and her words were intended only for Mr. Vasiliu's wife.

"They might well owe me something, either the one or the other. But I don't know how much."

"How is that? Didn't your husband sell them the sheep?"

"I couldn't say."

"Didn't he tell you?"

"How could he have told me? Those who are not with us cannot tell us such things. I have been like a widow ever since last autumn, my dear lady."

"Why, did he abandon you?"

"I cannot answer that either. God alone knows how things are."

The innkeeper's wife then asked confidentially, as if they had been alone, the two of them:

"What is your name?"

The woman told her, and immediately learned the other's name.

"Vitoria, my dear," the innkeeper's wife said sweetly and just as confidentially as before, "let me tell you what I learned from the wife of the other fellow, Ilie Cutui, a conceited thing, too—Gafita her name is—who thinks herself a beauty because her husband gives her money to dress up in fine clothes. She may seem beautiful to him! As for Cutui, she hoodwinks him all the time. He never knows what she does: it is as if she had cast a spell on him. Oh, she's good company for the other one, Bogza's wife. They look fondly at each other and speak with honeyed tongues, but they'd put each other's eyes out if they could."

"But why, Maria dear?"

"Life's too easy for them. They've come into a fortune. In the spring, more than a few hundred sheep will have lambs in the meadow by the Pruth. Bogza is drunk most of the time and goes about with his fur cap set jauntily to one side. When he rolls back from the inn like a full cask of wine, he gets her into a corner and knocks her about."

"Knocks about who, Maria dear?"

"Ileana, of course."

"And why should he do that?"

"Oh, just to prove that he's a real man and strong! But she doesn't care. She has a good time with others."

"And what about the second man?"

"You mean Cutui? That one drinks too, though not as much. And he's as meek as a lamb with his Gafita. It's from Gafita I learned what Cutui says about the sheep. He says he and Bogza bought them from a shepherd a long way off. They gave him all their money there and then, and he passed over all his sheep."

"Oh, so that's how it was? But what about this mountaineer! Did he go back home to the Tarcau or didn't he? Did he fall ill on the way? Nothing seems to be known of him. Did he spend his money on a green-eyed woman? Perhaps you can tell me, you or one of your neighbors. Has nothing been heard of him? Well, we'd better start asking. Somebody should be able to tell us what he's been doing and help us find him. He must have let someone into his secrets."

"We'll see what they have to say when they're asked. And perhaps after a few questions, some girls' pride will have a fall."

The women alone had participated in this quick exchange of words. Iorgu Vasiliu, closing his register, looked anxiously at each of them in turn.

"One moment, my good people," he said, "what are you thinking about? Is it possible that you suspect these men, whom everybody will vouch for as honest and decent fellows, of heaven knows what, perhaps even of murder? The fortune they enjoy has been honorably earned. How would they have dared to murder and rob anyone? Highwaymen might do such a thing but not our husbandmen here in Suha."

"H'm!" the innkeeper's wife exclaimed, crossing herself. "Who has spoken of murder and robbery? God forbid I should believe it, any more than this wife here, but it is fitting that they should render account to the poor woman who goes about the world like a widow. That they should prove they bought their sheep, show what money they paid Nechifor Lipan for them, and tell her which way the shepherd took. Isn't that as it should be?"

"Aye! surely, it is! Let her go and ask, then. It's the woman's right."

"So that's understood. And we are right to ask such questions. But I'd like to offer a piece of advice and say something like this: dear Vitoria, don't go alone with your son to places where you're a stranger, and especially to such a lonely spot as the Doi Meri. The ones you seek may not be at home, and, if they are, they might become angered if asked to render account of this and that. My husband here says that they may have knocked down the shepherd, so they might knock you down, too!"

Mr. Vasiliu listened to all this open-mouthed.

"Did I say such things?"

"Of course you did. And even if you didn't, I consider it best to send them word through one of our lads here that they are wanted at the mayor's. And let him tell them that it concerns an important affair and that it is to their interest to attend. I'll be there, too. You are busy here. But I'll go with this woman, just to keep her company, and to show her the mayor's office. She must have an advocate and a witness. No, no! Coming all the way from the Tarcau, as she has done, she cannot face such ravens as Bogza and Cutui alone, in a strange place."

"Why do you call them ravens, wife?"

"Because they are. Do you mean to tell me they are not? I say they are!"

"Have it your own way but don't breathe a word about your suspicions. No man in his senses would believe such nonsense."

"Where's the nonsense? Won't they believe this woman when she says her husband hasn't come home?"

"Whether he's come back or not is quite another matter."

"Do you think so? It seems to boil down to the same thing for me. Would you have us bind this woman and take her to the asylum, as a madwoman?"

"Did I say such a thing?" Mr. Vasiliu asked in horror.

"Of course you did, so let's send Ghitisor to ask them to the mayor's. This woman will ask questions civilly, and they will reply in the same way."

While the thin, young fellow with the long neck and freckled face whom they called Ghitisor gathered his coat about him and sped along a path that took him over the hill, Vasiliu's wife invited Vitoria into the room on the other side of the round window and there told her all the things that her eye and her knowledge had been able to reach, as well as those that had been reported, of the different, vain and conceited women of the place who thought themselves beautiful. She spoke about many women and with each she found fault, but the worst was the wife of Calistrat Bogza, because her mother had given her beauty and her husband struck her now and again. Of course, it was a good thing he knocked her about, though of little use, and the mayor's wife alone could compare with her when it came to making up her face—nay, Bogza's wife was superior, being past master at such things. And as to spells and charms, there was no one like the chanter's wife in that line. One winter she kept a Hungarian woman in her house for three weeks, to be taught how to work them.

Vitoria listened humbly to all that was said, bending her will as if to the waves and the winds and agreeing in every particular with Mistress Maria, although she was listening with only one ear, while she let her thoughts run elsewhere, to ferret out things as best they could.

When Ghitisor returned, it was about vesper time. Vasiliu's wife immediately took him in hand. He was to tell her, without beating about the bush, if Bogza and Cutui were at home.

"Yes! They were at home," the lad said.

"And when they heard that they were summoned to the mayor's, what did they say?"

"Bogza only grinned, and Cutui answered, 'All right!' "

"Didn't they want to know more? Didn't they ask questions?"

"They did."

"And what did you tell them?"

"Why, nothing. Such were my orders."

"What was Bogza's woman doing?"

"Bogza's woman? How should I know? I didn't look in through the window."

"And you didn't see Cutui's wife either?"

"No."

"What did I say? They're out visiting."

"No. Cutui's wife was at home. I heard her singing. And so was the other woman, messing about in the garret. Bogza asked me who was stopping at the inn."

"And did you tell him?"

"No."

But one could see that he had. Ghitisor's mistress cast him a sidelong glance of contempt.

"When did they say they would come to the mayor's?"

"They came with me."

Vitoria's heart gave a leap. Amidst much talking, Maria hurriedly put on her shoes and slipped on her short coat. They left Gheorghita at home, that he might listen to Mr. Vasiliu's wise teaching, and the two of them proceeded towards the mayor's office. There they found the mayor and the village clerk smoking and chatting with the two husbandmen. Keen of vision, the woman of the mountains had already seen them through the window. She entered in the wake of her protector, as meek and subdued as a lamb.

The thick, loud voices ceased their talk; the tobacco smoke circled towards the ceiling. Vitoria looked at the men and picked out Calistrat Bogza and the small, swarthy man, Cutui. The mayor and the village clerk, fat, well-fed people, were dressed in city clothes.

Bogza was the first to speak: "You will be Lipan's wife," he said with a laugh.

Vitoria looked sideways but still kept an eye on him. She nodded in agreement, waiting for what he would say next.

"Are you collecting a debt? As far as I know I paid Lipan all the money I owed him; perhaps Cutui still owes him something."

"I don't owe him anything," Cutui answered in a determined tone.

Calistrat Bogza grinned again. "Maybe you've come to see how we live here in Suha, then. Thank God our life is not too bad."

The woman of the mountains sighed. "Indeed there are people who live in comfort and are content. I alone am driven from home by my sorrows."

"Now is that so? And what is the reason, pray? Tell us; perhaps we can be of some use to you. Is that why you called us here, my good woman?"

This was spoken by Bogza, who looked surprised and cast a slightly amused look at the village clerk and the mayor, who were also looking surprised. Vitoria hung down her head in silence. Vasiliu's wife then spoke:

"You do not know, good folks, that this woman's husband has not yet returned home?"

Bogza gazed at her in astonishment. She winked slightly with her left eye, while he smiled uncomfortably out of the corner of his mouth.

"Well, and what can we do if her husband has not returned home?"

"There's nothing you can do," Vitoria said gently, without looking up. "I am a woman in trouble and I come to see friends who might tell me when and how they parted from Nechifor Lipan; what they talked about together; and which way they saw him go. Possibly he said something which might show me where to look for him."

Bogza thrust his hands into his leather belt and looked pityingly at Lipan's wife.

"What can I tell you?" he said with a shrug. "On our way from Dorna we agreed on the sale of the sheep. We counted out the money. Part of it was paid by Cutui here. The other part I gave. And then we parted. Lipan seemed to be in a hurry."

"If I could but know where the sale took place . . ." Vitoria sighed.

"Do you want to know? Well, it was along the way somewhere."

"But where, just where?"

"You want to know a great deal," Calistrat said laughing. "How can I tell you exactly the place? As far as I remember we stopped at the Talian's Cross."

"And after you paid him the money, which way did he go?"

"What do you mean, which way? He turned back. Back home, I suppose."

"Don't be angry, Mr. Bogza," Vitoria said. "I only want to know if he said anything about his intention not to go home."

"I'm not angry, my good woman, although I don't much like all this questioning. Maybe you've got something against us; if so out with it. Don't buzz about like a bee that wants to sting."

"Oh, woe to me!" the woman of the mountains answered, crossing herself. "Far be it from me to have evil thoughts or suspicions. I want to learn anything I can from what he said."

"I know nothing more," Bogza retorted sharply, letting his anger get the better of him. "I paid him the money and he went about his business."

"Separating at the Talian's Cross?"

"Yes. As I said before."

"And had the sheep gone on before you?"

"Yes, as they'd gone on all along the way."

"So no shepherd saw him either? No cowherd that he might have dropped a word to?"

Vitoria sighed and stood in the same attitude, her eyes cast down, turning and twisting the stick she had taken from the inn, as if trying to bore holes into the floor.

It was then that Iorgu Vasiliu's wife spoke in a tone of blank indifference.

But first she looked at the portraits hanging on the walls; then winked again, showing what she thought of the crazy, foolish ideas of a woman who was a stranger to their parts.

"You can't expect a cartload of words from those who know nothing, woman."

At which Bogza began to laugh, nodding his approval. Looking at the cigarette he was rolling, he remarked: "That's true indeed."

"A woman will tell you more. Men are tongue-tied folk, but never fear, there'll be others who will know—others who saw your husband afterwards: innkeepers at whose inns he halted on his way back, or those who witnessed the signing of the agreement, and the payment."

Slowly Vitoria raised her head. Bogza lighted his cigarette, puffed at it, and letting the smoke out through his nose, concluded:

"So that's all. I've told you what I know, what I can remember. If Cutui knows more, here he is."

"I know nothing more."

"If a shepherd had been by, you could have asked him," Mr. Vasiliu's wife insisted, addressing Vitoria. "If some stranger witnessed the deal, you might seek him out, provided you knew who he was."

"We shall see about that; if I remember anyone, I'll tell her," Calistrat said. "But for myself, my dear woman," he added, turning to Vitoria, "I rather think he was tired of the old and was after something new."

"What's that you say, Mr. Calistrat?"

"He may have found another woman," Bogza answered, grinning at her.

The others present in the room smiled, too.

"Yes, it might be so," the woman of the mountains agreed, and a slight smile even touched her lips. "If only it were not the ugly, grinning one he has gone to."

Bogza gave a few last puffs at his cigarette; then threw it away. A moment of silence followed. The woman made for the door.

"Then, Mr. Bogza," Vitoria said, "once again, I say, don't be angry, and I ask you kindly not to forget you've been Lipan's friend and, if you remember anything more, to tell me when I come to see you again."

"I'll do that all right," Bogza answered. "Are you going now?"

"Yes, I'm going, for there's nothing else for me to do here. I must needs look for him everywhere, for I have but one husband. I have sought for him along the highways. I shall seek him along the byways and in the ravines. Saint Ann of the Bistrita monastery will direct my footsteps."

All that evening Gheorghita was Iorgu Vasiliu's pupil, while Iorgu Vasiliu's wife and Vitoria, Lipan's wife, held council in the little room, planning many more inquiries. Vasiliu's wife was eager to go in person to the houses of both Bogza and Cutui, to see the women there—the recognized beauties of the world—to weigh intelligence against good looks and see which would turn the scale. Then, if the men could not even be fathomed through their women, if no inkling could be had of thoughts escaping them in their sleep or in drunkenness or through confidences to their wives—then God alone could lift up the darkness.

"One cannot do more than one's best."

"There was a favorite saying of Lipan's," Vitoria said with dreamy eyes.

"And what was that?"

"Nobody can overleap his own shadow. That applies to us and possibly to others."

"Those are true words and wise."

Vitoria closed her eyes, feeling altogether shaken. From the darkness into which he had receded, Lipan, for the first time, had turned and shown his face; speaking clearly, although for her ears alone.

In her sleep that night, she had this vision again. And another of Vitoria's expectations came true. The wind recommenced to blow, this time from the south. Now, having taken counsel and reached a decision, mother and son left their heavy sheepskin coats and some of their belongings at Iorgu Vasiliu's inn, and went for a few days to Sabasa on the other side of the mountain, where Maria had suggested they should make certain inquiries. Vitoria, however, pursued a secret plan of her own.

The sun was showing its strength anew. Going up the winding high-road, over the Stinisoara mountain, Vitoria and Gheorghita heard the voice of rushing waters, and, as they passed over the great, arching stone bridges that spanned the precipices, the sound of these waters grew tumultuous.

Coming down to Sabasa, together with the mountain waters, they halted at the inn of another friend, Mr. Toma. This man, with long hair flowing loose, was as bulky as Mr. Vasiliu was slight of build, and Mr. Toma's wife, Catrina, though a small woman, was as talkative as Maria. She said everything that occurred to her in a soft, secret voice. The very first moment she met Vitoria, she confessed that she had been afraid of her husband all her life, for even though he knew by heart the legend of Alexander the Great and the Holy Virgin's Dream—and knew them better and could recite them more beautifully than a monk—even though he crossed himself piously morning and evening in front of the icons, Mr. Toma's anger was often roused and at such times he would butt into anyone, right and left, like a unicorn. And yet he was not bad-natured. Oh, no! He soon got over his anger, and then never failed to remember he had not had his glass of wine that day.

Sitting down to a meal and to counsel with these friends in Sabasa, Vitoria told them what she had done, seen, and learned at Suha, on the other side of the mountain.

She asked them for advice and for a favor, too.

To their rather lengthy and confused advice she listened, without hearing any of it, thinking her own thoughts. Then, to comply with the wish she had expressed, Mr. Toma rose and prepared to accompany her through the village. He slipped on his new sheepskin coat, brushed back the long hair on either side of his head as he adjusted his fur cap, and, taking a strong cudgel from behind the door, came out into the street, with the strange woman walking behind.

Vitoria had brought with her the white stick, with which she had tried to bore holes into the floor of the mayor's office at Suha. She carried it under her arm as if she thought it might prove of some use, though of what use it seemed hard to tell. They went along a road flooded by water from the melting snows. The village folk were closeted in their little cottages beneath the mountain which sheltered them from the wind, only occasionally showing themselves on their verandas in the sunlight, to take a peep at the passers-by.

"When the water has drained away," Mr. Toma said, "they'll come out of their lairs. The mountain people's tradition now is sleep. It is a well-known fact that the sweetest sleep is in March."

As she walked along, Vitoria stopped every now and then to look over a gate.

"There's still a goodish way to go," Mr. Toma said, with a shake of his fur-capped head.

They turned into a narrow path beneath a steep slope. At the end of it rose a well-appointed homestead, with all its gates closed. As soon as they had passed along the plank fence, Mr. Toma knocked on the gate with his cudgel. The dog within gave answer. Vitoria hurriedly passed in front of her companion and pushed the little gate open, at the same time drawing the slender stick from under her arm, for defence. Mr. Toma walked behind her, twisting his neck to one side to see what was happening.

Three dogs rushed at them with surly growls. Suddenly, the middle one, the biggest, stopped short, while the others momentarily did the same; then, still barking, they withdrew out of the way. The one in the middle, however, stood motionless, pointing. It was a gray, long-haired mastiff with ears and tail cropped in the fashion of the dogs of the mountain shepherds.

Vitoria changed the stick to her left hand and held out her right towards it.

"Lupu!"

Her call was scarcely audible to Toma, though she had called with all the strength of her soul.

Lipan's dog recognized its mistress, made straight for her, and lay down at her feet. It gave a low whine, put out its tongue, and licked the hand that stroked it.

A feeling of sickness passed over the woman, which changed to a sensation of intense joy on discovering in the animal a link with her lost Lipan.

Although he had been told the whole story, Mr. Toma was surprised. He could hardly believe that such a thing had happened: that a woman from the high Tarcau had come and found her husband's dog here, at Sabasa. And the owner of the house looked just as astonished when he saw that the dog really answered to the name the woman called it by, and was overjoyed at seeing its mistress. In answer to the woman's questions, he explained that the dog had come to his homestead last autumn from the mountain ravines. He had seen it prowling about the place; after which it had gone back up the hill and howled as dogs howl in lonely places. Later it had come down again and humbly stretched itself upon the ground somewhere near his gate.

The mountaineer had thought it was a dog that had strayed from the sheepfolds. He appraised the animal as a clever and useful one, and had called to his wife to fetch a piece of cold corn mush. She had put the corn mush near it and left it there. The dog had swallowed it greedily in two gulps, and had waited at the gate to be let in. The husbandman had opened the gate and his own two dogs had rushed upon him. But without fighting them, without a snarl, only arching his back a little, the dog had let it be understood he was a stray looking for a master and for companions, and had gone straight towards the barn, while the hounds had accepted him as one of them. The men working in the yard had called him Pripas, a name the dog seemed to understand, and all winter Pripas had guarded the four corners of the courtyard at night, thus giving good service for the food he got.

Now, if this woman had found her dog and had need of him she could take him, giving due thanks to the new owner, the husbandman said. He himself had no objection, especially as the dog belonged to a sheep-owner who had disappeared without leaving a trace. In the first weeks, the animal had often gone off in the afternoon, up the mountain, seeming to be looking for something. He understood from what the woman from the Tarcau had said, he must have been looking for his master. Perhaps he went to some lonely, deserted place where the corpse lay. When the snow had fallen and piled up, the dog had become more settled. It would still go up the hill sometimes and lie there, but always returned home. A dog's mind is not like a man's. Perhaps it had forgotten the way, if it had indeed been going to see its dead master.

Vitoria now realized that her sudden idea to look for the dog had been a blessing. Where had this idea sprung from? Doubtlessly from Nechifor Lipan. He was no longer among the living, that was certain. But his spirit had returned to her, and prompted her. And it was also a decision from on high, to which her heart always submitted.

She undid the corner of her shawl and gave the man more than he expected. The husbandman thought she had made a mistake and held up the two hundred-lei notes for her to see. But the woman had made no mistake, it seemed. She pushed them towards him, again giving thanks.

The dog followed her, now and then whining gently. When he did this, she bent down and stroked his head with her hand. In her thoughts, she was asking whether he would be of any use to her. She had not the least doubt about this, for had she not been directed towards him by the decision of a superior power?

She would keep the dog and take him up the mountains, until the memory of the places came back to him. Maybe it was God's will that she should linger here until the floods had subsided and the torrents had run down from the mountains. And then she would seek her husband's bones and weapons on every slope, in every ravine. The horse had not been seen, either. Perhaps the enemies had taken it to some fair, down in the plain. Or, possibly it too had been pitched over a precipice and crushed and the ravens had picked its bones, as they had picked the bones of its master. She knew now that from the very beginning she had felt sure of this, her life's tragedy, and for this very reason, from the first moment, her heart had been as if in a vise. In one way it was better so: to know him to be dead, rather than away from his home in another woman's arms, in another woman's bed. And if this fate which nothing could alter had been ordained for Nechifor, God had also brought her, Vitoria, along devious ways and by the aid of the Saint of Bistrita to the very place where she was to find her dear one, that she might take him from the place of his destruction and lay him in holy ground, with all the customary rites.

Now, in accordance with the advice of Vasiliu's wife and Toma's directions, she would have to go all the way to Borca and ask once again if Lipan had not, by any chance, been seen returning from Stinisoara. Toma himself had not seen him. If he had returned, he would surely have halted at his inn. When someone has stopped at a certain place and finds that place to be comfortable, he stops there again. Even though he may not be hungry, he may be thirsty, and, if drawn by neither hunger nor thirst, he comes for friendship's sake. Nechifor Lipan had passed by once. Toma had seen him pass, riding between the two husbandmen. But he had not been seen returning.

Gheorghita, too, was glad to have found the dog; and, as his mother wished, put him on a chain and led him by his side. At vesper time Mr. Toma raised his huge frame, shook his flowing hair, and remembered that in former days, when he was a child, such a deed had happened in the lonely places of Stinisoara. But who murders a man cannot escape God's judgment, he said: he is doomed to be pursued and caught. It is man's duty to go in pursuit. And it is decreed that even the animals, the wild and the tame, also pursue him. If you know how to interpret the wind, and the cry of the birds, and the whining of the beasts, and the ways of gnats and all the other signs there are—though they cannot be known at once—you would soon find the guilty one. But find him you will in any case, though not immediately, perhaps. Therefore, Mr. Toma, as an honest fellow, helpful to people in trouble, never for a moment hesitated to harness his mare to the cart and drive Vitoria to Borca and back again to Sabasa, stopping again and again to make inquiries.

Until then, there might still have been a doubt. But now there was none. Lipan had perished between Sabasa and Suha.

When this had been decided, Mistress Catrina, Toma's wife, began to cry and pity Vitoria. The woman of the mountains, however, refused to mourn. Her task henceforth was to seek and find and plan ahead. She would cry later. There was no time for such things now.

So she mounted her horse and went over to Suha again, Gheorghita by her side, Lupu trotting quietly on his chain.

Rivulets of melting snow were sweeping down the slopes and a warm wind was blowing. They halted on the mountainside and listened to the ice breaking somewhere down in the valley, who knows where. Ravens flew overhead and vultures. But they brought no message to her.

They reached Vasiliu's inn in the evening. Vitoria knew that there would be news for her. And indeed she was right.

The village was talking. People were saying that a judge from the town should come and inquire into the matter of the sheep and find out if there was a deed of sale at Dorna and whether the two sheep-owners at Suha possessed a receipt for the money they had paid Lipan. Nobody hinted that such prominent village folk were capable of an evil deed, but it was as well that they should show proof of the deal. Apart from this, someone had said that the worthy husbandmen must give the names of the witnesses who were present when they bought the sheep and counted out the money. For it was agreed that only a stranger (or strangers) who had been present and seen the money paid over for the sheep, would have followed Lipan and killed him, to rob him of it. The witnesses might have been passers-by, unknown to anyone; neither Calistrat nor Ilie Cutui having seen them before or since. But, if this were the case, they should describe them, their horses and their dress. Trifling pieces of information might be clues to more important things and thus the perpetrators might be discovered.

"But there's another thing, Vitoria dear," Vasiliu's wife, Maria, pursued heatedly. "Just imagine, Bogza's wife suddenly remembered me and paid me a call. But I didn't offer her preserves and water followed by coffee as the mayor's lady does; I just asked her to be seated. And fancy, Vitoria dear, she reminded me of our relationship and said she had come to ask me about the source of all the rumors, so unfavorable, that were being spread about her husband. 'I couldn't tell you, my dear,' I said to her. 'Perhaps it's some of your friends, for the sake of the great love they bear you.' After which she tried to draw me out, asking whether the woman from the high Tarcau had gone back and what her intentions were. I answered her that you had no intentions whatever, apart from going about the world and mourning over your husband. At this, Ileana shed a tear and deemed it unfitting that you had called her husband to the mayor's, for new reports were spreading about the village. It would have been better if you had gone straight to them, where you would have found a glass of wine and a kind word—and readiness on the part of her husband to help discover the criminals, if there were any. 'They surely exist,' I said. 'And before long we'll know them.' And then, I added, 'the woman was wrong not to have gone to your place and ask for advice and assistance.' "

A sly smile played about Mistress Maria's lips, and Lipan's wife smiled too, in silence.

"So she went away, just as she had come, without finding out anything," Vasiliu's wife continued. "And would you believe it, before an hour had passed, my dear, who should I see but her fair companion."

"Gafita came to you, too?"

"Yes, Gafita, Cutui's wife, came to see me. She's more finely dressed than the other but sillier. She came to ask about this and that. Oh! and what things I told her! I admired her clothes and her looks; and lost no time in expressing my regret at the tales her best friend was inventing about her. Of course, I wouldn't tell her who the friend was, for I don't like intrigues. But I told her that she was a good friend and a partner's wife. 'Could it be Ileana?' 'No, not Ileana,' I said in uncertain tones. 'Oh, but it is Ileana, I can see, though you pretend not. And, pray, what does Bogza's wife say about me?' 'To begin with,' I said, 'it's not Ileana, Bogza's wife. And secondly, she doesn't say much, apart from the fact that the whole village knows who comes to your place at night when your husband goes to his sheep.' At which pleasant words she cried out so loud that she made my husband jump out there in the shop. 'Does she say that? The scarecrow, the miserable beggar that Bogza raised from poverty.' 'To begin with, my dear, let me assure you, I'm not speaking about Ileana.' 'Oh, but I know her and what she's capable of. When she looks at me from the corner of her eye in church to see how I'm dressed, she goes green with envy. Oh! I know her. But she'd better look to herself, and not speak about other people. In any case, my husband doesn't come home drunk, corner me behind the stove, and thrash the life out of me. And neither does he have bad dreams.' "

Mistress Maria ceased talking. The two women looked at each other. The woman of the mountains blinked hard and frowned.

"Tomorrow I'll go and see them, too," Vitoria said in a low voice, "to ask their pardon for the trouble I've caused their husbands, but I'll say it would be a good thing to know who'd witnessed the deal and to see the deeds and the receipts, and I'll also say I'm sorely vexed by the rumors that have spread about. And to follow your example, dear Mistress Maria, I'll work them up and poison their mind and force them to let out their secrets. If they have anything to tell, they'll tell it; if they have nothing, I'll leave them to God's judgment. It is not fitting to persecute innocent people. What I want to do is to find my husband. I shall have all the services held according to custom, so that his soul may rest in peace. He has appeared to me in a dream and now he faces me—and calls me."

The two women debated everything in detail and the result was an organized campaign. The next morning Vasiliu sent for Bogza and Cutui to draw up a contract for cheese, a business they had put off all through the winter; spring had come and trade was beginning to be lively again. So the husbandmen at the Doi Meri would come for the contract and take an advance in payment. As the custom is, they would also drink a glass of something to celebrate the transaction, and they would linger some time at the inn. In the meantime, Gheorghita would lie in hiding in the little cottage in the courtyard, while the two women would go first to Bogza's and then to Cutui's. Or perhaps one of them would go to Cutui's and the other to Bogza's. They were to say cutting things and perplex and wheedle and work them up to such a pitch that the young women would writhe like worms. In this way, Vitoria might learn what the women knew of their husbands' affairs, even of their husbands' secrets, entrusted to them, perhaps, under a solemn oath. And afterwards the woman of the mountains could continue on her quest. Vasiliu's wife would remain behind, to embroil the women still more.

Undoubtedly, only God knew the whole truth: but Mistress Maria would have greatly liked to see Cutui's wife less richly dressed! They did as they had planned and since the result was nothing but supposition they could only return home to the inn and talk things over. Later, Vitoria mounted her horse to cross the mountain again with her son.

The road was clear of water now and drying. The pines in the forest rustled gently. Earth showed in the sunny glades, and blades of grass were pricking through. Among the dead leaves in the shelter of a steep slope Vitoria found white snowdrops. She got down from her horse to pick them, holding them to the light by their slender stems. Looking up at the blue sky, she inhaled the fragrance of the forest.

Slipping the bridle over her elbow, she walked on along the path by the roadside. Her whole body felt young and blooming; song ran through her veins; sunlight and joy filled her; then, at once, everything within her seemed to wither like the snowdrops she held in her hand.

The dog whined, as if aching to be let free.

"Let him loose, Gheorghita," the woman said thoughtfully.

The young man slid from his mount and undid Lupu's collar. But the dog showed no wish to frolic. He raised his head and looked as if he wanted to sneeze. Snarling and panting, he scented every breath of wind.

They climbed at a slow pace from one bridge to the other. When they reached the top, they stopped. The dog was sitting on his tail, looking down at the valley attentively, like a man enjoying the beauties of the world. So it struck Gheorghita, who laughingly drew his mother's attention to the fact.

"He likes to look about, too," the woman said seriously.

When they had descended to the second bridge in the valley, on the Sabasa side, the dog stopped, growing restless again. Suddenly, he sprang at the horses; barking and trying to get his teeth into their muzzles.

"I don't know what's the matter with Lupu today," Gheorghita said, looking puzzled. "This morning, too, while I was holding him in Vasiliu's barn, he tried to break loose and started snarling. It was like thunder heard from afar."

"Did he do that?"

"Yes. And only quieted down later, when the people left the inn. Now a new madness possesses him."

"Let's stop the horses and see what it is."

The dog left them and, racing round the parapet of the bridge and on down the steep mountainside, kept going until he reached a grassy plot which shone in the sunlight; then tore back to the road again, rushed upon Gheorghita and seized him by his coat. The lad's leg flew out and the animal fled yelping into the valley following the same track as before.

"Tie your horse to a birch as I'm doing, boy," the woman said, "and follow the dog into the ravine. Last night, too, on our way up, he had something to show us here, but was on the chain."

"But why should I go down? It's a bare, steep slope, and there's no path."

"Go down, I tell you! Lupu's barking. He must have found something."

The blood rushed to the woman's face and her eyes shone. The boy understood. Rounding the stone parapet, he let himself slide down the abrupt slope. The woman leaned over and looked into the abyss. Gheorghita was sliding smoothly down the wet slope, setting the boulders rolling as he went. The dog could no longer be seen. His bark alone was heard from the ravine.

She caught sight of the boy skirting the foot of the slope. Then, suddenly, his fearful cry rose towards her. Sure of what was there, Vitoria gathered her skirts about her legs and let herself glide down as the boy had done. Her head in a swirl, she landed at the foot of the mountain slope amid the sharp, angry barking of the dog. Gheorghita was sobbing, his right arm flung across his eyes. Scattered bones with their wet joints made white patches on the ground. The boots, pouch, thick leather belt and brown fur cap were Nechifor's. And he was there too, at least what the wild beasts' fangs had left of him. The skeleton of the horse, picked clean of flesh, lay a little further away under the saddle and the rugs.

The woman cried out passionately: "Gheorghita!"

The boy gave a start and turned round. But it was the other Gheorghita, the dead one, she was calling. Kneeling down, she hurriedly gathered up the bones, noting the things he had carried with him. The man's skull, she saw, had been broken by a hatchet.

Hastily but tearlessly the woman performed the first rite. She took a rug from among the moist, mouldy things that had been Nechifor

Lipan's, and laid it over his remains. The boy seemed dazed, bewildered. It was only now that he really understood it was his father who lay there. Then he cried like a young child, his eyes growing small with his weeping, his lips swollen. The woman was standing, her hands over her heart, trying to locate the place. From the stone parapet up there, the ground fell away as abruptly as any precipice. The ledge above had been built up and covered with stone. It must have been some twenty meters to the ravine below. The bank here had been eaten into and had crumbled away, and before it stretched a little plateau surrounded by sharp-edged rocks. The ravine, though, went much deeper. It was a narrow, lonely and secret place! No path ascended from it, and the midday sun alone could reach into its depths.

It had been Nechifor Lipan's fate to fall into this ravine as if into a well, struck and pushed by the hand of an enemy. Nobody had seen it happen. Wayfarers had passed without a care along the higher ledges; while not even the shepherds had access to the spot. The autumn sun had risen and set over the lone dead man and over his crushed horse. Driving rains had beaten down upon their corpses; vultures and ravens had picked at them; and at night the wild beasts, emerging from their mountain lairs, had torn at the dead man with their fangs. Only the dog had known about it all and had watched by him until hunger had driven him towards the living. He had returned again and again, always waiting; and then one day the wind had swept the land, the snow had set in, and winter blocked up the ravine. Now the sun had cleared it, in accordance with God's will, and obeying the same will the dog passing along the mountain crest had scented the corpse and signaled his mistress.

Noticing that her son had not yet recovered from the shock, she took in at a glance the height of the slope, wondering how she was to climb up onto the road again. Placing her feet carefully, she looked for a hand-hold and with the help of jutting pieces of rock she made her way upwards, following a difficult, roundabout way.

"I have something to do at the top," she announced to Gheorghita, "I'll be back shortly."

The dog scrambled after her, and she ordered him to stay by the horses, to protect them against any passers-by. She then fumbled among her things and went downhill again with matches and a waxen candle. Lighting the candle,* she placed it in a protected spot, a cave-like depression. She felt a new strength surging within her, apparent in all her movements and in her face.

"Gheorghita," she decided, "you stay here and watch over your father, while I go down to Sabasa to let them know about everything.

---

* See note on page 76.

I'll soon be back with Mr. Toma and the cart; then we'll take the corpse to the village and perform the rites due it."

"All right, mother," the boy answered with a sigh, "I'll stay if you wish me to."

"Yes, stay here, Gheorghita; I shan't be long. And take care the candle doesn't go out." She climbed again to the road, mounted her horse and was gone, leaving Lupu to watch by the other horse.

The boy stood looking at the candle. He could hardly see it in the blaze of the sun which beat down upon it slantingly. At a loss what to do, he had sat down, leaning away from the rug that covered the remains of his father and all those things that had once been his possessions, now an indiscriminate jumble. Never before had he seen such a terrible sight. Looking up and away into the distance, he realized in what a deserted place he was, surrounded by the steep walls of the gully, with only the distant sky above. The forest was near and at the bottom of the precipices were islets of snow.

Then, suddenly, the sun's rays shot over the top of the fir trees, towards the mountain peaks. Out of the corner of his eye, he could see the light of the candle burning more clearly in the shadow of the cave. An immutable silence prevailed: it was as if everything around had become petrified in the light of the setting sun. He remained motionless, listening to his own heartbeats. On hearing high up in the golden sunlight the cry of an eagle, he gave a start. It had called twice. He saw it hovering above, merely moving its head: it seemed to be eyeing him. Another, more distant cry was heard. The eagle floated in that direction. The sky was empty now and twilight seemed to have been sifted gently over the world. Examining his feelings, the boy decided that he was not unreasonably afraid, but he would have liked some living soul near him. The dog was up on the road. He had barked but once. Now he was silent and darkness was over all; no wayfarer passing by.

The stars shone in the heavens. The wind stirred gently.

From the precipice below he heard the grunt of a beast. It may have been an illusion. A feverish restlessness overcame him. He jumped to his feet and made his way upwards, following in his mother's steps. Clutching hold of every support, sticking his heels in the ground, he pulled himself uphill, arriving at the top panting and sweating. The horse gave a low neigh. The dog came up to him. Here on the road it seemed to be less dark. As soon as the moon came out, everything would be fully visible. Even the cave below would be filled with light. Down there the dead man had risen to his feet, clad in the rug, and was waiting for the last blessing and the prayers which had not yet been said for him.

He listened intently. An almost imperceptible breeze floated past him. He seemed to hear the sound of wary steps in the ravine and a rustle all around him. He noted quite clearly the murmur of remote brooks. Later, strange birds passed over the fir tops in the light of the moon. The mountain solitudes pulsated with rushing spring waters; mysterious life again bridged the precipices of death. Nechifor Lipan took flesh and blood anew as the steps, the flights, and the cries went on around him. The boy was aware of nothing of all this but a secret fear that oozed from the earth passed into him and he began to speak to the dog and horse with words that had no meaning. And in order that he might not feel how heavily time weighed on him, he looked for the bag of barley to give the horse. After which, he prepared for himself a sleeping place and wrapped himself up in a rug. He could hardly distinguish the murmur of the night now and sleep was gradually creeping over him when Lupu barked across the valley.

Springing to his feet, Gheorghita struck his forehead against the bag of barley from the horse's head, which made him shout in fright:

"Who's there?"

He received no answer except from the dog, who barked again. Then, as the animal quieted down, the boy heard in the silence the rattling of a cart, a noise which came to his ears like bells.

And now, from somewhere near, he heard voices calling. He recognized Toma's voice. Vitoria Lipan was returning not only with the innkeeper but also with the village judge and a guard. They halted, unharnessed the mare, and lit a wood fire by the bridge parapet.

"Is the candle still burning, Gheorghita?" Vitoria asked.

"I think so," the lad answered doubtfully.

"How can you fail to understand your duty, boy?" the woman reproved him. "Go down and see. And take this: I have brought the church lantern with the cross on it. Light the candle inside and set it by your father. You must know that we can't remove him today and perhaps not tomorrow, either. But we must keep watch, however long it may be, and I have arranged with Father Tudorache to come and read the service here."

"But why can't we take him away?" Gheorghita asked sullenly.

"We can't, for they must look into the matter on the spot."

"Who's they?"

"The authorities. They have their own arrangements. They say that everything must be kept in its place until the sub-prefect comes, the one we saw at Farcasa, and the doctor and the public prosecutor."

"But why should they come? What have they to do with us?"

"They have nothing to do with us. Their duty is with the corpse. They must see how things are; ascertain for themselves that he was indeed killed, and after that set about looking for the criminals. At first I asked them to let me take my man in order that I might perform the rites of proper burial, and to leave me alone. But Mr. Toma, here, rose and advised me to submit, for otherwise the judges would imprison us. When I saw how things were, what was I to do? I submitted. They will do as they think fit and then allow me to take the mortal remains. After that they will have nothing more to do with me, as I will have nothing to do with them."

"But, my good woman," Mr. Toma put in, dissatisfied with Vitoria's explanation, "they do not make investigations out of ill will, but to be able to find the murderer."

"Please don't be angry, Mr. Toma. But will they know who the murderer is if they look at a few bones?"

"That's not the only thing. You'll tell them what you know and what you suspect."

"I?" the woman of the mountains said in astonishment, casting a sidelong look at the other people who had come up from Sabasa with her. After this she fell silent and stood with her left palm over her mouth. "I thank you kindly, Mr. Toma, for the assistance you've given me," she added in a gentle voice. "And will you kindly send your cart here with the priest tomorrow, as I have asked? I'll pay you what you think fit, and deem your assistance a blessing. And in the cart, with the priest, put some twenty loaves of bread, four pounds of olives, ten herrings, and five pint jugs of brandy. Put it all down in your register in addition to what we've brought with us now. For I should like to offer a glass of brandy, a piece of bread and a bite of something in my husband's remembrance to those who'll think fit to come to see the dead, or keep vigil over him. And I offer these things now to his Honor the judge and the guard. Gheorghita, take the jug from under the hay in Mr. Toma's cart and bring it here near the fire."

The men were glad to be treated so amiably and smiled pleasantly at the woman in the light of the candles. Vitoria poured out brandy for them, and they took turns in drinking from the one glass, always remembering to raise their glass to the memory of the dead. Mr. Toma, especially, spoke words after Vitoria's heart:

"May God forgive all Nechifor Lipan's trespasses done with or without his will; and may He kindly give him rest in the earth, from now on at least."

At these words, Vitoria cried a little. And before drinking her brandy she poured a drop of it out of her glass, for the dead. She had been doing that for a long time now; indeed ever since the truth had dawned upon her.

The young lad took the lantern down into the ravine. The others waited for dawn, now and then taking a mouthful of liquor. Later, they too went down to uncover and see what had been left of Lipan.

Mr. Toma returned to the village with the guard and, at Vitoria's request, hired a horse for him and dispatched him as her private messenger to Mr. Anastase Balmez, the sub-prefect, to ask him to be good enough to carry out his tasks in connection with the dead man as quickly as possible, for the sake of the wife who begged him to do so with tears in her eyes, promising to pay all expenses promptly.

In the course of the day the priest took the trouble to come up the mountain with the loaves of bread and flasks of spirits and to go down into the ravine, a difficult feat, although Vitoria had hired a man to cut out steps for him the whole length of the slope. His Reverence was old and bulky and only just managed to get down to the place where he was to officiate. He put on his stole, stroked his white beard, opened a book and began to read the words of old, pausing now and again to recover his breath. The widow removed a corner of the rug that the dead, too, might hear the prayers and look skywards with the black orbs of his skull. Villagers and wayfarers had gathered at the spot, though not so much for the service as for the offerings in honor of the dead. The women told one another what had happened for, surprisingly, reports had travelled on the wind from the far side of the mountain that the criminals were sheep-owners of the region.

Vitoria listened attentively to everything that was said, thinking that she would call on a certain friend and invite her to the funeral, that she might know what other gossip had been spread and what else had been discovered. And she even found pleasure in thinking that there were people there who ferreted out and discovered things.

The representatives of the authorities managed to assemble in the ravine only on the third day. Vitoria stood half turned away, listening to what men who had no connection with Nechifor Lipan might say.

Raising the rug, they looked at the bones, and one of them examined the skull; then they wrote down what they had seen and deduced therefrom. The woman of the mountains was especially hurt by the fact that none of them had made the sign of the cross or said a word to rest the soul of Nechifor, as Christians should.

Mr. Anastase Balmez, the sub-prefect, remembered having seen the woman before. "Is this the man you were looking for?" he asked.

"It is, sir," the woman answered.

"As I suspected then: your husband was killed and robbed."

"Yes, sir," Vitoria answered gently; "but money has been found in his bag; and the leather belt with the purse was not taken from him."

"Then someone killed him for revenge? Is that it?"

"How can I believe such a thing, sir, when he was traveling with friends from Dorna?"

"What friends?" the sub-prefect asked in wonder.

Vitoria then thought fit to tell him what she knew. Namely that, having bought sheep at Dorna, Nechifor had come as far as this spot with two partners and friends who lived on the other side of the Stinisoara mountain at a place called Doi Meri. These friends said that they had bought Lipan's sheep and paid out the money to him. After the payment, separating on the mountain road, Lipan had started for home. It was probably then that someone who was by, and had witnessed the deal and seen the money, had pursued and struck him. He must have robbed him of the money he got for the sheep. It could not be otherwise, Vitoria pointed out, for that was what the two friends of the dead man, Calistrat Bogza and Ilie Cutui by name, had said. Which meant that Lipan did not put this money with the rest; that he had kept it in his hands. The murderer must have struck him and snatched the money; for, as soon as he had been hit, Lipan had fallen into the ravine, horse and all. It was more difficult to believe that the murderer had followed Lipan into the ravine, for the dog had been with his master and would have fought hard for him. In order to rob the dead man, the murderer would have needed to kill the dog, too. But the dog had been found alive. It was necessary to find the witness who had seen Lipan receiving the money. As far as she could make out, the husbandmen at Doi Meri did not know who he was. But if the authorities questioned them closely, they might learn something more. At the same time, of course, they would have to prove the purchase of the sheep by the receipt Lipan must have given them on the mountaintop, although there was no notary's office up there, and the whirling wind did not bring either ink or quills. The paper showing that Lipan had bought the sheep was in his bag and not in the possession of the others. But, if they maintained that they had paid for the flock they had bought from Lipan, and had counted out the money in front of a witness, who would dare say that it wasn't so? It was true the world was full of misleading rumors, and that people on the other side of the mountain were even saying that this was no straightforward business; but she herself could not accuse anyone, being convinced that God would ultimately make truth apparent.

"My good woman," Anastase Balmez said, pursing up his lips in contempt; "I cannot make head or tail of what you say. Was there or was there not a witness when the deal was concluded?"

"I don't know, sir. You will have to ask them and they will answer you."

"Of course we shall. We know how to deal with such matters; we'll question them all right. But what do you know about this witness? Or did you invent him?"

"I did not invent him, sir, but there must have been a witness. For, if there was no stranger whom we could call to book, then the friends must account for it all."

"God alone can understand you, woman. Do you, by any chance, suspect his friends Calistrat Bogza and Ilie Cutui?"

"God forbid I should suspect anyone. But they will tell you what they know and account for everything, as good husbandmen should. Three men rode behind the sheep as far as Borca. On the other side of the mountain, however, there were only two. The third was eaten by the ravens and the wolves, as it is plain to see. They should show who struck him with the hatchet, for he was certainly struck. The skull makes that plain, too. More I can't know, nor can you; let them point out the witness who was by when the deal and the payment were made."

"What witness, woman? Why do you keep talking about a witness?"

"I talk as best I can, sir, though I'm but a weakminded woman."

"Leave the witness alone, then, woman. My duty is to force avowals out of those two. However clever they may be, they won't play with me. I've dealt with more difficult cases than this."

Vitoria shrugged her shoulders and closed her lips tightly.

"You will do as you think best, sir; only allow me to bury my man and perform the Christian rites for him. But I beg you to write to the shepherds, too."

"Which shepherds?"

"Lipan's shepherds who were in charge of his sheep. They must know about the sale, if there was a sale."

"Do you think there was no sale and the two murdered him to take his sheep?"

"I said no such thing, sir. I said you should write to the shepherds. Their master could not have dismissed them without first paying their wages and having a drink with them, according to custom."

"You're right; we'll investigate in all directions. And I think, my good woman, it wouldn't be a bad thing if you came with me to the other side of the mountain and witnessed my interview with Bogza and Cutui."

"I will come with you; why shouldn't I?" Vitoria agreed. "I have a little business there with a friend of mine, a dealer's wife. I want her to be present when these bones are taken to the village and laid to rest in the earth. And it is fitting that I should also invite these two husbandmen with their wives."

"What's that you say? I approach them to investigate matters, and you invite them to the burial?"

"Why shouldn't I invite them? I'll ask them to attend the burial and the burial feast like good Christians. I've nothing against them.

God has not shown me they are criminals. And what if people say this and that; what if Cutui's wife chatters about Bogza having bad dreams and speaking in his sleep? But you, as a representative of the authorities, can question them; for myself, I can only bury my man with all the rites due the dead. So I shall ask them to come; and why shouldn't I? I would ask you, too, if you didn't object. They would not escape your notice, then."

Anastase Balmez nodded his head thoughtfully. The woman was right again, though it was beneath his dignity to admit it. A discreet and wary investigation now appeared to him to be the best way to discover and lay his hand upon the criminals. Certainly, the husbandmen could not refuse to come to the burial at Sabasa. That was what in law books was called confronting them with the corpus delicti. He tried to explain this to the woman, for he seemed to understand what she meant at last and recognized her shrewd intelligence. Vitoria did not know what confrontation actually signified, but she accepted the decision of the authorities with a smile, thinking to herself that it was not a bad thing that this gentleman in the pointed fur cap should know about all the rumors, assumptions, and venomous speculations that were growing like a rolling snowball in the village of Suha, in the next valley. Even though he was a gentleman, and conceited at that, she and Mistress Maria could get the better of him and twist him around their fingers, together with the doctor, Bogza, Cutui, their wives and all.

The authorities having completed their investigations, the woman drew the rug over the bones again and changed the candle within the lantern. While sighing and keening softly, she looked out of the corner of her eyes at the strange people in black clothes and listened intently to what was being said and whispered.

In Suha, Anastase Balmez began his investigations with the cleverness of which he was justly proud. He summoned the two husbandmen for questioning, determined to listen to them with patience and kindness.

"How should I know, sir?" the harelipped man answered in a voice in which there was determination and a little anger. "I cannot know anything about this."

"I quite believe you, Mr. Bogza," the sub-prefect said in an attempt to pacify him. "You are a well-to-do man. You enjoy great consideration. But it is my duty to ask you. And your duty to answer me. For you were with Nechifor Lipan on the way from Dorna to here. You travelled together, you ate together. Isn't that so?"

"It is."

"Such being the case, will you please tell me where you parted."

"Let Ilie Cutui be called. He should be present and answer you also. He was there, too."

"Oh, I'll ask him, never fear. Every detail is of interest to me in pursuit of the murderer. Do you think I can raise a finger without being quite certain of the facts? It is not my intention to wrong anyone. So kindly remember where you parted, for I need a clue to this affair."

"What kind of clue?"

"A clue that might put me on the track of the murderer, something to build on."

"What track? Please don't worry me, sir, I've enough bother without this. I know nothing about the death of that sheep-owner. The only thing I can say is that Cutui and I parted from him when we reached the top of the Stinisoara mountain. When he saw how long the way was to the waters of the Moldova, and thence to the Pruth, he grew tired of it all and decided to get rid of his flock. 'I've enough sheep,' he said, 'on the banks of the Jijia. Pay me for these, at the same rate as for the other hundred, and the expenses I have incurred besides, and go your way. May God grant you prosperity. I'm going back home.'"

"Is that what he said?"

"Yes, those were his words."

"And did you give him the money?"

"I gave him the money. I paid him in notes of one thousand and one hundred."

The dead man's wife sat humbly in a corner of the room, her head bent towards the fire, her elbows resting on her knees and her forehead between her hands.

"It couldn't be otherwise," she said softly, not moving in the slightest. "The husbandmen counted out the money. The other one was by and witnessed it all."

"What other one?" Bogza said with a frown.

"Leave us alone, woman," the sub-prefect said curtly. "Don't mix things up."

"I'm not mixing them up. I want to help out this Christian who is not to blame for what has happened," said the woman of the mountains, turning a gently smiling face towards Bogza. "The stranger who witnessed the counting out of the money, we must know who he is and pursue him."

"But there was no stranger, woman; I've told you so before," the sub-prefect said.

"Maybe there was," Bogza put in.

"Didn't I tell you so?" said the woman. "Though you might have thought I was speaking about Mr. Cutui," she added reflectively.

The sub-prefect was becoming angry.

"If there was someone, let the man own up to it. Who was it? Does he know him?"

"I don't know him; maybe Cutui does."

"He doesn't know him either. How should he? Let us say thieves held him up, and that's the end of it."

"Then why do you keep bringing in that witness?" the sub-prefect protested.

"I don't bring him in, sir. But we mountain people are used to selling things before witnesses and not by means of deeds drawn up by judges. If you say there was no witness, I have nothing more to say. But deeds must have been drawn up. Or perhaps there was no need for deeds either—Mr. Bogza and Mr. Cutui being good friends of Mr. Nechifor Lipan. So know, good folks, that the only reason for my coming here was to invite you to the burial of my husband's remains. That's my only business in these parts, and afterwards I shall go home and leave the authorities to find the criminal. I know that you will find him, sir, so I have no care in that respect. As for you two, you will explain it all like the good husbandmen you are and you will assist in the matter as best you can. But I pray you will not fail to come to the burial."

The sub-prefect was impatiently striking his boot with the little stick he held in his hand. The secretary listened to it all from behind his table, although he did not know what he ought to put down. Vitoria had risen from her seat and was buttoning up her coat. She was no longer interested in the investigations.

"That man of mine was a worthy husbandman," she concluded. "It is fitting you should do him this honor."

"All right," Bogza agreed, though he was puzzled; "we will come if the sub-prefect thinks we should."

"Come with your wives, I ask you kindly. Tomorrow we will hold a commemoration in honor of my husband. It will be the last. The sub-prefect is coming too."

"I?"

"Yes, of course. Can't you talk with them there, as you do now? Perhaps Mr. Bogza will remember better there."

Calistrat Bogza fumbled in his leather belt, took out his tobacco case, opened it and rolled a thick cigarette. The woman laid her hand on the door handle. The sub-prefect was waiting for her to go. He was a little annoyed and would have ordered her to be off, but he was a considerate man.

"I should have liked to say a few things more," the woman now spoke in a high-pitched voice, "but I'll leave it for tomorrow. We'll talk afterwards."

"After what?"

"After burying Nechifor Lipan. He's had his say. I'll be expecting you, Mr. Bogza, don't fail me."

"All right," the man answered, puffing ceaselessly at his thick cigarette.

Vitoria went out. There were gendarmes in the next room. Cutui was sitting at the end of a bench along the wall, smoking a cigarette that was as thick as Bogza's.

The woman stopped near him with a smile.

"You've managed to roll your cigarette at the same time," she said. Then she added: "Mr. Bogza has given you away."

Ilie Cutui started to her feet. "What? Given me away?" he said angrily.

"And would you like to know how? He said you'd witnessed the counting of the money, but I was speaking about someone else."

"I don't understand you, my good woman," the husbandman said weakly, sitting down on the bench again.

"I was telling the sub-prefect that someone else must have been by, who had seen the money handed over to my husband, and that he must be the criminal. But it was proved there was no one. Some people might say, then, that if there were no witnesses the money was not paid. But if Lipan had no money, who would have killed him? And if no money had been paid him, there was no reason for him to return; he would have gone on with the sheep."

"What do you mean—no money was paid? What are you talking about? Didn't I tell you before that we counted out the money when we halted high up on the mountaintop?"

"I know, Mr. Cutui, I'm not speaking about that, and please don't be angry."

"You're not speaking about that? Then what are you jabbering about?"

"Just for the sake of trying to make things clear in putting two and two together, like the folk that have nothing to do except interfere in this affair of ours. You know better than any one what has been done and what you have to say. The dead man has said all that was required, Mr. Ilie. What he had to say, he has said. What are you staring at me like that for? Now it remains for you to have your say, and that will be all. After which the sub-prefect will see what there is to be done. As I rely on your assistance, I asked Mr. Calistrat and I ask you, too, Mr. Cutui, not to leave a friend in the lurch. Now that his remains have been discovered, please come and see him laid in the place where he will dwell forever."

Cutui listened intently, casting sidelong glances at her.

"What's that you're saying?"

"Do come, Mr. Ilie. Mr. Calistrat is also coming."

"If he says he'll come, I will not make difficulties."

"I'm glad, Mr. Ilie, and please bring your wife too. We shall feast together afterwards."

Vitoria went out with sprightly steps. On this occasion, in order to do honor to the dead, she had discarded her sandals and put on her best shoes. She went to Iorgu Vasiliu's shop by the shortest way, choosing the dry paths. There she found the hired cart, in which there would be room for such a good friend as Mistress Maria. She knew that behind the round window she would find Gafita, summoned in great haste by Ghitisor.

She entered, took off her coat, sat on a low stool and looked with pleasure at Mistress Maria. Then she turned to Gafita. She had never expected to meet her, she said, and she was especially glad to see her because she could tell her what was going on at the mayor's office, where the sub-prefect was carrying on his investigations. Mr. Calistrat had been the first to be questioned by the sub-prefect; then Mr. Ilie's turn had come. But Lipan's wife did not like the way in which he questioned them.

Gafita, looking rather worried, asked: "How does he put his questions? And what does he ask about?"

"Oh! He asks them this and that. But before entering, I saw Bogza's wife."

"H'm, did you, now? And what was she doing there, pray?"

"Now, really, I don't know. I stood by for a time, listening, while she chattered with some women. But I can tell you, my dears, that as I'm alive, my only wish is that my friends should not speak about me."

"Did she mention me? I'm sure she did."

"Well, I wouldn't say that. It's not my way to make trouble. But, after all, not everybody is ugly, stingy, and stupid. Not everybody carries on—now with the clerk, and now with the gendarme. I know that these are only rumors born of envy. And there's one thing I've still less sympathy with, and that's slandering the innocent. God forbid! I'm the most worried and embittered woman on earth; I'm a widow, and a poor widow at that, but I wouldn't dare speak about people who are decent folk, with their own homes, and especially about one who is fond of his wife and allows her money to dress prettily, nor would I, God forbid, dare throw out a word, lest anyone might think I had my suspicions. So I invited Mr. Ilie, too, to his friend's funeral, which will take place tomorrow at Sabasa, on the other side of the mountain."

Gafita was a fairly tall woman, slender, and with a beautiful, though expressionless face; with arched eyebrows and big, black almond-shaped eyes that held a certain liquid quality. She wore a peasant skirt with spangles on it, a blouse after the new fashion, and high-heeled shoes. On hearing Vitoria's friendly, impassioned words, she flushed. She looked still prettier now, with the roses blooming in her cheeks. Then she smiled sourly, thinking of the cunning of a certain friend of hers, and sought for suitable words to describe the sort of woman one might find in the world, especially at Doi Meri. As to slander, she had already said that those who are blameless have nothing to fear. Ilie Cutui kept his hatchet at home under the icons. He had gone about the world with it, without fouling it.

"I can swear for my husband. I can swear on the holy cross."

"I know, my dear, don't heed this twaddle, I'm the most sorrowful of women and never strike at anyone. I wait for God to clear everything up. His decision will be manifest in good time."

"That's as it should be," Gafita said, her voice high, her eyes wrathful. "Who has trespassed, let him be punished. Who laughs should know what it is to weep."

"I know," Vitoria said, quieting her down. "I know that Mr. Ilie answered the sub-prefect truthfully; I am not worried about this. Whatever people may say, I have my own opinion of Bogza, too. So far there are no other signs except those the dead man himself has already given."

"But you should know, Mistress Vitoria, that there are other signs as well."

"I know. I know those, too."

"Oh, no, you don't! You think what I say is merely idle talk. But I speak in sorrow and in anger, for in the past months I have had no rest on account of a miserable woman."

"I believe you, my dear."

And then Iorgu Vasiliu's wife interrupted in a soothing voice: "Don't mind her. You are what you are. God has given you that which you cannot lend anyone."

Gafita laughed and was relieved. And in laughter she looked still prettier. The two other women observed her on the sly, darting eager looks at one another. When there was nothing more to be drawn out of her, they let her go. And then, in the little room profusely adorned with rugs and embroidered towels, a sadness came into Vitoria's eyes as she turned towards the icons on the eastern wall. Three times she made the sign of the cross to greet the saints. Then, turning and catching the eye of her hostess who was looking at her eagerly, she quickly spoke, not about the investigations undertaken by the representative of the authorities, but of her wonder that the man who showed his teeth through his cloven lip should still fight against decisions that were above those of men.

"He is trying to fool us, dear Mistress Maria," Vitoria said passionately. "He does not know, poor fellow, that his fate is sealed. I have read him as one might an open book. The little man with the pointed cap has another day or two to play with him. He understands how things are, for he is neither blind nor stupid; but I have asked him to let things slide for a while. All the proofs against the enemy must be clear, according to God's will, and then I would like to see him struggling, as my own husband struggled for life in the ravine. If I could strike him with the hatchet with which he killed Nechifor Lipan, I would do so and feel relieved. But that cannot be; nor can I ask Gheorghita to do it, for he is still a child and too innocent. So I want to stab him and slash him in another way, that I may rid myself of the bitterness which has for so long stifled me. For, dear Mistress Maria, I have lived on this earth solely for that husband of mine, and I was contented and happy with him. But now there are only cloudy days left for me. Sometimes I wonder how I have found the patience to suffer so much, and to carry out everything as I have done. After I found him, I should have laid myself down and mourned for him. But I know who has urged me on and given me strength. I have carried through much already and I shall go on as long as there is breath in me. I have taken every road across this mountain; I have been to Borca many times, money I have spent on every side, and set men and priests afoot; I have spoken through a wire as far as Piatra, dear Mistress Maria, I being on this side, in the mayor's office at Borca, and the prefect on the other side; I asked him to allow me to bury my husband in a cemetery, my husband whose bones I found scattered in a ravine, that he might not remain any longer among the wolves, but lie among other Christians. I sinned thus, speaking along the wire. The men laughed at me when I was frightened by the voice I heard from Piatra. And I did many other things; but now the time is drawing near when I shall have completed my task."

Vitoria rested her head on the shoulder of Vasiliu's wife and began to weep and sigh. Then she wiped her tears with her sleeve and prepared to go.

And on the day of the funeral all the miscellaneous company in that corner of the land in Suha—with its enmities, friendships, intrigues and idle talk, with its hidden fears and hopes—climbed into carts and crossed the Stinisoara mountain to stand beside the corpse as it waited beside its candles for the last alleviation.

Mr. Toma had taken care to bring a good wagon with two beautiful oxen. He had decorated the wagon with fir branches and placed an empty coffin in it. In accordance with Vitoria's order, he had arranged for three priests, three men with mountain horns, and four mourning women. And Mr. Toma had chosen the mourning women from among those who could cry and keen the most effectively; two were from Borca and two from Sabasa. The offerings in honor of the dead were brought in the chanter's cart, while the priests traveled in a green carriage. The villagers lined up with banners and the cross. Some of them carried the coffin into the ravine and when they had laid it down, Vitoria herself turned up her sleeves, carefully picked up the bones of her husband and, one by one, placed them in the deal coffin, sprinkling them with wine. The men carried their fairly light burden up the slope and laid the coffin in the wagon. They covered the lid with a narrow rug with red and black stripes and announced that everything was ready. Then the men who stood by the oxen prodded them on and signaled to those who were ahead with the banners and the cross. When the first halt was called, the priests got out of their carriage, prayed, and raised their voices in song. Vitoria hovered about while they officiated, seeing that everything was done as it should be; an old woman following behind her with the rolls of cloth to perform the rites at the bridges. When they set out again, the mountain people blew upon their horns, proclaiming the event everywhere as far as the most distant valleys. And when the horns ceased, the hired women began to cry and keen with great effect. Vitoria looked on and listened and, although this was her most trying day—her torment being far greater than that of all the wailing women—yet she also felt she had reason to be content.

The authorities and the two husbandmen of Doi Meri were present. Bogza walked apart from Cutui, each keeping on opposite sides of the road. They had not spoken, not even looked at each other. And only when the villagers had brought the coffin to the top of the slope, laid it in the wagon and taken off the lid, did Calistrat Bogza, not being able to refrain, crane his neck over the other people's heads to see the remains of the dead man.

This was certainly Vitoria's impression—that Bogza could not prevent himself—but, in fact, the man had never for a moment considered holding himself in check. He burned, as if with a fever, impatient to examine, and if possible examine closely, the condition of the skull. For if the skull showed no mark of an iron weapon, then it might easily be thought that Lipan, unsteady with drink, had fallen into the ravine at night, together with his horse.

And the men's wives kept apart, too, although they shot hostile looks at one another now and again. The woman of the mountains observed it all, and weighed things carefully in her mind; though at the same time she did not forget any of her duties and even found a moment to join Mistress Maria and hastily whisper some words to her. Gheorghita was not present. As soon as they had reached the site of the tragedy on the Stinisoara mountain he had mounted his horse and, at his mother's request, had ridden on down to Sabasa, ahead of the procession, taking with him the dog and the dead man's belongings.

The procession, moving slowly into the valley, was seen by the hired watchers in the belfry of the church. The bells began tolling. And through the sound of bells came the harsh note of the mountain horns. The villagers stood at their doors, shading their eyes with their hands. Small groups began to make their way to the cemetery.

Seldom in Sabasa had there been seen such a service as that held for the dead man. The golden April sun beat down obliquely on the uncovered remains of Nechifor Lipan. The priests prayed to the Lord God to give peace to the soul of His servant, Nechifor, and then raised their strong voices to sing the requiem.

Vitoria came up to Mistress Maria and asked her hurriedly to see that every rite was performed to the very end. In particular, she was not to forget to ask for the wine at the right moment, to sprinkle over the remains of the dead man; nor for the black hen to hand across the grave. The old woman she had engaged to assist her had everything in her knapsack; there was nothing to do but ask for what was necessary. She begged Mistress Maria to do her this great favor, as she herself had to be at her husband's side at the moment of leave-taking. This would be her last chance to look upon him. After that, she would see him only on the Great Judgment Day.

Approaching the coffin, she raised her hands to her forehead and pushed back her black kerchief. Then, bringing her fingers towards her eyes in a clawlike fashion, as if ready to scratch them out, she cried:

"Gheorghita! Why did you forsake me?"

And her voice held such depths of grief that a shiver went through all those present. Then, falling on her knees, she laid her forehead on the edge of the coffin.

Mistress Maria rushed to her, thrusting the crowd away on either side of her with her hands. She leaned over the woman, took her by the shoulders and drew her aside. Vitoria allowed herself to be taken away, but almost immediately released herself gently, returned to her husband and knelt down by him again.

"Let the boy come!" she shouted.

The lad was near and came at his mother's call, his right arm raised to his eyes. He was at a loss what to do, for he was ashamed of lamenting like a woman in front of all the men present.

Maria lifted up Vitoria once more and the lid of the coffin was quickly nailed down. Instantly, it was let down into the earth and the muffled sound of falling clods was heard. Vitoria returned to the grave but she was calmer now and, like the others, she threw a handful of earth over her husband.

* * *

Note: In Romania there is an age-old burial custom of lighting candles on the occasion of a person's death. This custom is probably based on the belief that darkness reigns supreme in the beyond. Lit candles are placed in the hands of dying persons and at the head of their deathbeds, and kept until the burial. Similarly, candles are lit whenever a mass for the dead is held.

Liviu Rebreanu

(1885-1944)

Liviu Rebreanu is one of the creators of the modern Rumanian novel, a leading figure in Rumanian letters of the interwar period.

His novels *Ion, The Forest of the Hanged,* and *Uprising* are highlights of Rumanian prose that have already long been included among the important works of world literature. He was also the author of a number of short stories and plays, as well as being a dramatic critic and essayist of high standing.

Ion is an admirable epopee of Rumanian village life before the first World War.

The Forest of the Hanged, an analytical novel, is a vast evocation of the first World War with its profound national and psychological implications. This novel initiated a fertile trend that dominated Rumanian prose between the two World Wars.

Uprising, a masterpiece of the Rumanian novel, is an artistic synthesis of village life at the turn of the century. The writer evinces in this work his masterly gift as portrait painter of the masses in movement; his exceptional merit resides in the powerful creation of a memorable collective hero: the peasants in revolt.

Other works include *Adam and Eve* (1925), *Ciuleandra* (1923), *The Little Prince* (1929), *Embers* (1934), *Gorilla* (1938), and *The Two of Them* (1940).

Before embarking on his career as a novelist, Liviu Rebreanu wrote short stories (*Vicissitudes* [1912], *Confession* [1916], *Getting Even* [1919], *Three Short Stories* [1921], *Dream-nest* [1927]). These first literary attempts foreshadow the virtues of his mature work, appearing as preparatory exercises to his great future epic compositions. The heroes of his short stories—humble peasants oppressed by the authorities, or petty clerks pictured in their modest and precarious social existence—are rendered without sentimentality, in crude strokes, with a power of observation that heralds the great master of later date.

Rebreanu wrote three comedies, *The Quadrille* (1919), *The Letter* (1923), and *The Apostles* (1926), and he was also an outstanding essayist and drama critic.

The Death Dance

For two days and two nights Ion Haramu has not budged from his corner of the railway truck. Crouched upon his kitbag, his arms folded around his rifle, he sits plunged in thought and gloom, his eyes riveted upon the floor. Now and then, at rare intervals, he raises his eyes—eyes in which a look of terror has crept in, the terror of a strange and gruesome foreboding—staring around in bewilderment. He breathes heavily, like an exhausted beast of burden, mumbling over and over again the torturing thought that keeps running through his mind.

"I'm going to die . . . I'll be killed in the battle . . . I shall die. . . ."

His lips are parched and his throat is dry as dust; his temples are furrowed by rivulets of sweat that keep trickling down his face no matter how often he mops his brow.

The train rattles along endlessly, and the heavy wheels never cease their maddening grinding. The engines puff and snort like dragons, belching forth thick clouds of smoke that whirl up and up and then disappear into the air. The yells and songs of the weary soldiers form a sinister duet with the clickety-clack of the wheels, like the bleating of a flock of sheep being driven to the slaughterhouse.

Forty men are crammed into the cattle car. Most of them are clustered round the open door, as though wishing to bid farewell to the fields, villages, hills, and to the forest trees that bow and sway as the train speeds by. Their caps pushed over the back of their necks or tilted over one ear, their cheeks drawn and haggard with lack of sleep, the soldiers keep on singing in their hoarse, unsteady voices. A few of them snore away, quite indifferent to their surroundings, huddled among the knapsacks and rifles piled up against the walls.

Haramu rubs his eyes with his fists. It all seems a bad dream and again he murmurs:

"I shall die . . . die. . . ."

The songs suddenly cease. The men burst into stupid fits of laughter, yell, glare at each other as though they had not seen one another for ages, then abruptly lapse into silence, their voices suddenly stilled as if dead. From the other wagons come wailing chants and cries largely crowned by the rat-a-tat of the wheels.

The silence grows deeper, and in the air, dank with sweat, stifled forebodings creep into their souls—millstones weighing heavily upon the spirits of men called on to face death. The same question is on the tip of everyone's tongue. They keep racking their brains to find an answer, which when found they fear to voice.

A corporal, as tall and hefty as a mountain, his small gimlet eyes sunk into their sockets, with a sparse, fair moustache and protruding jaws, breaks the silence:

"Come on, boys! . . . What's come over you? . . . Carry on with your song, come on!"

In a corner three shy, lanky lads talk and laugh in hushed tones. Vasile Fodor of Magura, with his squirrel face, calls back in his shrill voice:

"Right you are, Boroiu. . . . Yes, as soon as we stop singing, cares and worries come over us and we start fretting and grow homesick!"

And in a high-pitched whining treble he suddenly strikes up a love song.

"That's the spirit, Fodor!" mutters the corporal, baring his teeth in a smile.

Fodor stretches out his neck and lustily bellows out the refrain while the others, one after the other, join in, keeping up a droning chorus.

The evening light glides stealthily into the truck. The sky has turned ashen, the horizon disappearing into the mist-covered earth. Wrapped in the thin veil of dusk the singing soldiers seem to recede into the shadows.

Boroiu listens to the melancholy song for a while and then, casting a searching glance around, catches sight of Haramu, still squatting glumly in his corner. He stands watching him for a time and then calls out to him in contempt:

"And what are you sitting there and moping over?"

Haramu raises his forehead, looks up, and stares blankly back but makes no reply.

"Letting it get you down, eh?" says Boroiu as he moves closer, his lips curled into a grin; he stops in front of him with his hands folded behind his back.

Haramu's face is drawn and waxen. His sparse moustache bristles with fear; his filmy eyes are straining to leap out of their sockets, his nose seems thinner and longer, and the furrows round his mouth are deep and more numerous. Peering straight into the corporal's eyes he bursts out in a cracked and grating voice:

"Of course, it's easy for you to scoff. What do you care if you're alive or dead! But I, I've got children, land, and a wife."

Tears well up in his eyes. He pauses for a moment, gulps, and then goes on:

"My children will be left homeless. . . . My wife will remain . . ."

He dares not end his sentence, afraid to voice his fears. He casts an appraising glance at Boroiu, mumbles a few meaningless sounds under his breath, and lapses into silence. His head drops onto his chest, and he begins to moan. A soldier, who is trying to fall asleep, gazes at Haramu sullenly, curses, turns over on his side, and grumblingly dozes off.

Boroiu is rather taken aback. Startled by Haramu's outburst he clenches his fists, involuntarily. He quickly pulls himself together however and says:

"Chuck it, man; there's no need to get so scared. . . . You're not going to die."

"I know I am," replies Haramu emphatically, "I can feel it in my bones. I know I'm going to die."

"Well, I for one know I am not going to die!" mutters the corporal puckering up his brows. "I won't die! . . . Why should I?" He sits down beside Haramu, pulls off his cap, and scratches his scalp. The other man watches him out of the corner of his eye, sulkily, not saying a word. Both sit there, locked in silence, deep in thought.

They are from the same village, in the Somes Valley, and they have been enemies for about six years, since the day Haramu married Ileana, the daughter of Paraschiva and Grigore Bulbuc. Ever since Boroiu has never found rest; nor have Haramu and Ileana for that matter.

Boroiu had loved Ileana and Ileana had returned his love. They went together to the village dances and were inseparable on every holiday; while during the week they always somehow contrived to run into each other several times a day.

But the time came for Boroiu to leave for his military service. Ileana wept bitterly on the day of their parting and, accompanying him to the village boundary to say goodbye, pledged herself to wait for him. She'd rather die than forsake him or marry anyone else.

So Boroiu left for Bosnia, full of trust and hope, and from there he wrote to Ileana and Ileana, overjoyed, answered his letter, and her letter was written in red ink and stained with hot tears.

A year later Boroiu returned home for Christmas, on a week's leave. He was proud of the two white stars that adorned his collar; he had been promoted to the rank of corporal. He was a smart young man, Boroiu was, alert, hardworking, and always willing to help. All the villagers stared at him in wonder and showered him with questions and with mouths agape listened to him showing off his knowledge of Bosnian and recounting his exploits and adventures. Ileana would cling to him, scared like a bird, watching him with entreating eyes. Boroiu seemed quite unaware of her agitation, or, if he had noticed it, had misunderstood its cause. And no one dared tell him that Ion, the son of the wealthy Alexe Haramu, was running after Ileana, determined to take her for his wife, come what might.

Shortly afterwards, Boroiu left for Bosnia and did not return until two years later, during which time he had not received a single letter from Ileana. And when he came back, he found Ileana married to Ion Haramu, and a baby in her arms.

And then, little by little, he learned everything. The villagers told him that Ileana had resisted as long as she could and had succeeded in putting Ion off for a whole year, but, in the end, her father, realizing what her game was, began to take a stick to her and went on beating till she gave in. Old mother Firoana, the village midwife, told him of the hard life Ileana was leading with Haramu and that she cried all day and night; she also told him how her father used to thrash her and bawl at her:

"So it's Boroiu you want, is it, eh? It's Boroiu you're waiting for. . . . Well, then, take that, you slut! . . . . So that's what you're after? To live in misery, be a pauper." And he would shout at the top of his voice for all the village to hear: "You'll either marry Ionica or I'll thrash the life out of you. . . . !"

From his father, Ionica got seventeen plots of land, a large piece of woodland, three pairs of Hungarian oxen, God knows how many horses, two Swiss cows, and an entire flock of sheep, as well as a stone house in the village and two other houses out on the plain.

Boroiu felt that if he were to talk of Ileana with Haramu, he would be unable to control himself and might even kill him. Boroiu had a fist as hard as a sledge hammer while Haramu was as weak and rickety as a starving nag.

They did talk together now and again. Haramu felt guilty about his marriage and constantly tried to soothe him. One day he suggested to Boroiu that the latter marry Haramu's sister and promised to give her a dowry of six plots of land, a house, and a pair of oxen. Boroiu looked him straight in the eyes and replied in a loud voice, so that everybody in the tavern could hear:

"No Ion, I am not marrying. I'll stay single all my life!"

Haramu understood and never brought the subject up again.

Time wore on. Six years passed.

When the Emperor's orders were issued drafting all the men for military service, everyone in the village was distraught and bemoaned his lot, except Boroiu, who rejoiced at the prospect. He was not afraid of death, and had nothing of value to leave behind. He lived a life as solitary as that of a cuckoo, his heart empty and without hope.

On the eve of his departure, who should turn up but Ileana!

"Have you forgiven me?" the woman asked, her eyes brimming with tears.

"I have forgiven you," was Boroiu's desolate answer, his head bent down to his chest.

Ileana would have liked to say more but she did not dare. She stood for a while wiping her palms against her sides, waiting for a word of encouragement. And it was only as she moved towards the door that her voice returned:

"Forgive him too," she said softly. "Take care of him and protect him and don't let my children be left fatherless."

From beneath his bent brows, Boroiu could see her tremble with shame. At length he replied:

"It shall be as God wills, Ileana!"

They parted without shaking hands and without even glancing back at each other. And yet a ray of hope stole into Boroiu's heart. He was afraid to admit the thought that had risen in his mind. He tried to banish it, but instead found himself cherishing it all the more fondly. Ileana was, he felt, dearer to him than ever before, even though she had had three children by Haramu. He loved her. And now he could not suppress a surge of joy to see Haramu tortured by the thought of death.

Haramu is moaning and he can hear him mutter:

"I'm going to die. I'll die . . ."

Boroiu draws a deep breath, tugs at his moustache, and whispers:

"Don't be afraid of death, Ionica! Only those die who are ordained to die!"

"I am one of them, Boroiu; I know I'm going to die!" Haramu replies in a stifled voice.

The corporal, ashamed of his thoughts, lapses into silence. He listens for a short while to Moise Tripa, singing in a hoarse voice at the door, his legs dangling out of the truck, the other men laughing and stamping with their boots, the wheels clanging incessantly like a row of little hammers striking a giant anvil. Again Haramu's voice breaks through:

"If we only knew where they're taking us to, Boroiu."

"Wherever the Emperor wishes," says the corporal; then, after a short pause, he adds: "Keep close to me, Ionica; you'll be safe near me."

"Yes, Boroiu, I know I will . . ."

"For death never comes stalking after me. . . ."

Swiftly Haramu turns his head in Boroiu's direction searching his face. It's too dark; he can see nothing. But he hears the man's powerful, regular breathing, and a strange feeling shoots through him, making his blood tingle, his heartstrings twitch and his body stiffen. He feels as though a rough, invisible hand is clutching at his throat, slowly tightening its ruthless grip. He is afraid of this man who is not afraid of death. His mind wanders to Ileana, to the children, to the Boroiu he knew before.

"He's a good chap, Boroiu . . . generous . . . if he said nothing at the time! . . . Now, there are plenty of other things to worry about . . . God forbid."

Night has closed in.

Now there are only three or four sitting in the doorway of the truck. The singing has ceased. The soldiers have stretched out on the floor and are talking in whispers, lest they should disturb their comrades' rest. The whispers are mingled with deep sighs and from a distant wagon a solitary, mournful tune is heard in snatches, cut off every now and again by the noise of the wheels and engines. The telegraph posts flash past, tracing a black stripe against the patch of dark-blue sky that, with its twinkling starry eyes, casts its tender gaze upon the heavy-hearted soldiers.

Sighs and moans fill the trucks. An invisible terror has gripped the several hundred soldiers rolling on to a grim destination. They would all like to sleep, to forget what they are and to dream about what they would like to be. But sleep refuses to come.

Hundreds of men lie there, racked with fatigue, their eyes wide open, peering into the darkness, striving to pierce an impenetrable future. And through the hundred fear-stricken looks that find recognition in each other's eyes, runs the same anguished foreboding.

A soldier tosses restlessly in his sleep. Suddenly he leaps to his feet and rushes towards the truck door, crying out in terror. Startled from their thoughts, the others spring forward to hold him back and quiet him.

"Grab hold of him quick, or he'll jump out of the train!"

"Stop him, lads!"

There follows a sudden flurry as if a badger had broken into a hen coop. All cluster around the fear-ridden sleeper, soothing him with comforting words. Quite some while passes before peace is restored; the silence then is even more depressing and more agonizing.

Haramu mutters a prayer and is irritated at not being able to remember all the words. It is a prayer that in his childhood he used to say every evening and from which he now hoped to gain some encouragement and relief. From time to time he turns his head with concern to Boroiu, who quietly snores away beside him. He is acutely aware of Boroiu's peacefulness and this makes him still more restless. His thoughts keep returning to Ileana and to Boroiu and he feels guilty towards him. At one moment he is on the point of begging Boroiu's pardon and almost utters the words of apology, but then changes his mind. He had better leave things as they were.

And the corporal feels perfectly contented . . . as if he were going to the fair or to a party.

Towards midnight the soldiers gradually drift off to sleep, worn out by their thoughts and anguish. Their slumber is broken by frequent sighs and on and off by a burst of laughter or a doleful groan.

The train keeps rattling. The engines chug wearily along. The earth races past the trucks. The sky smiles down like a forgiving mother.

Then, after miles of running non-stop, the train halts with a heart-rending series of jerks. All the cars are asleep; only the engines blow out clouds of steam through their steel nostrils. The stillness weighs heavily; the entire world seems to have been turned to stone under the sheer weight of darkness.

All at once the hoarse blast of a bugle rends the stillness. A startled murmur is heard throughout the reawakened cars, like a shudder running through them all.

"The Russians! . . . The Russians!"

A warrant officer shouts sternly before every door:

"Five minutes! . . . Alarm! . . . Five minutes!"

The noise in the trucks increases; the clatter of rifles colliding, the creak of kitbags flung over men's backs, repeated curses hissed between teeth, vain moanings. A stout, moustached officer runs breathless between the lines, waving his sword about:

"You blithering idiot! Do you think the trumpet is blown when the enemy's around!"

A group of sleepy and shivering officers crack their bones on the station platform, which, with its two lighted windows, looks calmly and indifferently into the night, heedless of what is going on around it. In the haze flurried orders and short commands ring out above the general commotion.

Another bugle shatters the night's slumber, despite the stout officer's intervention, who, cursing, presses his hands over his ears. The next moment there follows a prolonged stamping, as if a gigantic dance were about to start. Like lightning, the companies line up in front of the empty railway trucks that look like greedy mouths exhaling a foul stench of human odor.

"The dance is beginning, Ionica. . . . Now we're in for it!" says Boroiu in a whisper so as not to be overheard by the officer who is nervously walking up and down in front of the sergeant major, yawning all the time, his sword dangling behind him.

Haramu gives a start. He misses the meaning of Boroiu's words, but feels the cold air. A slight, wet breeze is beginning to blow. The company marches off along a narrow, muddy lane.

"Seems to have been raining here," thinks Haramu. "It was quite warm when we left home."

The man in the back of him keeps treading on his boots. "It's damned annoying. Who the hell can it be?" He can't make him out. Boroiu, though, is at his side. He recognizes his heavy, firm stride. He knows it all too well.

They seem to be marching through a village. Some dogs bark quite far off, only for some more to join in close by. A speck of light, yellow and faint, flickers for a moment and dies out almost at once. "It must be a village . . . . Yes it is . . . a village."

They walk on for a time and then come to a halt.

"What are we waiting for?" says Haramu to himself. "Why don't we start fighting?"

They all fling themselves down in the ditches on the side of the road. Left on the road itself are only the piles of rifles and the groups of officers looking like ghostly shadows. In the sky in the distance, thick, black, threatening clouds are gathering. The stars—such as they are—weep in alarm. The main road glitters in the dark as if it were made of old silver. An early cock crows, followed by several others in turn, some hoarse, some shrill, some furious, forming the respective parts of the morning concert. An alarmed cricket chirps his repeated shrill signal. The dry leaves scurry about before the wind with an occasional crackle.

Haramu lies on his back, motionless, staring up at the gray sky, overwhelmed by his thoughts. A smell of dank earth tickles his nostrils, reminding him of home. And all at once the sky is no longer alien and these strange noises fade away. He is back in Prislop. Down the main alley the poorer houses shyly hide their faces behind their rickety fences made of twigs. His house alone, built of stone, rises haughtily up with its red tin-sheeted roof. He strides proudly into the courtyard. The cows and oxen chew their cud lazily and cast a long glance at him. The sleepy stableboy is bailing out water; he can hear the creak of the well sweep. In the hall kitchen, Ileana, with her tearstained eyes, is sitting near the fireside with the youngest child in her arms. The fire crackles in the hearth and the fluttering flames give out a soothing warmth. In the upside-down bed, the other two children lie asleep, uncovered, Toderas smiling as he dreams.

A cold shiver runs up and down Haramu's spine; he shudders, sweeps his hands over his eyes, and heaves a deep sigh.

"All's over . . . I am going to die," he thinks, suddenly flooded by his old fear.

He feels an immense emptiness inside, as great as if someone had wrenched all his insides out and left a void. The same void is all around him, stretching away into infinity as though the universe had been atomized, and he alone had survived, terrified and distraught.

The lieutenant, a tall, lanky, red-haired Saxon with a waver in his voice, gathers the platoon around him in a cluster. He speaks broken Rumanian. He tries to appear energetic, but his voice trembles.

"The enemy's not far away, lads! . . . We will soon have our baptism of fire. . . . Be men! Rumanians are brave. . . . Be Rumanians!"

The soldiers listen in silence, their mouths wide open as though unable to grasp the officer's words. The lieutenant keeps on talking. "The Emperor . . . Rumanians . . . Russians . . . Enemies. . . ."

Not long after an officer comes galloping up. He reports something in German to the colonel in such a loud voice that he gives the impression of being scared. The men understand nothing. The officer continues to shout, then turns his horse around, and vanishes. Hurried commands are given out. All the men cross themselves of their own accord, as if by order. Then the feet start marching and the road seems to shake under the cadence of their steps.

The winding road follows a bend here, another there, climbs up some slopes, crosses several villages. The freshly strewn gravel crunches under the soles of their hobnailed boots. The soldiers trudge along in silence as if they were going to a funeral. Now and again an officer mutters: "Cheer up, lads!" But the voices too sound hollow and die out without an echo.

Haramu drags himself along, his eyes wandering to right and left in search of something, he himself doesn't quite know what. The dawn breaks, but the sun has not risen yet: the clouds in the east are holding it back fettered. Haramu feels the same void in his soul. His brow is burning. His face is as white as a sheet but a smile flickers on his lips.

"In these parts they've already done most of their harvesting," he says to a soldier who is also surveying the stubblefields and cornfields.

"Another people, another country, other customs," the man replies shaking his head thoughtfully.

"What a lovely crop there was at home! . . . The crows will be gathering it now!"

Haramu laughs bitterly. The soldier laughs too and shakes his head again.

All of a sudden, God knows why, Fodor leaps out of the line and begins dancing a jig, yelling like mad. The entire company breaks into boisterous laughter, and Haramu suddenly braced up, urges him on:

"That's the stuff, Fodor!"

They plod along, marching without respite. By now the sun has moved behind them. The heat burns into their soles and their feet ache. Heaven knows how long they've been marching!

The road wedges its way through a broad valley that looks more like a giant ditch. The companies make a brief halt and move aside to let a long convoy of carts pass by, loaded with heavy white cases, marked with red signs. The drivers sit smoking their pipes on their boxes, utterly indifferent to their surroundings. An officer on horseback keeps milling about around the carts, cursing for all he is worth, and threatening people left and right with a broken riding-whip.

"Ammunition," whispers Boroiu, and a strange gleam of joy lights up his eyes.

Just as the convoy is passing by, a long, muffled rumble reverberates in the distance. A deep silence follows, broken only by the grinding of the rusty wheels. In the sweltering heat all eyes are raised inquiringly, searching the sky towards the east.

"That sounds like rain!" breathes Haramu after a time.

"No, it's the big guns!" replies Boroiu, the same exultant joy in his eyes.

Haramu eyes him suspiciously. He laughs and bares his teeth like an angry dog. His voice trembles:

"It's beginning then. . . . High time it did!"

The column is now climbing up a slope. The thunder of the gunfire slackens. The soldiers begin to pant with the effort. They go on climbing higher and higher.

On the hilltop the sky is suddenly rent asunder as if a window had been flung open: the earth shakes with the impact of the blasts. Instinctively the men cross themselves and duck their heads.

Before their eyes a wide, endless, smooth valley stretches out. Far in the distance, a dented range of hills adds its bluish outline. The valley in its full expanse looks like a vast map spread out upon a giant table. Silvery roads wind their way through pale-green patches. Here and there are scattered violet patches of woodland and bushes. Then wide strips of yellow cornfields. Scattered about at random are a few villages, their houses standing seemingly terror-stricken under the rolling gunfire that never ceases. Far to the left, there is a village in flames, its smoke rising to the sky. Straight ahead, another village is wrapped in a cloud of yellow-gray smoke, and every now and then black columns whirl up from it when a stray shell bursts in the cluster of ruins. Further off, lost in the distance, blazing fields can just be made out. The smoke rolls over the land, reeling like a drunkard wandering across a field.

The companies turn to the right along a narrow path lined with thick poplars. They tramp along . . . on and on.

Again they pass through a village. In one of the broader lanes there's a string of twenty carts lined with straw. The drivers wear the Red Cross insignia. Raised on the church steeple is a large white flag with a red cross fluttering in the wind. A very young doctor, standing with his hand raised to the peak of his cap, smiles gaily, crying out from time to time: "That's all!" Boroiu cannot refrain from putting Haramu wise. Peering straight into his eyes as if thrusting a knife into his heart he explains:

"That's for the wounded. . . . You know, if you're mortally wounded, it's here they bring you to die."

"I'll die on the battlefield," stammers Haramu under his breath, stretching his neck forward like a sick duck. "There'll be no need to carry me to this place."

"Shut up, man! Talking of death all the time. You are a miserable cuss! Harping incessantly on the same theme. And suppose you do die. What of it? You just go out like a light and that's that. There're plenty of men here to bury your corpse!"

Haramu fearfully looks up at Boroiu and shudders. There's a look in the corporal's eyes that makes his blood curdle. He'd like to tear himself away from him but cannot. A thought flashes across his mind:

"Boroiu would be happy to see me dead!" But no word breaks from his lips. He trudges along, dragging his leaden feet behind him, sighs and finds comfort in the thought: "As the Lord will have it! His will be done!"

The rolling thunder of the guns gets more and more savage as they move closer. Like tiny toys some guns can be seen behind a flat hillock, with the men moving around like black beetles.

At their sight, Haramu brightens up with childish delight, and cannot take his eyes away from them. The hoarse, loud blasts are music to his ears. He is suddenly seized with a feeling of boundless, blind self-assurance and he bursts out joyfully:

"Look at the guns! . . . Our artillery! Our guns!"

He catches Boroiu by the sleeve and tugging at it cries proudly: "Look at our guns!"

At that very moment a terrifying crash rends the air. A shell bursts somewhere behind the troops with a blinding flash. A white cloud, no larger than a haystack rises, swells out, hovers for a few moments in the air, and then breaks up and fades away. Boroiu retorts with a sneer:

"The Russians have sighted us and have started shelling."

"We've got guns too," cries Haramu triumphantly. "Look at them down there!" He points to them, laughs buoyantly and goes on: "I don't know what's come over me, but I feel as strong as steel! I'm not afraid of anything. If now a bullet were to strike me dead I wouldn't utter a sound. After all, one can only die once, right?" He laughs boisterously and starts stamping his feet, as on parade, calling out in a loud voice: "Left! Right! Left! Right!"

The corporal eyes him wryly, mops the sweat from his neck, and walks on in silence.

A wounded gunner comes staggering up the road. He sits down on the edge of the ditch to let the column pass. His head is swathed in dusty, blood-soaked rags. A wide dark-red stripe trickles down from the collar on to his gray tunic. There is an oddly terror-stricken gleam in his eyes and from time to time he murmurs horrified:

"It's hell on earth!"

At these words Haramu suddenly feels his confidence drain away. He marches along with the others but no longer seems to be aware of what he's doing. The image of the bloodstained gunner is constantly before his eyes and with it the haunting thought of death.

He finds himself all at once in a cornfield, running forward, his rifle in his hand. "How did I get here? What am I doing here?" Boroiu is a couple of paces ahead of him. "Why does Boroiu want my death?" The soldiers are dispersed in all directions; panting heavily they trample over the cornstalks. The lieutenant with a buoyant step cuts his way through the corn, as if testing the sharpness of his sword on the dry stalks to right and left. Every now and then he turns back and hisses something, keeping his voice as low as possible. The guns continue their booming. To his left the rat-a-tat of rifle shots. A faded leaf strikes Haramu in the face and the light blow suddenly drives his thought back home. He remembers that the plot near the brook had been mown but hay left ungathered. "Let's hope there was no rain to spoil it. It would need seven men to stack it up. And what hay! Silk, nothing less! Ileana will certainly attend to that; there's no need to worry. But she'll have to hire women to gather it in. Women, of course. The men are all away. . . . Quite a large number of the men, that is, have left. God knows how many will return. . . . It's Friday today, isn't it? Yes, Friday. A fast day. One can't fast out here, though, can one? You're thankful for any morsel of food you can get. . . . " It occurs to him that he had not eaten anything since yesterday morning and that he's hungry. He pulls out a piece of pie that he has brought from home, made by Ileana, and hurriedly gulps down a few large mouthfuls. It may be the last time he'll ever eat anything, God knows. "In wartime you're alive now and you're dead the next moment. . . . God forbid!"

The cornfield is endless. Nothing but ridges, ditches and cornstalks. "Where are the Russians?" Haramu murmurs to himself. The question begins to drill into his mind.

"Where are they? Where can they be?" Before him all he can see is Boroiu's back, his knapsack, the back of his cap, and his water flask that keeps dangling and clattering incessantly. The thought that Boroiu wants him to die flashes through his mind, but a second later he returns to his query: "Where the hell are these Russians?" He is as nettled as if he'd been slapped in the face. "Call that war, and no Russians to shoot at! . . . Absolute disgrace!"

The next moment he finds himself lying flat on the ground, next to the corporal. They're at the end of the cornfield. The lieutenant is peering through his field glasses. All of a sudden, in front of him, a volley rings out followed by the officer's shrill order:

"Fire! Open fire!"

To his left, out of the cornfield, there leaps a string of soldiers who advance in formation like an accordion. By his side, Boroiu aims and fires. The rifle booms like a cannon. Haramu wonders why it booms so loudly. He would like to shoot too, but sees nothing in front of him.

"Where are the Russians?" he asks angrily.

"Are you blind? Don't you see them?" mutters Boroiu, aiming again.

Haramu stares out across the field in vain. He shoots away however just to appease the same torturing urge to do something. He keeps firing, though he is unable to see the slightest trace of enemy, and feels exceedingly pleased with himself.

Just then the lieutenant cries out in a scared voice, "Forward!" and leaping up, bounds off like a hare.

The men all rush after the officer.

A shrill whistling sound shoots over his head as he races along. "That's a bullet!" he thinks, peering to right and left out of the corner of his eye. After a few paces he hears another buzz, like the drone of a humming bee passing by close to his ear.

"The bullet seems to be after me! It's on my heels!"

When he finds himself once again sprawled on the ground he heaves a sigh of relief and starts firing like mad. He happens to be lying between the lieutenant and Boroiu. They all keep shooting, even though there's no sign of the Russians. Large beads of perspiration flow down the officer's cheeks. Haramu hears him clearly ask Boroiu: "Have any of the men been hit?" and Boroiu answer in a remote bass voice: "I didn't look back. . . ."

Immediately after, the lieutenant bawls out another order and the wave surges forward again. The whine of the bullets seems to get shriller at every step. He feels them whistling past, but no longer pays any heed to them. The same idea keeps darting through his mind: "Where are the Russians?" As he charges forward, a heart-rending cry strikes his ear. A soldier—it seems to be that Fodor chap—rolls over on the freshly plowed soil like a dog with its spine broken. "They've killed him!" cries Haramu frightened. To his right, Trifon Mocanu swears lustily, limps on for a few paces, then drops down in a heap, moaning and wheezing. The bullets keep flying past without cease, more savagely, and in steadily greater number like crazy adders. Haramu feels as though he has been racing since Adam and that the race will never end. His feet are numb, his head is spinning.

When he comes to again, he is in a ditch, his rifle at the ready, and he hears the lieutenant's voice:

"Range one thousand, lads! One thousand!"

And all down the line the order is passed on from man to man growing fainter and fainter.

"Range one thousand. One thousand."

A couple of paces in front of him the earth spurts and a little cloud of yellow dust rises like a fur cap.

"It's still after me," Haramu says to himself, but he has no time to think of the bullet, for the haunting thought returns: "Where are the Russians?"

Two further charges forward. The bullets buzz around them like a swarm of maddened wasps. Cries, moans, oaths keep resounding, soldiers keep falling and rolling over with a groan. The rifles crack incessantly, now at longer, then at shorter intervals. The gunfire has abated, but every now and again a shell lands, and pieces of shrapnel fly through the air. Haramu never stops asking himself: "Where are they?" He is boiling with rage.

"We cannot advance any further," he hears Boroiu say. "More than half have fallen."

"Right, dig in! Dig in!" the lieutenant urges them. "Not all at the same time! In turns! Take it in turns!"

Before Haramu has time to unfasten his spade, he notices some of the men crawling up to a ridge that separates two burned-out stubblefields. He creeps up warily and slips safely into a ditch. Then, he pokes out his head to look for the Russians. In the distance, at the edge of a cornfield, lined with trees, he catches a glimpse of the tips of their caps.

"Look, Boroiu! There're the Russians!" he cries out with a sigh of relief, as if a weight has been lifted from his chest. "Look at the enemy! Look! Look!" He feels as happy as a child.

"All right; I see them too," murmurs Boroiu taking aim with the utmost care. "Come on, Haramu, shoot or they'll get us first!"

Haramu starts firing, and after every shot settles down even more cosily in the ditch. He seems relieved of a great worry. His spirits rise. He even feels chatty, but Boroiu is in a foul temper and keeps cursing and fretting. Haramu shoots, works out accounts and plans, and is no longer willing to die.

"After all, why should it be me? Why not other chaps who have no one and nothing to return to. I won't die since I don't want to die! . . . I won't!"

And yet he feels fear working its way into his heart, and refusing to be chased away, no matter how often he repeats: "I'm not afraid!" The lieutenant lying next to him begins to moan. "They've got him,"

Haramu thinks, as he sees the officer's head drooping to the ground, a large bloodstain on his left shoulder. "They've got him in the shoulder, the poor chap! It's all a matter of luck. . . . What's the good of being born under a lucky star if a bullet gets you!" Then again his thoughts wander to his hayfield near the brook and he starts worrying lest the rain has spoiled the hay. . . . "Damn the hay. Is there nothing else to worry about!" He tries to change his thoughts, but in vain, and for the twentieth time begins to work out how many carts of hay he can get.

"Ion!" Boroiu's voice rings out. "Look out! Another company is coming to reinforce our lines. Do you hear me? When they get here, we'll be going over the top again. . . . Do you hear me?"

Haramu stares at him with wide open eyes. "What does Boroiu want with me?" he muses suspiciously. There seems to be an air of exultation in Boroiu's glance. "What is he so happy about? Does he think I'm going to die? . . . Yes, he does, most certainly. . . . He wants me to die, that's it. And after I die he'll return home and take Ileana. He has a grudge against me on account of Ileana!" He shoots a look of hatred at Boroiu and shouts:

"Ileana, eh? So you think I'm going to give up the ghost here, do you? Don't delude yourself, I'm not!"

Boroiu does not hear a word, since the din is as great as in hell. But he grins back joyfully, as if he can guess Haramu's thoughts. From the rear, heavy steps, panting breath, clatter of arms, quick commands keep moving nearer. Just when Haramu is turning round to see what's going on, a wild cry bursts forth: "At them, boys! Forward! At them!" He springs forward to join in the assault but he advances no more than a step when a blow in his left hip stops him short.

"They've got me!" he grunts, rolling back into the ditch. "They've broken my leg." He tries to lift himself up but fails. He feels his leg with his fingers, raises the flaps of his tunic, and his fingers are instantly stained with blood. A bullet has bored a hole through his belt.

"They'll have to cut my leg off. . . . I'll be left a cripple." His eyes grow dim. The wound becomes more and more painful. "I'm fainting. . . . I'm dying," he thinks, terror-stricken. He tries to call for help, but his lips refuse to open. The blood trickles down his skin. He feels the heat of the blood. "If only I could stop the blood," crosses his mind. His hands tremble but he cannot move them. He begins to murmur the "Our Father" and feels a little more comforted.

He expects to faint every moment and is surprised not to have as yet. "I'm bound to die. There's no hope. I'll bleed to death in this ditch like a stray dog. . . . Will no one come to stop the bleeding!"

He remembers the carts with straw at the end of the village. "And Boroiu will remain with Ileana. He'll survive all right. . . ."

Time passes heavily as if it were melted lead. The sun is on the wane. The air all around smells of gunpowder.

Then all at once, Boroiu and several other soldiers appear in the ditch. They all look terrified and try hard to keep under cover, firing back desperately. Boroiu's face is as black as a gipsy's. He swears savagely. Haramu strains himself to call out but only a moan escapes his lips.

"Good God! What's the matter, Haramu? Have you been hit?"

Boroiu's voice calls up the picture of Ileana. Haramu's eyes close, his lids are too heavy. Boroiu runs his hand over him and murmurs:

"Where did they get you, man? Oh, I see! For Heaven's sake, the blood's gushing out as if you were a stuck pig."

The wounded man feels first a piercing pain then a moment later a soothing relief.

"I've tied it up, Ion," thunders Boroiu's voice in his ear. "It'll be all right . . . provided they don't attack!"

Haramu gives a faint groan and then hurriedly, parrot-like, begins to mutter a prayer under his breath.

After a while—Heaven knows how long—terrified whispers reach Haramu's ears: "They're coming! . . . There they are! . . . Coming straight at us!" and soon after Boroiu's voice, harsh and hoarse: "Back . . . All back!"

Haramu is seized with terror. He sees the soldiers leap out of the trench and make for the rear lines as fast as they can. "The Russians are coming!" he thinks and all pain vanishes, replaced by a feeling of horror that freezes the blood in his veins, conscious that he will be left behind and trampled under the enemy's feet like a worm. He musters all his strength and cries out in despair:

"Boroiu, brother, don't leave me behind!"

Boroiu stops short, undecided.

"Don't leave me, brother, to die among strangers! . . . For pity's sake!"

They peer into one another's eyes. Haramu entreating, Boroiu irresolute. The corporal's first thought is to leave him there, at the mercy of the Cossacks. Just as Haramu had ridden roughshod over his life so should the enemy trample him under their feet. But at the sight of his face, turned as white as a sheet and his eyes overflowing with tears, his heart melts. He recalls the picture of Ileana standing before him, her downcast eyes in tears, and he seems to hear the echo of her trembling voice: "Look after him and protect him!"

"All right, come along!" grunts Boroiu curtly, stooping to raise him on his back.

The bullets whiz and whistle in the air without respite. Panting heavily the corporal staggers along with Haramu on his back moaning and wailing. The whole expanse of stubblefield is filled with soldiers fleeing in panic, aimlessly, anxious only to escape the shower of bullets.

The pain grows fiercer and unbearable. He feels like yelling out but is afraid of Boroiu. He smothers his cry, clenches his teeth with all his might and only when the pain is too great does he let out a stifled groan.

"Now then, stop it; it's not so bad as all that," says the corporal cursing him beneath his breath, plodding away as heavily as a buffalo.

"I'm dying . . . dying," thinks Haramu feeling his last bit of strength giving out. "I'm done for . . . all's up with me!"

To chase away his torturing forebodings, he begins to talk, attempting to assume a cheery or at least lighthearted air:

"Oh, Christ! . . . I've left my rifle in the ditch."

"To hell with it . . . you're lucky I didn't leave you in the ditch!" is Boroiu's terse reply.

"I'm afraid the Russians have got the better of us," Haramu goes on.

"Too bloody true they have. The place's swarming with them."

"And what shall we do next?"

"Run, that's all we can do," says the corporal gloomily and after a while he adds: "You're a hell of a weight. . . . I feel as if I were carrying a sack of potatoes on my back."

Haramu, though scared at these words, gives a forced, dry laugh. Boroiu laughs too, a satisfied and rather harsh chuckle.

"We've lost a lot of men," the wounded man begins again. "You're telling me. And there're many more who'll be soon giving up the ghost, too." After a short pause he goes on: "A hell of a lot. . . . Ilie Onu is one of them. A bullet got him in the head. . . . Then there's George Bucur from Tihuta. And Dolga Mihai, you know, that young lad from Birgau, who was always playing pranks. . . . They're all dead!"

"May God rest their souls."

"Hell of a lot indeed . . . Dumitru Hrisca was hit right in the heart. He staggered another few paces and then dropped down like a log, without even a cry. And there must be many more. The field is full of them. And the trenches are crammed with corpses."

"God's scourge!"

"That's war, Ion! . . . War means blood, death, pain, and misery for everybody."

"Can you hear? They're still firing at us," says Haramu listening to the bullets rending the air with their shrill cry. "They're after me. I can feel them on my tracks."

"Listen to me, Ion," grumbles Boroiu in a stern tone. "The bullet gets the man who's afraid of it. Mark my words. If you're scared, you're done for; you're doomed."

Haramu begins to tremble. Boroiu's words are like a dagger thrust right into his heart. Fear digs its claws ever deeper into his brain, his bones, his flesh, into his very veins.

"That's the end of me . . ." the thought flashes through his mind. He still keeps struggling against it, fighting to withstand its grip. His tongue rolls nervously in his mouth. His words are mingled with a raucous, croaking laughter:

"I'm not afraid! Honest I'm not. . . . They shot a hole in my leg? Well, maybe that's God's way to get me out of this hell. The carts lined with straw will take me to the hospital. They'll cut my leg off. . . . Well, and what of it? I won't be the only cripple. There's heaps about. One leg or two legs, it's all the same to me . . . to live, to be alive that's the only thing that matters! . . . I've got a wife, land and children to look after . . . I must live, I must."

His rambling stops short. He hiccups, as if someone had struck him a cruel blow on the back of his head. He gives a short gurgle, draws a deep breath, and goes dumb as if his tongue had been suddenly cut off from its roots.

The corporal does not appreciate his comrade's chatter. He can't help recalling all the harm Haramu had caused him and he calls himself a sucker to be carrying on his back the very man who has ruined his life. "Why not drop him on the ground and leave him there?" After all, that's what he'd been hoping for ever since he left home. That was the dream he had been constantly cherishing. Why then should he fight against destiny? Just as he was turning these thoughts over in his mind, he stumbles against something and almost trips over. He peers down; an oath rises to his lips. But his curse sticks in his throat. At his feet is Marin Prislea from Salva, his closest friend, stone dead, shrivelled up like a tortured worm, his face a misshapen mass, his neck ringed with a red collar of clogged blood. A shudder runs up and down his spine and he steps up his pace. A few more paces and they'll reach the edge of the cornfield. A captain, his sword raised, bawls at the fugitives who keep flowing in. Threatening the men who refuse to stop, he shouts wildly:

"Stop, you lousy buggers! Down, get down on the ground! . . . Make a stand at the edge of the forest. . . ."

"We're almost there, Ion," cries Boroiu more cheerfully. "Maybe from here the stretcher-bearers will come and carry you to the straw-carts."

He pauses, laughs, and waits for Haramu to answer.

"Well, have you nothing to say?" and then, hearing no reply, goes on: "So you refuse to talk? . . . You've gone dumb with fright, haven't you? Remember, Ion, fright's a bad companion."

The corporal laughs lustily, but there's still no answer.

"Well, if you don't feel like talking, don't," he murmurs after a while, with indifference. "He may have fainted, the bastard," he thinks next. "Fright does such things, no doubt about that!"

He works his way into the cornfield. A couple of soldiers have turned back towards the enemy and have started firing listlessly. The captain, his eyes bulging out of their sockets, keeps shouting desperately: "Stop! Stop! Make a stand here."

"Here we are, Haramu!" says Boroiu. "Let me help you down."

As soon as he detaches the man's legs from his waist, Haramu's body drops like a log to the ground and rolling over remains lying face upwards, his hands and legs stiff.

A painful grin is frozen on the dead man's lips, and his open eyes are stamped with the craving to live, mingled with a savage terror. In the region of his heart, from a round wound no larger than a silver florin, a thread of murky blood trickles down lazily.

"The bullet hit him in the back; that's why he stopped talking," thinks Boroiu, his eyes staring at the corpse. "God's punished you, Ion, for having ruined my life and Ileana's."

He crosses himself slowly, three times.

He feels happy. It's all turned out as he had wanted it to. Ileana is free again. No doubt Providence had meant them to belong to each other.

Boroiu gives a start. He hears the captain's voice; he hears the rifle shots and the weary thunder of a distant gun.

"The Russians!" he says quickly.

He begins to realize that it's not over yet. It's the Russians first; Ileana comes after. And who knows what may still be in store for him?

He crawls up to the edge of the cornfield. Scattered about in the sun-flooded field he can see the bodies of the soldiers lying as they had fallen, struck by the lightning of death. In the sky a flock of ravens wheel overhead, keeping up their croaking; they alight for a moment, hop up to the dead bodies, soar up into the air again, indifferent to the presence of men or the random shots. The straggling soldiers come racing back, their faces distorted with terror. And in the distance, from time to time, thick rows of enemy troops can be seen swaying, vanishing, reappearing, moving closer and closer towards them.

"The Russians are going to overrun us!" stammers Boroiu as he struggles to take careful aim in the hope of stopping the hostile flood. His hands, however, tremble and thoughts that are dear to him keep racing through his mind and haunting him. He would rather not think of them now. He knows too well that they'll only leave care and worry in his heart and probably cause his undoing. And yet, struggle though he does to chase these thoughts away, they keep on and on returning.

A deep groan rises from the cornfield.

"That's another one who's had his lot. . . . One after another," he thinks to himself.

There is no compassion for others in his thoughts. He's happy he's alive. He can't worry about them. Do others worry about him? As long as he's alive, that's all that matters. He must live!

And little by little, he begins making plans for the future. He takes aim, fires, but all the while his mind flies home to his village in Prislop. He sees himself returning from the war, Ileana coming to welcome him at the outskirts of the village. She looks younger, or is it only his fancy? Tears flow down her cheeks, the darling! She says: "So you're back?" And he replies: "Yes, I'm back!" "Thank God you've come back safe and sound." He'd like to fold her in his arms and crush her with kisses, but he dares not, out of shame, for meanwhile a crowd of people have gathered and they all smile, happy to see him back. Father Grozea comes up to him and says: "Now then come along to church with Ileana; you've waited long enough!" Some one says however: "How can Ileana go to church with Boroiu? Haramu's not dead!" "What do you mean, he's not dead?" "Well, he's not, look at him coming along!" With a wooden leg and a red hole in his chest, Haramu limps along laughing. As Ileana sees him she cries: "You didn't look after him, Boroiu! God won't help you! The Lord shall not help you!" "You're raving!" Boroiu thinks, and he blinks furiously. But in his heart he feels a void; a threatening void that keeps growing mercilessly. And the next moment doubt creeps into his soul: "Maybe Haramu isn't really dead. Maybe it was he whose moans I heard a few minutes ago?"

He would rise and creep back to the spot where he had left Haramu to make sure, but he feels too ashamed to do so. He tightens his grip upon his rifle till the bones of his fingers crack and then scolds himself: "For shame, you stupid bastard!"

And yet the doubt has wriggled its way into his soul and gnaws into him like a worm.

In the stubblefield, not more than six hundred yards away, he sees a wave of men, moving nearer and then flinging themselves flat on the ground. One is slow in his movements. He's pot-bellied and wears a red beard. "I'll get him!" he says to himself, swiftly raising his gun to his shoulder. The Russian stops short, raises his hands to the sky in terror, and then drops down, his face touching the ground as if in worship.

"I got him," murmurs the corporal with satisfaction, but the next moment the thought returns: "Suppose Haramu is not dead!"

A fierce rattle of rifleshots proceeds from the Russian lines. The entire edge of the cornfield hisses in alarm. Boroiu hears the steel wasps buzzing past his ear, carrying their menacing message. "I must have got scared," he says to himself and all of a sudden cries out in frenzy: "I won't! I won't! I won't!" He strains all his forces, as though he were fighting a ruthless foe and despite his gigantic effort drops his rifle. He hears the thump of his rifle and an instant after a gay whistle in his right ear: "I'm dying," thinks Boroiu, as a veil of darkness covers his eyes. "And maybe Haramu isn't dead . . . maybe. . . ."

His grip stiffens on his rifle, blood wells up into his mouth, and his head drops on one side as if overcome by fatigue.

The enemy moves steadily forward. The captain cries out plaintively:

"Take aim! Fire! Fire!"

The bullets shower down, whistling like a stormy wind. The sun sets angrily, staining the sky and the earth with its blood-red hues.

Ion Slavici

(1848-1925)

Ion Slavici is one of the classics of Rumanian literature. He wrote short stories, novels (of which *Mara* is the most representative both of the writer's genius and of the prose of his time), plays, and philological, political, and educational essays. He is the creator in Rumanian literature of "peasant realism," a literary approach subsequently adopted and developed by a long series of Rumanian prose writers which attained its most accomplished artistic achievement in Liviu Rebreanu's novel, *Ion*.

His short stories and novelettes ("Father Tanda," "The Mill of Good Luck," "Dad's Little Boy," *The Girl of the Forest*, "Scormon," "The Neighbours," "Village Gossip") depict the life of the villages in robust, unidealized strokes. Slavici's heroes are not divided into positive and negative characters, according to their virtues or vices, but are rendered with their complex qualities and failings, with that combination of good and bad that is typical of every human being. The personalities of his heroes—genuine in their character—stand out with striking vividness and vigor. In *Mara* the peasant soul is painted with exceptional dramatic force and authenticity. Slavici used "popular orality" as an effective instrument for depicting rustic life.

Psychological analysis is another valuable aspect of Slavici's individuality in Rumanian literature. His types remain printed in our memory not only for their picturesqueness but for the genuine and forceful precision of his character-painting. His analysis of erotic passions in rural life is piercing and dramatic. Whenever he endeavors, however, to endow his characters with spiritual refinements or traits of city life, his tone becomes false and didactic.

The Girl of the Forest

Wealthy Busuioc was a man who knew his own mind. By wishing hard enough, by striving and scheming, he had become a prosperous farmer who tilled his land for ten days running with four ploughs, and sowed his furrows with only the choicest grains, and so he felt he could achieve things of which others dared not even dream.

There was cholera in the country, but it was of no concern to Busuioc. Cholera at harvesttime? He had 40 acres of land under wheat —one single stretch of grain bending under the weight of the heavy ears. Cholera or no cholera, he had three days to bring in his wheat. Otherwise, with the ears full to bursting, he would lose much of his grain and, though the poor might have little to lose, he would suffer greatly.

There were, indeed, many who would have much to lose—a vast amount in the course of years—were it not for the work of the hungry woodlanders. As they felt harvesttime drawing near, the woods would arise and stir; from hut after hut, from village to village, the people gathered, and whole valleys would set out for the wide plains; and in a few days the whole district from the river Mures to Oradea, and right up to the source of the river Cris, would be empty of people except for helpless old men, women, and children. The thirst for life would draw all the others to that great yearly festival where the daily bread was being distributed.

But this time, the authorities had forbidden the festival. It had been announced by the village crier, and even in church to all those present, that no one was to leave the boundaries of his village, nor to hire harvesters from other villages.

"I'd like to see the man who'd stop me bringing in my wheat," shouted Busuioc. "Sheer madness! How can the authorities stop us? Have they thought of that? On the one hand it's: 'D' you want to starve, man?' and on the other: 'Look out or you'll catch the cholera!' Give me cholera every time. For, if it's in the books, wherever that may be, that I'm to die of cholera, it's not the authorities that are going to wipe out my name. If it's written down, there it is—and if it isn't, well, it isn't, and that's that."

Busuioc had made up his mind: he had only to harness his horses to his carts and go to the upland villages to fetch the people himself, and he'd like to see the man in Curtici who would dare say a word.

"Look here, dad, I'd better go myself," said Iorgovan, Busuioc's son.

Busuioc was not one to consult with people, and one of those he particularly avoided consulting was his son, Iorgovan.

Iorgovan was, of course, younger than his father, but just because he was younger and the son of a rich man, he had learned more in the course of his life and was smarter than his father. Iorgovan felt it, and so did Busuioc, who was secretly glad of it.

For five years Iorgovan had attended school at Arad. He was expected to become a gentleman; but one fine morning Iorgovan had turned up at home. "Dad, I've been thinking it over and I want to take up farming, too," he had said.

Busuioc had given him a long look, had pondered a while, and then had asked him: "So you'll be a ploughman, too, like me; now why didn't you tell me that before?"

"Because," Iorgovan had answered, "I've been telling myself: 'If

I ask him, he won't agree; if I do it, he will be sorry for it one day, and if I wait till he thinks it over, I'm afraid I might change my mind.'"

"He is quite right," thought Busuioc; "better a first-rate ploughman than a second-rate boyar."

Since then, Iorgovan had set about his business quietly waiting for his father to cheer up. And Busuioc, being a father, did cheer up, even without any special reason for doing so.

"All right, my boy, but be careful," Busuioc finally answered his son.

As a matter of fact, Iorgovan was a sensible boy. But the sense of a man depends on time and circumstance; the lad was twenty, and at harvesttime a mind of twenty would be a poor thing indeed, if now and then it entertained no mischievous thoughts, however fleeting.

Harvesttime is a joyous time, and Iorgovan wanted to choose the men himself—reapers, sheaf-binders, and the girls who walked along the furrows gathering the wheat from under the scythe of the reaper.

Last year it had been great: lusty lads, eager at both talk and work, three musicians—one bagpipe player and two fiddlers—and there also had been one who never ceased to crack jokes; and then the girls, one finer than the other, so that Iorgovan had been dreaming of harvesttime the whole winter.

And in the midst of the harvesters he always saw Simina, the daughter of the verger at Zimbru, and when her vision rose before him, his memories wandered from harvesttime to threshing time and further to grape-gathering, because Simina had only gone back when the wine had begun to ferment. At Busuioc's house there was always work for a girl like Simina, for her father, and for two or three others who came along with them.

But Simina herself, Iorgovan would not like to see again; he had long made up his mind on that point. He'd been nearly knocked off his balance at the time; it was as well she had left. Whenever he thought of her, however, he wondered ruefully why he had been such a fool as not to kiss her just once. He was not a shy fellow, and when she first came to stay with them, he had wanted to do so.

"You know that I'm willing, why then are you trying to steal a kiss?" she had asked him.

After that he had no longer wanted to kiss her, and now that he was a year older, he was angry for not wanting to, and yet he didn't wish to see her again, lest the devil should prompt him to show her that he could want even more.

Thus, Iorgovan was not thinking of the real Simina, but only of a Simina who came and went, leaving behind her a short-lived joy. But Busuioc had no idea of all this, and when Iorgovan crossed himself three times and said "God be with us," the father was thinking of his forty acres.

Sofron, the farm hand, had also said "God be with us" but he had thought of nothing but the job that his master had set before him.

Busuioc had been right. The authorities hadn't been strong enough to stop the people leaving their homes. They had spent the winter evenings telling each other what they had seen in the plains during the summer. In spring, they would stop the travellers on their way, to find out how the crops were looking in the plains, and as they knew that the year had been a good one, they were impatiently awaiting the news that the grain was ripe. As soon as they got the news, they started off towards the valley.

And why shouldn't they? There was no cholera in their parts! The authorities? Why, the authorities asked nothing of them! They only stopped the villagers for their own good, to protect them from danger, but it was up to them whether or not they wanted to benefit by this measure.

The country road of the White Cris Valley forked in two when nearing the plains at the village of Maghierat. One part of the crowd went through Pincota village towards the center of the plain, while the other set out for Siria village and thence to Arad, crossing the river Mures into the Banat. On reaching Siria, the crowds crossed the village and stopped on the commons, on the outskirts of the plain.

The village sprawls at the foot of the last range of hills. Overlooking the village, there are vineyards; higher up, the slopes are covered with raspberry bushes, and at the top of the range, the forest begins. On the highest peak, over the plain, stand the ruins of the Vilagas, an old fortress, where the eye takes in the plain as far as the horizon.

Iorgovan had left Curtici at dusk and had driven straight towards the heights of the Vilagas. He drove quickly, being driven by some unknown force. Sofron was annoyed that Iorgovan drove so quickly and wondered what possessed the lad to be going at such a rate.

Nightfall came quickly, and Iorgovan parted company with Sofron. Having set out with the idea of making a long journey on difficult business, his thoughts went far ahead, and whenever he caught sight of the fortress it seemed to him that he was making no headway, and he urged his horses on. But he was only a man. Finally, he dozed off and the tired horses, feeling the reins loosen, slowed down. Near the village he suddenly shook off his fatigue.

For some time he had thought he heard music and merry shouting. Having crossed a stone bridge, he caught sight of fires at the outskirts of the village and of people crowding round them.

Iorgovan drew up his horses and glanced around in a daze. People here, people there, people everywhere, hundreds, thousands of them—as many girls as there were young men. Iorgovan jumped from his cart, unharnessed the horses, and made his way towards the crowd. The people were merry and Iorgovan was no longer sleepy.

Near the road he happened on some people gathered round a fire of dry branches. Some were sitting on the ground, others standing about, but all of them were listening breathlessly to the song of an old man seated on a small cask by the fire. It was "Novac's Song." Iorgovan had heard it before, but it seemed a little different now, and he resented not being able to hear it better with all this noise going on.

Behind him, a flutist and a fiddler played a Transylvanian folk tune, and one of those fellows who are the life and soul of a party was dancing with five girls. The people who had gathered round them burst into laughter at each of his jokes, then quickly checked their mirth so as not to lose the next.

On hearing the shouts and the laughter, Iorgovan turned on his heels, then gave a start; he stood quite still for a moment and finally drew a few steps back.

A pang pierced his heart. One of the five girls was Simina! No, it was not Simina; it was another forest girl, and girls and forest girls look much alike about midnight.

For months he hadn't seen her in his mind's eye. He was aware of having seen her once; he knew what she was like, but gone was the sourness that had filled his heart during her stay at Curtici. Now, alongside the other forest people, her image had come to haunt him again and the sourness had returned; no bitterness, no—but sourness like the acidity of fermenting wine which had not yet settled down. During the time she had stayed at Curtici, no smile had lit up his face; he had enjoyed neither food nor sleep and yet, whenever her leaving was mentioned, he had wanted to howl and dig his nails into his sides. It is terrible to struggle against desire, to feel that you are powerless and that another's will is leading you. And Iorgovan had the same terrible feeling now. He trembled all over.

He did not want to meet her, but he wanted to see her, to find her, to know whether she was here or not. And as his mind was haunted by her image, he saw her wherever he looked, and when he saw that he had been mistaken, he saw her elsewhere.

He had passed through the crowd in all directions—at first rather shy and frightened, then boldly and ever more boldly, elbowing people out of his way and butting in wherever he saw a group of people.

"Whom are you looking for, man-of-the-plains?" a lad asked him.

"I? For nobody," he answered; "I'm just looking round."

"How stupid I am!" he burst out. Every village has its own particular dress. He had but to look for a man from Zimbru in order to find out if Simina was there or not.

Simina was not there; neither was she expected. He was certain now that she was not coming, that she could not be—still, he saw her everywhere. He felt as though he had gazed at the sun too long and now his eyes were flashing. In vain! There was but one Simina, one forest girl in the wide world and of her he would never be rid. He had been afraid of finding her here and now that he knew he could not find her, he was disconsolate. He wanted to go to Zimbru right away.

Sofron had found the cart and the sweating horses by the roadside, in the cool night. He had been cross with Iorgovan for leaving them thus and had taken the cart to the village inn. He had fed the horses and then returned to the common at the end of the village.

"Well, what do you think of it? How d'you like it?" he had asked.

"I don't quite know," said Iorgovan. He thought the forest people were rather a dull lot. True, they were merry enough, shouting, dancing, and laughing, but Iorgovan wanted to see them mad with delight, so that they might sweep him off his feet.

"Let's start something, to make the world talk," he shouted. "Go fetch a cask of wine! Company we are sure to find."

A cask, two casks and more if he wanted, Busuioc's son could afford. And company, thank heaven, there was plenty of that. In the dusk, the lads were stamping the ground and Iorgovan was sitting on the cask by the fire, beating time and shouting without pause: "Upsey-daisy, upsey-daisy, hop!"

He had just touched his wine cup once or twice, but he felt giddy, very giddy. Suddenly, tears welled up in his eyes.

"I've had enough of it!" he shouted querulously; then he got up and made for the village.

Sofron, a man of thirty, had served as a soldier in the emperor's army and had been a farm hand for several years; he therefore knew his duty and obeyed his master's orders.

As long as the casks were full, he had taken his share and no small one either. He was not exactly a giant, but, looking at him, you felt that no cudgel and no amount of wine could fell him. He was not very tall, but big-boned, broad-shouldered and of a heavy build—a tough man. Yet, when he returned to the inn, the ground swayed under his feet and the road seemed too narrow for him. At the stable door, he stopped and pulled himself together.

"I'm giddy," he said to himself, "there's no doubt about that. I'm very giddy, but I'm not drunk. Busuioc is an honest boy; Iorgovan is a decent fellow, and mistress Vica a good soul. Well, and what of it? I don't care a fig! In the autumn I'm getting married anyway."

And Sofron could afford to marry. He had money lent out at interest and a plot of ground for a house at Curtici. He had entered Busuioc's service because he wanted him as best man at his wedding. Everything was quite ready, only he hadn't found a wife yet. And now that Sofron was not drunk but giddy, he would have been glad of a wife, so that he might have someone to kiss. That was his way when he was giddy—he was in love with all the world.

Lying down in the doorway for his forty winks with his head on the threshold, Sofron was soon smiling in his dreams.

After a brief nap, he jumped alertly to his feet to water the horses and curry them, and as the sun peeped from behind the hills, he went back to the common at the end of the village to see how matters stood and to inform his master when the latter awoke.

Sofron was a forest man himself; he knew how to talk to the forest people and that's just why he felt that it would be difficult to come to an understanding with them.

Busuioc had reckoned upon so many reapers, so many binders and so many boys to gather up the wheat for the binders, so as to bring in his grain in three days. But the forest men had their own plans. For the harvest they gathered in groups of from five to a hundred. Each of these groups had chosen a man who spoke for his group. Separate workers were not to be had, because a forest man would not for the world part from his group. In vain did Sofron try to hire the number of people Busuioc had demanded—either there were too many binders or too few reapers. The worst of it was that there were always too many who wouldn't do a stroke of work. Each group of at least eight men had a bagpipe player or a fiddler and a boy to carry the water cask after the reapers, and the fiddler was to be counted as a reaper and the boy as a binder. Busuioc had decided on one bagpipe player, one fiddler, and two boys, but Sofron was always faced with four fiddlers, two or three bagpipe players, and about five or six boys.

"Iorgovan will have to decide," said Sofron and returned to the inn, rather angry.

He grew angrier still when he heard that Iorgovan had not got up yet, and, going to the stables, he began to scratch his head. Vulpoi, one of the horses, stood with drooping ears and obviously had the glanders.

"I knew it," said Sofron. "Iorgovan is not quite himself; he isn't. I said yesterday that he was killing the horses. Last night, he left them sweating in the middle of the road and now he is sleeping as never before."

He knew that Iorgovan would not want to have his father's servants interfere with him; but Vulpoi was ill and, worried as he was, Sofron went to rouse him.

Iorgovan was neither asleep nor awake. He did not rightly know what he was doing. Used to getting up early, he had awakened at much the same time as Sofron, but he didn't feel like getting out of bed. It was awkward to see the people who had watched him last night, and so he shut his eyes and locked out the world.

He looked rather crossly at Sofron. "Why bother?" he said. "You don't want me to be out of humor as well as out of pocket, do you? Let the horse go to blazes if his days are up."

And Iorgovan shut his eyes again; he would have liked to sleep forever, not to wake up the same man any more. But he could sleep no longer. A horse? What of it? Yet, it was not a good omen. But he wanted to show Sofron that he didn't care. He wouldn't have got up for anything now, nor, in getting up, would he have asked about Vulpoi.

"What about the men?" he asked, glancing stealthily at Sofron's face.

"Come and see for yourself," answered Sofron.

"Are there or aren't there any?"

"There are and then again there aren't."

"Speak properly," Iorgovan said sharply. "Have you looked for them or haven't you? Have you found them or haven't you?"

"I've found them and then again I haven't," answered Sofron. "Such as the master wants them I could only find in a village where you can choose as you please."

That was just what Iorgovan wanted to hear. If he could not sleep, he wanted to go on and on to the end of the world.

"Then harness the horses and let's be off," he said in a firm voice and went to pay for food and lodging.

Sofron harnessed the horses, three to his own cart, to Iorgovan's only two.

Iorgovan got into the cart with two horses just as if there had been three. No need for Busuioc's son, thank God, to trouble about such a small thing as the loss of a horse.

"What about the skin?" asked Busuioc's son.

"We'll find it here," answered the servant.

"You go first."

Sofron left the courtyard first, Iorgovan following his servant.

"My word!" grunted Sofron. "I wish it were not such an ill beginning."

At night, when the cocks were crowing, Iorgovan had reached Cil and haggled with Iutu, a man from that village, while Sofron was sleeping as usual in the stables, his head on the sill.

"So, you'll be here tomorrow morning with the men!"

"Leave it to me!" answered Iutu. "If I don't find them here, I'll look for them in the neighboring villages. Plenty of time till morning to scour all the villages as far as Dulcele and Zimbru.

Iorgovan started. "Zimbru isn't far from here?" he asked nervously.

"About an hour or even less," answered Iutu. "I keep to the country road to Iosasi and there I turn left up the valley, and come right into Zimbru."

"Well, be off! Don't let's waste time!" Iorgovan said impatiently.

When he was alone, he began striding nervously through the big and desolate courtyard.

There was plenty of time till morning. He could go and return and Sofron would be none the wiser. Yet the horses were tired and he had had one loss already. Besides, Sofron was sleeping in the doorway of the stables.

It was sheer madness! Why see her? What had he to do with her? Nothing, nothing, nothing! That forest girl was his misfortune, but the calamity had overtaken him and he could no longer avoid it. The thought of riding over to her had taken hold of him and he couldn't resist it. The freshness of the night, the moonlight, the shadowy trees—all beckoned to him.

"Lie down and sleep," he commanded himself sternly and he went to a haystack at the back of the courtyard, made a bed for himself in the hay, lay down, and shut his eyes.

He tried hard to sleep and he succeeded after a while, but as soon as sleep overcame him, he set out on his way. In dreamland the roads are short—once started you can't stop except where your wish takes you. At length he started with fright from his sleep, looked round quite lost for a moment, and, seeing himself in the same place, jumped to his feet and went to the stables.

He was only half awake and had he gone to sleep again, he would not have been able to tell later whether he had just dreamt of the journey or actually taken it. However, he took the poorest of the five horses from the stables.

Sofron jumped up, ready to attack the intruder.

"Keep quiet, it's me," Iorgovan murmured.

"What are you doing?"

"I'm going to look for harvesters."

Sofron waited till he had gone out with the horse and went to sleep again quietly, his head on the doorsill.

"Never in all my life shall I do a thing like this again," Iorgovan said to himself once he found himself on the main road.

The way to Iosasi was pleasant enough in daytime, but now, before dawn, in the cool of night and in the moonlight, it was like a fairyland, and Iorgovan was riding along as if in a dream. But only from Iosasi on began the real, the unspeakable wonder, especially for a man brought up in the plains.

Here, the way wound through a narrow valley, keeping to the banks of a noisy brook, now through tilled fields and hayland, farther on crossing meadows and glades, and still farther, going through thick woods, overhung by steep, rocky slopes on which birches grew here and there. Daylight was breaking and the birds flew from branch to branch. Now and then he heard a jay or a thrush; the wild dove cooed; the woodpecker hammered at the bark of a tree; the wild cock heralded the dawn; and the nightingale which had accompanied Iorgovan on his way sang its song with increasing passion, as though frightened by the daylight which was spreading over the hilltops into the valley.

When the valley opened out, it was full daylight. Moma, a high mountain with steep slopes covered with thick forests towered in the background. To the right rose a rocky hill and to the left another hill of a more gentle incline on which the village was spread with its church and the graveyard above it. Iorgovan stopped and felt like retreating.

This was where Simina lived. What could he tell her? What could he do? What did he want of her? Should he, a man full grown, tell her that he had come all this way for her sake? Or should he tell her that he had come across her by mere chance? But how could he tell what he should or should not do?

Being industrious, Simina had got up early as she had work on her loom, and a weaver's zeal is measured by the yard. Neacsu, her father, had gone to the forest to find some wood for yokes and she was sitting by herself before the loom placed in a clearing in front of the house.

Simina might have been thinking of anything but Iorgovan. True, there had been a time when she had thought of him very often and thinking she would find herself weeping. But girls cannot go away with young men as their thoughts might demand; they stay at home and think and wait and weep. And the very thought leaves you when it sees that you don't follow and then there is an end to weeping too. Simina was beautiful and she knew it. When she was a child she felt that everybody was looking at her, and now, a young girl, she was told every day that she was beautiful, and, besides, she saw it herself in the eyes of the lads. Beautiful girls may choose among many. Yet, it was not she who had chosen Iorgovan.

It had just happened. While other lads were always looking out for her, Busuioc's son would keep away and only now and then would he say a word or two to her which she alone could understand; no love word either, but the short words of a man who wants to hide his pain. Thus, she had dwelt almost three months near him and when she was about to leave, he had stayed away from home for three days on end so as not to face her.

When she now saw him entering the gate, she stopped her work, looked at him, lay her shuttle down gently on the linen in her loom and then got up and crossed herself. A thrill shot through her body, taking her back a year; she felt like closing her eyes and rushing to him.

He came up smiling and quiet as though they had parted only yesterday. "You are surprised, aren't you?" he inquired, stopping in front of her but without looking straight at her.

"I don't know," she answered, beginning to tremble, "but I know that I am glad to see you."

"I've come to fetch you for the reaping."

"Have you?" she replied. "Dad did not mean to go this year."

"And you?" he asked.

"Neither did I," she answered firmly.

"Well, then, I've at least seen you," he managed in a choking voice. "Perhaps it's better like that."

"Is it?" she said and the tears welled up.

Iorgovan bit his lips and looked around. He would have liked to tear, to rend, to break something. He dared not look straight at her; he would close his eyes when he saw her, because on seeing her he longed to take her in his arms and hold her tight so that she would stop weeping.

"You need not look around," she added, "nobody is at home; and even if they were, I'm not ashamed of crying."

"But why are you crying?" he queried, drawing nearer to her. "Have I come to see you weep?"

"How should I know why you have come?" she answered, sitting down and turning her face away from him.

Iorgovan started tearing with one hand at the nails of the other. Finally, he touched her sleeve with his fingertips.

"Simina! I say, Simina! Be good or I shall lose my head. And what's the good?"

She dried her eyes and looked at him.

"I've always wanted to ask you," she said, "and I don't know why I haven't done it before. What do you want of me?"

He shrugged his shoulders. "Nothing! I just know that you're so dear to me that life is hell."

"Love to no purpose!" she said. "To be loved and yet to be consumed with aching and longing!"

"That's it," the lad answered, "I know that it is so."

"Then leave me alone!"

"And you, why don't you leave me alone?"

She gave him a long look but she did not answer.

"You're right!" Iorgovan spoke, ill at ease. "You didn't run after me, but you made me run after you. Who knows, perhaps it is better like that."

He wanted to say many other things to her and she wanted to ask him many more questions, but after this, things followed he did not care to speak about and which she would have liked to find out without asking. So, they remained silent, she sitting at her loom, he leaning against a pillar of the hay-loft, and both of them felt that being silent together was as it should be.

That is how Neacsu found them when he came home from the forest. "Now, what is the meaning of this?" he asked himself, casting a puzzled look at Iorgovan. He didn't quite know whether he felt glad or sorry.

But nobody asked him, anyhow: the question was whether he would take the girl to the plains. He had only one daughter. Had he not cared for her, what kind of a man would he have been?

He looked round him, at the house, at the shed with the loom and his carpenter's tools, at the orchard and the gate of his courtyard. He looked with tenderness at all these things and then he said: "Of course, we'll go! We have to," he added softly as if speaking to himself, "so that we may not say later that we didn't do it."

On the way from Zimbru to Cil, Iorgovan kept reining his horse. The more he advanced, the more he regretted his move. At last he reached Cil and once there he walked about impatiently up the road on which he had come, but stealthily, so that Sofron should not suspect him. Simina was to follow him on foot.

When Sofron first caught sight of Simina, he looked at her indifferently, then stared and then gaped as if his whole life were spoiled from now on, and there came a single thought into his mind: to hide the girl, so that he alone should know about her.

"Come along, young woman! You'll sit with me," Sofron told her when the people started to get into the carts. He jumped up briskly, took his coat from under the grain-sack and put it on the board next to himself.

Simina wavered for an instant, of two minds as to what to do. She glanced at Iorgovan, then she got into the cart and sat down on the coat next to Sofron.

Iorgovan saw everything and was cross, but he could not betray his feelings in front of a servant; moreover, he wouldn't lose Simina wherever he might leave her. It was enough to know that she was near and that he could see her every minute. Simina, however, would have liked to be alone and have a good cry.

* * *

The big gate at Curtici opened for Iorgovan and his two carts full of harvesters around noon the next day.

When Busuioc noticed that there were but two horses attached to Iorgovan's cart, he muttered to himself: "Things like that will sometimes happen." It was really only a trifle. Better not notice it.

And yet. . . . He knew Iorgovan to be a reliable fellow and he could not understand what had happened, what had possessed the boy; for such losses just don't happen.

Meeting the newcomers, his glance swept over all of them and his eyes rested on Simina. His heart filled with dismay. He knew her quite well, and it was enough to see her to understand a great many things.

The year before, Busuioc had felt that his son was fond of the forest girl's eyes and he might have been vexed if he hadn't liked those eyes himself, for they were made to please. But that a year should pass and the boy should not forget them, that he should like them so much as to get all worked up and kill his horses for their sake—that set the old man thinking.

Busuioc beckoned to the girl to approach. Simina shook her clothes smooth with one single movement and then she went up to him, her head held high. She bent down and kissed his hand.

"Bless you!" he said. "You've done well to come. Go into the house; the mistress will be pleased to see you."

"Vica!" he shouted, turning towards the house, "come and see the newcomers." Then he went up to Neacsu and greeted him.

Sofron stood motionless and looked on. In those seven years that he had worked for wages, he had made a nice little sum. Busuioc had lent it out for him to people who paid good interest, and he had two acres of land, as part of his wages, one sown with wheat, the other with maize. They gave him great satisfaction and around them centered all his dreams for the future. As he was standing and looking, he wished he could gather all his possessions and buy straw, heaps and heaps of straw, to make a huge bonfire and then laugh, laugh till he could burst.

"Let's unharness the horses," Iorgovan told him, wondering that he had to remind him.

Startled, Sofron looked up at him. "I don't want to," he said. "Let him do it who owns them."

Iorgovan was speechless for a moment, then he looked round to see if anyone had heard these words. "I have no mind to quarrel now," he said. Then he unharnessed the horses, took them by the halter and led them to the stables.

"Here! What are you doing with the horses?" shouted Sofron roughly and he hurried to take the halters away from him. "Don't you see they are still hot from the road?" So saying, he led the horses round the courtyard.

Iorgovan was Busuioc's son and he could do as he pleased with his father's horses; but the servant was right. So, Iorgovan went and unharnessed the horses from the servant's cart, took them by the halter and walked them around too.

So, both of them walked around the yard watching the front door in turn, to see Simina come out. Finally, Iorgovan lost patience and took the horses to the stables. Sofron would have liked to tell Iorgovan that he had not walked the horses long enough, but, as that was not true, he could only follow him to the stables.

From the stables they could not see whether Simina had returned or not. They were secretly of the same mind: to hurry and finish their work and to get out into the open as quickly as possible.

Busuioc had plenty of servants and there was no need for his son to unharness the horses, walk them about and take them to the stables, but nobody could stop him if such was his pleasure, and now, after having done everything that was to be done, Simina still being with the mistress of the house, he could pull the carts under the shed, see that the oxen had their fodder and that everything was as it should be. There was much work for an industrious man in Busuioc's household.

But, after all, he was his parents' son and he had just arrived home. Industry is a good thing indeed, but it is no excuse for seeing to your work without exchanging a word with your parents first. So that, willy-nilly, there was nothing for it but to go in. And Iorgovan found it awkward to face his parents.

He didn't want them to imagine, God forbid! that he was thinking of marrying Simina. But he loved her. Still less did he wish people to find out that he was fond of her and yet would not marry her.

Sofron's eyes followed him as they might have followed a torrent ready to sweep him away, and, when he saw him enter the house he leaned against the door-post of the stables, feeling quite giddy.

"Thou hast struck me hard, oh Lord," he said and, somewhat relieved, he entered the stables and set about his work. But he was unable to do anything.

The misfortune had come upon him like a thunderbolt; he was bewitched, nothing less. He went out into the yard again but in vain, because he could see nothing of what was happening in the house, and there wasn't a thing to do but to wait and to long, and so great was his longing that he felt it would reach her and bring her out to him.

And who knows if after all it was not Sofron's longing which made Simina leave the house and look into the courtyard though none of her companions had remained there.

Sofron had longed for her to come out because he did not want her to be with Iorgovan, but he was afraid to see her or meet her face to face. He had seen much of her, too much already. He therefore hurried to tell her that the others were resting in the big barn which stood on the threshing-ground behind the stables. And Simina, who had sat on his coat during their ride, was shy of him now.

So she did not ask any more questions, but made her way towards the back gate near the stables, where the others were.

Sofron had to prevent Iorgovan from meeting Simina. Whenever he pictured those two alone together, he felt that he would go mad and there was murder in his heart. Yet Iorgovan was Busuioc's son, and Sofron, being Busuioc's servant, could not follow him into his own house. On the other hand, Simina had told him that she had spent three months at Busuioc's house, and, as she had stayed once, she might stay again. And if Iorgovan wanted to be alone with her, he had only to send his servant on an errand.

"I must talk to him," said Sofron firmly.

In the barn everything was quiet. The people prepared their beds in the hay and they were all sleeping except three of them who were sitting round the fire at the barn door. Neacsu was among them. Simina's father was not an old man; but throughout the summer he had been suffering from a fever and one illness follows another. A sickly man thinks continuously of his state of health. Neacsu was speaking about the cholera with the others, saying he was afraid of it. Cursed be the hour when he said so.

The father of a pretty girl, Neacsu was accustomed to men whose minds were set on marriage, and a word or two with Sofron had been enough for him to see how the wind was blowing. Sofron had told him in detail what he had and what he hadn't, what he could do and what he couldn't. He had tried hard to impress him and he had succeeded. That's just why Neacsu would have preferred to be asleep when Sofron turned up. If Sofron had been a man like the others, he would not have cared; but he was not, and so Neacsu was sorry for him, because all his comings and goings were in vain.

Sofron felt that he was not welcome. By his intrusion he had stopped the talk of the men around the fire who, after silently loitering for a while, started yawning and finally bedded down.

Sofron remained alone with Neacsu and found it hard to leave. They sat in silence by the fire, glancing at each other now and then, and they each knew what was in the other's mind.

"I've got it badly, Father Neacsu," murmured Sofron finally, "and at my age too. I would never have thought it possible."

"I know," said Neacsu, deep in thought.

What else was there to say? They stayed on for a while and then Sofron got up and left, without so much as a good night. Neacsu took a handful of twigs and, one by one, he threw them into the fire.

Meanwhile, Busuioc was walking about the house, now and then glancing at Filip, his younger son, a boy of about eighteen, who was seated near the table, his pen poised over a sheet of paper.

"Write!" his father said finally, " 'Dear brother-in-law . . .' "

"Why can't I write in my name?" asked the lad.

"Write as I tell you," said his father quietly, "it will sound better."

" 'Tomorrow, we start reaping,' " he went on dictating, " 'and I've brought forest people here, fifty-two of them, as many as I need. But you know that the authorities have forbidden their coming. That is why I ask you to get into your cart and come here as quickly as you can. I want your advice about what I should do. Don't delay, for I'm in great need of you . . .'

"That's all," he said and took his seal from the table-drawer and, having pressed it on the colored ink-pad, sealed his letter.

At cock-crow, Busuioc's people were up and about: the fiddler was stringing his instrument; the bagpipe player was looking over his pipes; and the people were preparing for the feast; boys shouldering their scythes and girls tucking their sickles in their belts. Day and night hadn't definitely taken leave of each other, and they had already gathered in front of the house, waiting to wish the host good luck with the harvest.

As soon as they heard the key in the lock of the front door, the piper blew up his bags and the fiddler drew his bow across the strings.

Bagpipe and fiddle there were to your heart's content, but both bagpipe and fiddle sound desolate when there are no human voices to accompany them, and so it might have been the dusk of the dark autumn night instead of the dawn of a summer morning.

The people were ready to be cheerful, of course, but if you are in someone else's home, you expect your host to lead the fun, but here, their hosts seemed mirthless.

If you had asked Simina whether she felt happy or not, she would have shrugged her shoulders smiling. She felt like soaring, as a bird returned to its nest, like singing and playing pranks. Still, she moved as if on tenterhooks and was afraid to speak or look at anyone, because she might have stirred ill will. But she could not stand gloomy people. She would have liked to strike a bargain with them: tomorrow is tomorrow, but today, let's forget our troubles.

Sofron knew but one thing: reaping day had come. And a man who works day after day the whole year long and who likes his work, doesn't postpone reaping day. When it's a question of marriage or christening, you might stop and think, they are but beginnings, but on reaping day you don't. But Sofron was not merry. Neither could he be sad. He would worry, become angry, occasionally feel beside himself, but his moods never lasted, and in no time he was his old self again, that is to say neither one thing nor the other.

While Sofron had been on his journey, Petrea and Matei who looked after the carts, had made ropes of rye-straw to bind the sheaves and they had piled them in a cart to take to the fields. They were heavy as they had been sprinkled with water to dampen them. They struggled with the cart to turn it towards the gate but the place was narrow and they could not cope with it. Sofron coming down from the garret with a sack of maize stopped halfway down the ladder and smiled at their efforts.

Women are easily frightened. Seeing that the ladder was bending under Sofron's weight, Simina guessed how heavy the sack must be and she nervously came towards the ladder.

"Get down; you make me feel giddy," she told Sofron. "You'd better go and help them."

He was glad that Simina had seen him early in the morning, that she had spoken to him and told him what to do; he had to respond in return. He seized her two hands and looked at her face in a puzzled way.

"Do you know that I have a mind to kiss you?" he said.

Simina was eighteen years old and she was not a stranger to kisses. One kiss more or less meant nothing to her; but Sofron was a man of thirty and girls feel awkward towards men of thirty. Besides, Sofron was no trifler.

"If you want to, I suppose you could," she answered, "for you are stronger than I, but there is no sense in a forced kiss."

"That's where you are wrong," he said, taking her head in his hands and kissing her right on the mouth.

Simina set her lips tight.

Sofron didn't like that. When a man is longing for a deep drink, he is not satisfied with the dew on the leaves.

He lowered his arm around her shoulders and hugged her to his breast, kissing her throat, her eyes, her mouth; the tighter she closed her lips, the longer his kisses were.

She put her hand to his face to push him away.

"Let me go," she whispered in a choking voice, "I am ashamed."

"Give me a kiss then," he answered, "I won't let you go until you kiss me."

Simina closed her eyes and raised her lips to his.

A kiss, whether extorted by force or given willingly, is still a kiss.

"May God reward you," said Sofron letting her go.

"A grown-up man," she said troubled, "and without any sense. Go now and help them."

Sofron leaped up to the cart, seized it by the axle between the back wheels, lifting and twisting it so that the two others had only to turn the shaft to move it to the gate.

"What could I do when he is so strong," said Simina to herself, "and after all, one kiss won't do much harm."

Iorgovan had seen everything. He had stood and looked on, but he pretended not to see or mind. In fact he did not mind very much. He knew that Simina had not given Sofron leave to kiss her, that she was angry at his having done so, and that was enough.

Neither was she angry with Sofron, nor did she reproach herself. She went straight to the house, looking at Iorgovan as if she wanted to say: "You ought to do something, so that nobody dares kiss me any more." Iorgovan understood her look and, feeling guilty, he pretended not to understand it and tried to look gay and unconcerned.

There was one, however, who would have been angry to see what had happened and that one was Busuioc. Should a miserable servant kiss the girl for whom his son had killed his horse? But he didn't know.

He only knew that it was reaping day and that the village would watch his people going out to the fields.

"At it, boys! Don't lag behind, girls!" he shouted, raising a glass to their health. "Simina, Sofron, and you, Iorgovan, go ahead; you belong to the house."

The lads whirled the girls round and shouted lustily; then Vica, the mistress of the house, came out. Filip followed with a gun on his shoulder, and the younger children came too; and when the merry-making was at its height, the girls began to sing and the harvesters went dancing and singing towards the fields.

Everybody was so merry that Sofron quite forgot that he ought to feel unhappy because Iorgovan was near Simina. He did not sing because he couldn't; he didn't crack jokes because he always missed the point; he did not tell tall stories because he couldn't invent any. But he hummed the tune the others were singing; he burst with laughter when the others cracked jokes; and he listened open-mouthed to those who could tell stories. It was his job to gather the sheaves and build them into good, solid crosses so that the wind should not overturn them or the rain spoil the grain, and whenever he took a sheaf on his fork, and it was a heavy one, his heart leaped with joy. To feel still happier, he took two or three sheaves at once and held them upright on his fork like a flag. And when he happened on a quail that had been hiding under the sheaf, he jumped after it and wondered why he could not catch it in its flight.

Simina and Iorgovan did not hum songs. Neither did they laugh at jokes or listen to the stories. They did not run after quails. They lived their shining day.

The reapers went on step by step, cutting down the heavy grain in long and broad furrows, stopping now and then to take the whetstone out of its sheath and sharpen the scythes; and the sound of the stone upon the scythe rang out far and wide. Behind the reapers, nimble girls gathered the wheat into bundles with their sickles. Then, strong-armed lads stretched out the straw-ropes, laid the bundles on them and tied them securely, flattening them under sinewy knees, making them into tight sheaves. Last, there came the bagpipe player, the fiddler, the boys with water casks and Sofron with his three-pronged iron fork.

Iorgovan advanced with them, binding a sheaf here and there, resting a while, seeing that the crosses were well stacked. He was master, and the master must try his hand at everything.

As if by chance, he went to bind into a sheaf the bundles Simina had gathered more lovingly than the others gathered their wheat, for she knew that his hands would touch them after hers. Now and then she glanced at him over her sickle, and now and then he looked at her over his sheaf, and so they spoke without words and they understood each other.

"You are not angry with me," she said at last.

"Sofron is a silly fool," he answered and went off, but was soon back again.

Simina's eyes followed him, called him, brought him back and kept him at her side. They didn't talk; only the golden wheat passed from her hand into his.

"But you see," she said, and again she was the first to speak, "the pushy ones always come in first."

Iorgovan dropped his bundle and looked at her, wide-eyed. "What do you mean? Would you like me to do the same thing?"

"No!" she said laughingly. "I shall do it."

Iorgovan blushed violently. He was ashamed and did not really know whether it was because he was such a weakling as to let a girl say such things to him, or because he loved the girl who said them. But he was ashamed and the soil burned under his feet. He tied another sheaf and went away.

Simina blushed in turn. She was angry with herself for having uttered such words and angry with him for having driven her to say them. Her eyes no longer sought him. Slowly she approached the other girls and talked to them. Iorgovan glanced at her once or twice and, as he met her eyes no longer, he felt impelled to return to her. The girl slowly put a distance between herself and the other girls; but she dared neither look at him nor talk to him.

"You're easily upset, aren't you?" he said after a while.

Simina turned to him and looked at him calmly. "Am I?" she answered. "There, you might as well know it: you may ruin my whole life, but never shall I harbor one bad thought against you."

"Nobody knows what he is going to think tomorrow," said the lad, troubled.

"One knows," answered the girl gathering another armful. "One knows," she said again, taking up her sickle, "because one feels what one does not know." She didn't mind whether the people round her heard her words or not, because she could put up with all things but one: that Iorgovan should doubt her love.

"You know," she continued calmly, "I see and I feel every moment that you are ashamed of your love for me and that you are careful so that people should not suspect it. If that does not make me angry, Iorgovan, nothing in my life ever shall."

"Don't say such words to me," he said choking, "or I'll kill myself. Don't. Let's be silent. It's enough for me to know you are near, without seeing you, without hearing your voice; the ground you have trodden leaps under my feet, and the wheat you've held in your hand bewitches me. God knows that my life is a sad one, but I wouldn't miss one day of it, had I to suffer the tortures of hell."

"Nor would I," said Simina, moved.

"Then let us be silent," he said, "for words are made so that men can ask for their daily bread; for us no words have yet been made, nor is there any need for them. Look into my eyes as I look into yours and if you don't understand me, then there is no understanding in you."

"I do understand you, Iorgovan," she said, "but look," and pointing at Sofron who was again running after a quail, she added: "I should like to see you as merry as he is."

"Maybe he has some reason to be happy," answered Iorgovan.

Simina looked at him to see if he had said those words in rebuke. But Iorgovan was not thinking of what had passed in the morning. She was thinking of it though, and her cheeks became crimson. "He hasn't," she said, "He only believes he has."

"He who believes is just as happy as he who has some real cause," said Iorgovan.

"Then you, too, should believe!"

Iorgovan grew sad and lost in thought. "When your wish is a slight one, hope springs up easily," he said after a while, "but my wish is a great one and I'm afraid to hope."

So their words led them again to the same impasse from which there was no escape.

Sofron? He saw them exchanging words now and then, but what did he care about a milksop like Iorgovan. Had he seen Iorgovan kiss Simina, he would have cleft his head open, while Iorgovan had not even been angry.

Neacsu thought the same. For love is love, and if you care for a woman, you will not stand for any liberties.

Late in the evening, when everybody was settling down for the night, he managed to remain alone with his daughter. He, too, loved Simina, and he would have loved her even if she had not been beautiful. But he had never loved her so much as he did now, so tired from reaping that all his joints were aching.

He felt a sudden longing for his home, for his village, for the people with whom he had spent his life, for the church in which he had taken holy communion so often, for the graves on which he had lit candles on All Saints' Day—candles of yellow wax melted from the honeycombs of his beehives. Many long years had passed since the last pitcher had been broken on his doorstep and he remembered his parents, his brothers, his wife and children as if they had been characters in a book; but now, as he looked at his daughter, all his dead seemed to come alive in her face, one by one. He beckoned her to him.

They had never spoken about Iorgovan; they had gradually come to a silent understanding to leave this subject alone. Now he took her hand. "Do you think," he said, "that Iorgovan will marry you?"

Simina caught her breath and her heart missed a beat. It was difficult for her to answer him, but she was glad there was somebody to whom she could speak about it. "I don't think so," she answered.

"You are wise, my child," said the father. "It would be bad enough if you thought so, but it would be worse if it were to happen."

"Why, dad?" she asked amazed.

"Because a marriage against one's will is not for people of our sort," he answered.

"What do you mean, against one's will? Who is going to force him?"

"His passion," answered the old man, "and that won't last a lifetime. Nor have the others any feeling for you. Don't become a young cuckoo in a raven's nest, my daughter," he said after a while. "You are not cut out for it. You have been sleeping here on an armful of hay and you have slept well. But they have slept in their beds on pillows of down and they'll never forget that you've slept in their barn."

Simina had never believed that Iorgovan would marry her; at least she had told herself that she did not believe it. But now, seeing her father so anxious about her, she wanted to prove to the old man that it wouldn't be a misfortune either for him or for her, if the marriage did take place.

"Dad," she said, "I've been thinking over everything, but, you see, if I were only his servant, I'd still be happy. He is good and kind-hearted."

"He is a coward," answered the old man. "If he were like Sofron, you might have gone through fire and water with him, but it is hard to be the partner of a man who doesn't look straight ahead but is always looking right and left to guess what other people might want him to do. But what's the good of talking?" he said after a short while. "As it is written, such luck you'll have. But I should like to know how things are going to turn out for you."

Finally he rose and said: "May God guide you on your way!"

"Don't go, dad," she begged. "Who knows when we shall have another chance to be together like this."

He sat down again near her and asked her what she wanted.

"Nothing, dad," she replied. Then she put her head on his shoulder and wept.

The priest Furtuna of Socodor was Busuioc's brother-in-law. The name of Father Ioan was not Furtuna,* but the people called him that and with reason. On receiving his brother-in-law's letter, he had smiled. It was not the cholera, he was sure. The physicians had proved that only those died of it who hadn't sufficient strength to recover. That's why the authorities had changed their orders and had decreed that people should eat no cucumbers, melons, or unripe fruit, "but if they died, nevertheless, their grave should be a palm span deeper than the others." Busuioc was sure to know all this, but even if he didn't, he certainly had no need of priest Furtuna's beard to put a check to the cholera.

The priest started to run his fingers through his beard. It was his habit when he was deep in thought. He himself had about twenty acres under wheat and he was expecting the harvesters to come, preferring not to humble himself by begging the villagers to help him. It was perfect; he would just take on Busuioc's harvesters. Besides, the priest liked going and coming, being on the road and out in the fields.

* Furtuna—storm.

"Wife! Wife!" he shouted, looking around him to see what he might need for his trip—his gun, his game-bag, his gunpowder horn, his three-legged stool, his tumbler, and his knife and fork. He could not do without these things. Even when he left after lunch and intended to be back at dusk, he still took all these things with him, for otherwise he could not enjoy hunting. Shooting was hardly the thing for a priest, but if anybody had thought of stopping him he would have shaved off his beard and done what his nephew Iorgovan had done. For, without a dog and a gun, Father Ioan's life was barren.

"What is it, man? Is the house on fire?" asked his wife, standing in the doorway.

"Ah, yes, I called you," he said quickly. "Never mind! I'll do it myself. I don't need you. Wait! What else do I want?" he said stopping in the middle of the room, putting a finger to his forehead.

"Where do you want to go?" she asked with a laugh.

"To Curtici," he answered, gathering his things. "I'll bring back harvesters, too. Look!" he added, handing her the letter, "read for yourself. Something must be up. I'll be back in no time."

Speaking thus, he pinched her ear by way of saying goodbye, and when his wife came into the courtyard, he was already in his cart, his gun on his right, his bag on his left, and his retriever at his feet.

"Get going!" he shouted to the driver, "and don't go to sleep, block-head!"

Busuioc knew of his brother-in-law's approach; the dogs of the village barked the news as they always did on his arrival—scampering around the light cart of the priest who made his servant use his whip on them, sorry that he couldn't do so himself and delighted whenever the servant touched one of them.

"What's up? What's happened?" the priest asked before he had got down from his seat.

"Everything in its proper time," said Busuioc. "For the moment, my thanks for not forgetting us."

But the priest Furtuna was not to be put off; he wanted to know now, on the spot, why he had been called. Entering the house, he greeted his sister and gave his niece Persida his hand to kiss, then he drew his brother-in-law aside to question him.

Busuioc was over forty, about ten years older than his brother-in-law, but the latter was a priest, nay, a priest among priests. That's why the family never did anything without consulting him first. Neither was Father Ioan unworthy of his reputation in the family. Quick and stormy as he was, he was never rash in thought but took his time. He listened attentively, now nodding, and now and then smiling as if doubting what he was told.

"A pity about that horse," he said regretfully. "Didn't I tell you to sell it to me, you having nobody who knew how to manage it?"

"Never mind the horse," said Busuioc vexed. "Tell me rather what to do now."

"Nothing," said the priest shortly. "Let the young manage their own affairs."

"Wait," said Busuioc quietly. "Since that girl has come to my place, I've been on live coals, not knowing how to behave to her. What am I to do if that lad of mine marries her?"

"You don't know your son," said the priest.

"And you don't know the girl," replied Busuioc. "I don't at all want her for a daughter-in-law, but old as I am, if I were a widower, I'd marry her by hook or by crook. She's clever, Father, well-built, and as pretty as a picture."

"Don't I know our Iorgovan?" laughed the priest. "There must be something in her if he went such a long way for her sake. But he won't marry her, brother. You should because you are old, but he won't because he's young and doesn't need to. Let him sow his wild oats, brother!"

"I would gladly let him," answered Busuioc, "only think how hard it would be to have a daughter-in-law that I'm ashamed of. You see," he added quickly, "I don't know if she should sit at the table with us or not."

"She shouldn't if you don't want her for a daughter-in-law."

"But if the boy wants her?"

"Don't agree to it."

"I can't do that," answered Busuioc firmly. "He is my son and I can't, because I don't know if I would be doing right or wrong. That's why I ask you to worm it out of the boy, so that I may know what to do, where to place her, how to speak to her."

"Be sensible, brother!" said the priest impatiently. "Don't be afraid of shadows. Let him alone and little by little he'll grow weary of her."

Busuioc gave him a long look and nodded several times. "Go and have a look at the girl," he continued, "talk to her and then come again and let me see what you have to say."

The priest had had enough of being in one place, and he was glad to get a move on. He gathered his belongings, took Filip with him and the retriever for a bit of shooting.

Iorgovan was moody. His life was bitter again. Simina had kept silent the whole day and stayed close to her father so that he could not come near her. When he caught sight of his uncle, he drew still further away from Simina. He was fond of the priest and God forbid he should suspect anything.

On reaching the harvesters, Father Ioan wished them godspeed and then he began to give criticism first to one, then to the other, now to a girl who didn't hold her sickle properly, then to a lad who did not know how to bind a sheaf or do it tightly enough, then to a reaper who cut the grain badly—he picked on all of them, finding fault with everybody. Iorgovan followed.

"And who might you be?" he asked one of the girls. The girl kissed his hand, telling him her name, her village, and the name of her parents. "Very good!" said the priest, turning to another.

Simina knew the priest. She had seen him once and she had tried to find out all about him. Though for Simina it had been sufficient to hear his voice and to see him walk, to know what he was like.

"This man will quarrel all his life without ever being really angry," she said to herself when she saw him coming towards her. She spread out a handful of grain to look at the ears, chose the most beautiful ones, tied the stalks so as to form a wing and finally she broke the stalks several inches below the knot.

When the priest approached, she waited for him with the fan of wheat in her hand.

Iorgovan felt his cheeks glow.

"What's that?" asked the priest, looking at her with bewilderment.

"It's harvesttime, Father!" she said, holding out the fan.

The priest took his hat off, stuck the wheat in it, then took the girl by the hand and asked her kindly: "And where do you spring from?"

Simina kissed his hand. "She's my daughter, Father," answered Neacsu.

The priest turned around, looking intently at the thin, old man, dried up by disease and by the summer sun. "Your daughter?" he said. "And from where might you be?"

"From Zimbru, Reverend Father. I am verger there."

"Zimbru is it? And how is Father Toader?"

"In good health, God be praised," answered the old man. "Just before Easter, in Lent, the good Lord blessed his home."

The priest went on from one man to another, leading Simina along with him by the hand and holding his hat in the other, Iorgovan and his brother Filip following.

It is a queer thing to be taken along like that. Simina could scarcely check her laughter at being dragged along, but Iorgovan wanted the earth to swallow him, he was so embarrassed. At last, they had left all the reapers behind them and on reaching a wheat cross, the priest stopped. "Haven't you anything to say?" he asked Simina.

"I, Father?" she answered with a smile, all her small teeth showing. "Perhaps I should say you'd better put on your hat, or you'll get sunburnt."

The priest put on his hat, let go of Simina's hand, and stroked his beard. "Any quails?" he asked, turning round to Iorgovan.

"Lots," answered the lad.

"Let's go then; take your gun and come along."

Iorgovan turned around once. He did not know whether to return to the girl or to go and not look at her again.

"Hurry up!" said the priest. "Your mind seems to be elsewhere," he added after a while. "Take care, Iorgovan, my boy, or you'll get into a hell of a scrape. You know me well. Don't get mixed up with the girl. If it's girls you're after, your father is rich enough to get you a wife and he has enough relatives to find you the right one. Understand? That girl is not ugly and she's more cunning than a tigress defending her little ones. Don't let me hear you've been up to any mischief."

What could he answer?

There were three men and Sboru, the priest's retriever, was the fourth of the company, but only Sboru felt in good form. The priest missed all the birds; Iorgovan saw them too late; and Filip thought it preposterous to believe that one could hit a bird which was not sleeping on a branch. Having missed the first time, the priest was convinced that the hour when he had started from home had been unlucky and that he would not hit anything that day.

"You've spoiled my pleasure," he snapped at Iorgovan, slinging his gun over his shoulder, and on his way back to the village he kept calling Filip names—milksop, whipper-snapper, ninny, and so on, and so forth.

"Well?" asked Busuioc when he was alone with him.

The priest flung everything topsy-turvy on the bed—his gun, his tumbler, his gunpowder, his game-bag, his knife and fork in their case. "What can I say!" cried the priest hotly. "And after all, why should I always shoulder the responsibility?"

"Didn't I tell you?" said Busuioc calmly.

"Didn't you tell me what?" he replied, drawing out his words. "It's as I told you. You were not right at all. The girl has caught him; that's all there is to it. She's playing her cards for all she is worth."

"But that's what I told you," said Busuioc astonished, "and that's what I asked you to find out, because it's hard for me to question him."

"Let them settle it among themselves!" shouted the priest furiously. "Why should you interfere? Let her break her head against the wall!"

"And if he breaks his?"

"I'll shave off my beard!" replied the priest promptly. This was his greatest oath, but he would not have minded a bit shaving off his beard.

But Busuioc was not satisfied with his brother-in-law's beard.

"Who the devil brought that forest girl here?" shouted the priest finally, gathering his belongings one by one.

"I did, brother," answered Busuioc with his heart in his mouth, "none but I, and I remember how glad I was to have found her, for people work better when they have girls like that to look at."

"Then stop complaining like this!" said the priest and went away, shouting for his horses to be harnessed.

"You'll come again tomorrow to reach an understanding with the reapers, won't you?" shouted Busuioc.

"I will."

"You'll think about it, won't you?"

"I have nothing more to say!"

Coming back from his shooting, Iorgovan strode with long, measured steps. These last days had been lived more intensely than whole months in the past. It seemed to him that years had passed since he had set out to hire harvesters. The night he had spent on the common at Siria, the way from Cil to Zimbru, the meeting with Simina, everything seemed remote and separated from the present moment by many important events. And all belonged to the past. Simina was sadder than she had been the whole day; she had her reasons. He was not sad; he had no reason to be. Formerly, he had dreaded approaching her; now he didn't mind whether she was near him or not, whether he saw her or not, whether he spoke to her or not. Simina glanced at him from time to time and she felt that he was no longer a man struggling against himself.

"Iorgovan! I want to speak to you today," she said when the harvesters made for the village.

"Why not now?" answered Iorgovan.

"I can't now," she said.

"As you please," he said, "and when you please. You won't be able to say again that I'm ashamed of people seeing us together."

"But I'm ashamed," she whispered tearfully, and they went on their way silently, side by side, Neacsu behind them and Sofron now three steps to their right, now three steps to their left.

In the evening, when people had settled down, Simina walked about restlessly, yet she could not leave as the old man's eyes did not leave her for a moment.

"Father, I have a word to say to Iorgovan," she said frankly.

The old man squeezed her hand, but he neither approved nor disapproved. If she wanted to go, he wanted it too. She bent over him, kissed the hair on his brow and then went away.

As for Iorgovan, he was calm indeed. He was waiting like a man who is certain that his waiting is not in vain and who can afford to wait. He pretended to be busy in the yard.

Sofron, who stood at the stable-door, was waiting too, but like a man who hoped his waiting might be in vain. When Simina came into the yard, he coughed but once.

Simina withdrew, her heart beating quickly. She did not know if he had noticed her, but she would not go in again for the world. Iorgovan followed her out. . . .

Sofron coughed again.

"So he is watching," said Iorgovan to himself, and went towards Simina with a determined step. Sofron came out, fork in hand. Iorgovan pretended not to see him. Sofron flung his fork away and went straight up to meet his master's son who stopped and waited for him. Simina stood stupefied, and Neacsu, who had become fearful at his daughter's absence, went up to the two young men.

"What do you want with that girl?" asked Sofron quietly, very quietly.

"And you, what do you want?" asked Iorgovan.

"I want to marry her," Sofron answered.

"And I don't want to," said Iorgovan frankly.

"Then, leave her alone!"

"It's she who doesn't leave me alone!"

Sofron took a step back. "Liar," he shouted.

Terrified, Simina stepped forward and placed herself between the two men. "He is not lying, Sofron," she said, raising her hand.

Sofron cast his eyes to the ground and wondered why the earth would not open to swallow him. Then, raising his eyes, he looked at Iorgovan, then at Simina; he would have given anything to know what Iorgovan possessed that she should love him so, and what she lacked that he would not go through fire for her sake. "This is not the end of it," he said, turning away.

Sofron had left as if never to return; Simina had sent him away and nobody could call him back.

Neacsu looked straight into Iorgovan's face. He would have liked to say a few things to him, but Simina had cleared him by her remark.

"And if you don't want to, why don't you?" he said at last.

Iorgovan did not want to hurt this sickly old man.

"Why don't you want to, if you'd like to; for you would like to, wouldn't you?" Neacsu insisted.

"Because my wife must not only be a wife to me," answered

Iorgovan. "She will also have to be my parents' daughter-in-law and a member of the family and there would be well-nigh murder about it."

Simina burst into tears. . . .

Busuioc had been an observer of all that had taken place. His son and his servant quarreling over a girl, and his son not man enough to leave alone a girl wooed by a servant!

Priest Furtuna was the wisest after all.

"Haven't I told you?" he said when Busuioc had related what he had seen. "It is as I told you. If he meant marriage, he would not seek to talk to her on the quiet. Leave him alone, brother, and let him sow his wild oats."

"I won't," said Busuioc curtly. "Take her with you," he said finally, to his brother-in-law, "and I'll see to it that she doesn't return."

* * *

In the fields, the next day, the harvesters continued their labor, cutting the wheat in broad waves, binding it into sheaves and gathering the sheaves for Sofron to pile up in crosses. The priest came along to reach an understanding with the men.

Iorgovan who had been calm and rather stern all the time, laughed unpleasantly when he heard that Simina would be going to the priest's at Socodor with the others.

And then came the news that an awful thing had happened at Busuioc's mill. The threshing machine had crushed Pupaza, the treasured retainer of Busuioc's.

"And what about it?" asked Iorgovan callously. He could not understand how such a small thing could upset everyone so much. He set out with the priest for the scene of the accident. . . .

Having reached the mill, Iorgovan looked at the dead man. It was Pupaza, the same old Pupaza he had known in his childhood, who had carried him on his back, whom he had annoyed so often and who had never annoyed him.

He turned round to look at the machine. . . . The driver showed him how the wheels had caught Pupaza, how they had thrown him into the other wheels and how his bones had been crushed. Now Iorgovan understood.

So, Pupaza was dead and would not come to life again. That happens every day and is the way of all flesh. He looked again at the wheels, then he left the scene, determined to forget about them.

Simina's eyes searched the road. He was coming back with a swinging gait, his head well up and his eyes no longer hidden under their thick lashes, but looking around boldly. He was wealthy Busuioc's son, proud and sure of himself, not afraid of anything.

"I can't go away," said Simina to herself. She looked penetratingly at him, as you look at a man whom you want to do your will. "Iorgovan," she whispered at last, "you lied last night and you do so now."

"I?" said he smilingly. "I have a weakness for lying, and if the devil were pleased to ride on my back, I'd boast of having ridden him. Unfortunately, the devil doesn't want to."

"But he does, and very much so," she replied. "Do you know that I am supposed to leave here tomorrow?"

"I do," he answered.

Simina was silent. She was hurt by his indifference. "Iorgovan," she said bitterly after a while, but with her usual calm, "you know what you are doing and I suppose you have your reasons. I don't ask you what has happened to make you as you are. But don't you think that my feelings should have been considered?"

"I do as I please," he said, laughing in her face.

"What if I should refuse to leave?" she said stubbornly.

Iorgovan looked at her somewhat taken aback. "But if your father tells you to go?" he asked.

"He won't."

"But he wants you to go."

"It's just because he wants me to go that I must do as my heart wishes and as my head advises me to do," she said. "My life and my happiness are at stake, Iorgovan, and I don't want to curse anybody. I'd rather repent all my life."

"Then, stay here, girl," he said laughingly. "I brought you here and I've got to keep you. I suppose every man has to carry the burden he has taken upon him of his own free will."

"For shame!" said Simina and turned away disgusted.

She was not disgusted with him but with herself.

In the evening, there was a death vigil at Busuioc's house and, according to custom, there should have been much noise. And noise there certainly was. Busuioc wanted everybody to know that those who had lived with him would be honored in death. He wanted to show Father Furtuna what he could do: his house was full of people, the priest had consented to read the service over the corpse and the alms for the dead man's soul were his affair.

But the priest had not given in to Busuioc's wishes entirely. The corpse was not laid out in the big room, but in a servant's room. Vica, the mistress of the house, had locked herself in a bedroom, and disapproved of everything.* The grave was not to be dug among the other graves but close to the surrounding ditch. The priest had promised

---

* Because Pupaza had not died a natural death and had not been attended in his last moments with a lighted candle, custom demanded that he be buried on the scene of the accident, without ceremony.

to read the service, but it would only amount to a prayer for pardon, and there were no women wailing over the body, as women are easily frightened. The people were playing cards, beating their palms with knotted kerchiefs, telling each other stories, and there was some laughter; but the priest had said that this sort of thing would never bring them luck and, after all, a priest was a priest. They did as they were bidden, but did not feel happy about it. They kept glancing at the windows and the door to see if the devil or a ghost was not peeping in at them to ask what they were doing, making such a noise.

Busuioc himself felt more than any other that what was taking place was not a good omen. He felt broken and weak, and he looked so upset that Neacsu eyed him with pity, and deep down in his heart, he did not doubt the rumor that Pupaza had actually been Busuioc's illegitimate brother.

* * *

Lost in thought, Simina was sitting on a log at the corner of the house. Now and then, a tear trickled down her face and she let it dry there.

In one room there was the body, in the other Busuioc, and in the third there was Vica, but Iorgovan was nowhere. Having come back from the fields, he had stayed for a while and then he had left. He was supposed to have gone to the mill to see how things were there. Simina was waiting for him to return, and her heart ached and the earth burned under her feet. What was he doing? Where was he? Why didn't he come back? Could anything have happened to him? Dear Lord! He couldn't have wearied of life? She had to see him and never let him out of her sight again.

She wiped away her tears and got up. But where was she to go, and so suddenly too? Her old father was with the corpse. She could not go in there; she had no heart to see a dead man laid out on a table, just now.

Sofron stood in the stable door leaning against the door-post. She went straight up to him. Sofron trembled when he saw her coming.

"Sofron," she told him, "if my father should be looking for me, tell him that I shall be back very soon."

He took her hand, squeezed it, and kept it a while in his. Then he asked: "Where are you going?"

"You know where. Why do you ask me? Why do you force me to tell you?" she answered in a choking voice.

"Look here!" he said. "I have been rude to you, but don't think that it is my way. I don't know why, but I am very glad that you have come to me now—let me go and find him for you. I know how it feels, Simina!" he added as he left.

Simina covered her face with her hands and went into the stable, weeping softly. Sofron left at a run and returned in the same way.

"He doesn't want to come," he said troubled.

"Where is he?" she asked.

"At the inn," he answered, looking worried.

Simina stiffened, made as if to go away, and then asked shyly: "Does he make a habit of it?"

Sofron was not the kind of man who understands what he is not told, but he had a kind heart and what he could not understand he felt. "I have been here for a year and I have seen him only once making a night of it, and this is the second time."

"Come on," she said. "Come on, I can't go there by myself."

Sofron followed her with firm steps. Iorgovan was having a good time. In a room separate from the big bar, five people were sitting around a table loaded with bottles and glasses of all kinds, some of them full, others overturned. Iorgovan was sitting alone on a couch at the back of the room; on his right, there was Vasilica, the notary's clerk, on his left, Sarica, a girl from Curtici, seated on the corner of the table among bottles and glasses. Five gipsies were playing near the door, and Buczy Arpad, one of Iorgovan's schoolmates, was dancing with another girl from Curtici, in the middle of the room.

Iorgovan was beating time, whistling the tune, and seemed very gay. . . .

"I want to have a word with you, and then you can do as you please," said Sofron, going up to Iorgovan. He told him in a whisper that Simina was outside and wanted to see him.

Iorgovan stood confused for a moment. Then, hitting the table with his fist shouted: "That's fine! Let her come here and make merry with us. I'll fetch her."

Simina retreated when she saw him drawing near to her with uncertain steps.

"Come along," he said, putting his arm around her. "There is no time like the present. It's now or never!"

The girl was frightened but did not try to resist. She stood shyly in front of him like a quail caught unawares. "Sofron," murmured Simina moving away with Iorgovan, "I have to go with him."

But when she got to the threshold of the separate room, she stopped short and stared at the loaded table and at the occupants. She looked at Iorgovan and the two girls and she passed her fingers over her brow. She felt a sort of giddiness come over her as if she were looking into a deep pit—its very depth drawing her down: the atmosphere created by the upset glasses, the gipsies' faces, and the dishevelled hair of the two girls seemed horrible to her.

"If you are not disgusted by this, let's stay and be merry," she said in a low voice.

Iorgovan also looked at the table. He glanced at Simina and the two girls; then his glance fell on Sofron, who stood behind Simina like a pillar of stone.

"I don't want to!" he said, softened. Then he turned around and staggered towards the door.

Simina caught his arm to support him, and Sofron tip-toed out behind them so as not to anger them by the noise of his steps. He was both unhappy and glad.

"Let go," said Iorgovan after a while, drawing himself away. "I can walk alone."

"If it annoys you. . . ." she answered.

"It does annoy me," he retorted, letting go of her arm and walking on; but finally he burst out weeping.

Simina covered her face with both her hands and stopped, but she could not weep. Iorgovan stopped, too, looked at her for some time, and then suddenly threw himself on the ground in front of her, as though he wanted to kiss the earth under her feet. The girl clasped her hands in despair.

"Come on," she said, bending over Iorgovan, "we must take him home to bed."

* * *

"One has to get angry sometimes, otherwise one gets either addled or rusty." With such words did Father Furtuna end his fits of anger. Early in the morning he was at Curtici. He had not come to fetch the harvesters. They could go alone. His wife was at home and she knew more about running a household than he did. He was a priest and he had to look to his parochial duties; he had come with his stole, his prayer book, and his chasuble to read the service over the dead man in Busuioc's house, for Busuioc was his brother-in-law, and their two houses were of one family.

Busuioc knew his brother-in-law well, and so his coming did not surprise him; and yet he felt a sort of pang at his heart when he saw the priest alighting from his cart.

He did not jump down as usual, but got off sedately, shaking off the dust and smoothing his clothes; he even stamped his feet to clean his shoes, which he would usually never dream of doing except perhaps on the bishop's doorstep. Busuioc eyed him thoughtfully.

Father Furtuna was not the man to be silent when he had something to say. "Haven't I told you?" he said rather roughly when he was inside.

"What's that you told me, brother-in-law?" asked Busuioc nervously.

"The cholera is here. Yesterday two people died, and today there will be other victims."

Busuioc stood motionless for some time. "God's will be done," said Busuioc finally.

On seeing Busuioc so meek, the priest and Vica did everything to please him. Vica insisted on having the body moved into the big house, and the priest proposed that seven priests should celebrate at the burial and the grave be dug among the other graves. But Busuioc lifted a protesting hand and said that everything should remain as it was. For, if a man does no harm, he need have no remorse.

Iorgovan brooded in his bedroom. Overwhelmed by what had happened, he had no strength to face people. "A worm, a good-for-nothing," that's what his servant had called him, and justly so.

That's how things were when Neacsu prepared to take his leave. The men started slowly towards Socodor, and he saw the long column leaving the village. Simina was sitting on a log at the corner of the house and did not stir.

She had seen the priest get down from his cart, she had seen Vica somehow different from her usual self, she had seen a very subdued Busuioc, and she had seen Iorgovan leave the stables with downcast eyes. She saw the whole house in discord, and she was unable to move, nor could she understand the insistence of her father that she leave with him.

Neacsu had given up the idea of persuading her to go with him, but he supposed that she would follow him soon. He went to the servants' quarters to say goodbye to Sofron.

"God grant you good luck," he said, holding out his hand. Sofron pressed his hand, keeping it in his for a long time as though he wanted to keep him back, to tell him something. For he had something to tell him, something the priest's servant had whispered to him. "Look here," said Sofron, keeping the other's hand in his, "do you know that several people have died of cholera at Socodor?"

Neacsu freed his hand, remaining for some time tall and bony-faced in front of him. "Then give me a candle," he said.

Sofron went to the house and came back with a small loaf of bread and a candle, for bread and wax-candles are given as an offering when someone has died—the bread for one's living days and the candle for the hour of death.

"May God forgive him," the old man murmured, taking the bread.

"May God accept the offering," answered Sofron.

Tucking the candle inside his shirt front, the old man went to his daughter, the bread in his hand.

"I'm going, my child," he said.

Simina rose and arranged the bundle on his back. Then they went into the road without a word, the father in front, she a very small way behind. When she bent down to kiss his hand, he kissed the top of her head. Then he took her face between his hands and looked at her with happiness in his eyes.

"And if you should happen to have difficulties," he told her, "don't be afraid of him."

"Yes, father," she answered.

After this, Neacsu set off at a quick step to catch up with the others.

On the way to Arad there is a broad, deep well with two beams, two long troughs—one placed on stumps for the cattle, the other on the ground for sheep—and two buckets—one in the well, the other always swinging in the air, creaking from time to time in the wind.

It was Sunday. The wheat was gathered and carried home. Far and wide, the steppe and the plain were deserted, closed in on every side by waves of heat raised by the scorching noonday sun. Here and there a tree appeared, a well-beam, a house, a church spire, inconstant phantoms, now immersed in water, now projected upside down in the air as the wind changed and the eye moved. Sometimes, the whirlwind gathered straw, leaves and dust, lifted them high in the air, and the column rolled, rolled over fields and dusty roads, till it broke up and scattered its burden all over the fields.

At the side of the well there was a cart with two oxen. The cart must have been there for a long time, as the animals had nothing but the remains of corncobs before them, which they tried to take up with their tongue, scattering them, looking wide-eyed at the corn in the cart and now and then at the troughs of foul water. In the cart there was a man with a water jug near him; neither asleep, nor dead, he lay there ill.

Busuioc was returning from Arad with Iorgovan driving his best horses and making the dust soar far behind.

"Stop!" Busuioc wanted to shout when he saw the suffering animals. "Drive on, Iorgovan, faster!" he said when he had seen the man. He wanted no one to see what he had seen on his way, and nobody to feel what he had felt. Death is terrible, sudden death is more terrible, and still worse is death among strangers. But death by the roadside, without shade or shelter, is the worst—it can't be God's will.

And he, the wealthy Busuioc of Curtici, had sent his boy with two carts on a two-days' journey, to bring those carts back loaded with men. It was impossible not to feel bitter remorse.

Coming home, he found the priest there, anxious to tell him about Neacsu's death. Iorgovan was thunderstruck.

"It could not be otherwise, could it?" laughed Busuioc. "It goes without saying. What sort of cholera would it be if it did not strike my people, and especially Neacsu. Good and merciful is God!" So saying, he kept pacing up and down, and the priest stood aside and looked at him with a sort of satisfaction, beause he liked unexpected things to happen.

"Well, he is dead and we shall bury him," said Busuioc at last, stopping in front of the priest, "but what about the girl?"

"How should I know?" the priest answered. "You look at me as if I had brought him here. When you sent Iorgovan after the harvesters, you knew that the cholera had broken out, and didn't mind. You should not mind now. He whose days are up must die."

"And I shall never have another happy day in my life if that girl remains homeless," shouted Busuioc.

"You know how you feel," said the priest, "so don't ask my advice."

And Busuioc took to his pacing again. There were three men in the house: Busuioc, Iorgovan, and Sofron, and only Sofron knew what he wanted, but he did not dare. The other two were afraid that they might do, out of weakness, what they did not want to do. Busuioc had set his heart on atoning.

"Iorgovan," he said, stopping in front of his boy, "it is not because you want it, neither because I wish it, but it seems to be God's will. . . . You know what I mean, don't you?"

Iorgovan trembled all over. "No!" he said, humbled. "Let us leave all that."

Busuioc, without heeding his son's words, turned on his heel and went to Vica.

A bit later, the whole house except for Simina knew that Neacsu had died. The priest had told her that Neacsu was all right.

Simina had got into the habit of walking about warily. For four days after her father's departure, she had felt like a slave in Busuioc's house. Humbled by what she had done, shortly after Neacsu's departure, she had gathered her few belongings to follow him, but she had had Vica to reckon with.

"He is sending the girl away," she cried whenever Simina prepared to leave. "She makes my boy unhappy," she cried, whenever she saw her son with downcast eyes. And Simina could not leave a house in discord behind her.

So Simina was accustomed to go about warily, but lately, life had seemed unbearable. She noticed that their faces had changed, that they avoided her; that there was secret conversation at times, and she struggled hard to understand the meaning of everything. One thing she knew for certain: all this change, all these glances had been brought about by the arrival of the priest. She often remembered the day on which she had remained alone in the stubble field.

But despite Vica's authority, things couldn't go on as they were. There was one man in Busuioc's household who dared everything. As soon as he heard about Neacsu's death, Sofron uncovered his head, hung his hat on a peg, and went to find Simina without a moment's delay.

In the middle of the courtyard he stopped her. "Simina," he said, "what relatives have you?"

"A cousin and an aunt at home, at Zimbru," she said astonished, "and an uncle here, at Cherechi. I don't know him but father often speaks about him. Why do you ask?"

"Your father has died," said Sofron tonelessly.

"Father—dead!" she whispered. "How did he die?" she asked, frightened.

"Of cholera."

Simina raised her hand, passed it across her forehead, and then her fingers went up and down between her eyebrows. "What am I to do now?" she asked.

"I don't know," he said. "We must ask an old woman. Go and loosen your hair. I will ride to Cherechi and at midnight I'll be back at Socodor with your uncle, so that they may wash and lay him out for the death vigil. By then you must be there also to mourn for him."

"Where are we going to lay out my father? Where is the death vigil going to be?"

"In my house," said the priest, hurrying up to her.

Simina kissed his hands. Then she began to weep and went up the front steps, loosening her hair.

For nine weeks Simina had not plaited her hair, for nine weeks she had closed her prayers every night with the words: "Forgive me, Lord, my trespasses; God rest his soul!"

The priest had buried him, had given out alms, had read the prayers of pardon, had kept the dead man's daughter in his own house.

In vain, Vica, the uncle from Cherechi, the aunt from Zimbru asked her to come to them. Simina could not leave Socodor; she could not leave her dead father alone. She didn't weep, but she stayed and wanted to stay on in the village.

And if she had wanted to go, the priest's wife would not have let her, because she was lonely, and before Simina had come to her house she had not known how bad it is to be alone.

And yet, it was the priest's wife who reminded her that the house at Zimbru was empty and that she had to look for another home. . . .

"Busuioc is coming on Sunday."

Simina hung her head. "On Sunday? Next Sunday?" She knew Busuioc's intentions and she had got accustomed to the idea that it would be so; but it seemed too early yet. For two months she had had no time to think of it, and now it seemed that she could scarcely remember all that had happened.

In the evening, before going to sleep, she remained awake for a long time, thinking of the past and future. She had been through it all; she had felt and suffered everything, but now, when looking at things with eyes purified by sorrow, she could not believe it all any more. Thoughts and feelings had settled quite differently in her heart now, and whenever she thought of Iorgovan, her cheeks grew hot and she felt a harshness in her heart.

So much madness, so much pain she had left behind! She now felt sensible and she wept. She did not feel dazed any more, but life had lost its charm, and whenever she thought of beginning where she had left off, the same words came ringing in her mind: "A cuckoo in a raven's nest, Simina, my daughter." No, it was too early yet. She needed time to think. And yet she did not feel strong enough to oppose Busuioc.

"I have an uncle and an aunt," she said. "I'll see what they have to say about it. He must ask them."

Father Furtuna had settled down to a quieter life. He still went shooting, continued to drive his horses, was as fond of his retriever as ever, but he did not put his heart into anything.

He would have dearly loved to call Neacsu to life again. It was no fault of his that he had died, but he would have preferred him to be alive or, if he had to die, that he should have died in his own house. And as Simina, the dead man's daughter, lived in his house, he was reminded of him whenever he saw her.

Wherever the priest went, he could not get rid of Neacsu, for his brother-in-law Busuioc was well known to everybody, and who would not have liked to know whether it was true that Busuioc had taken it into his head to have a girl of the forest for his daughter-in-law.

Busuioc's relatives, especially, were very much surprised. Some of them thought that Busuioc was quite right, that Busuioc, being a rich man, did not need to look for a rich girl, and there is nothing better in the world than love between husband and wife. Above all, Simina was beautiful and a beautiful daughter-in-law is like a jewel in the home.

Others were of the opinion that Busuioc did not at all wish his boy to marry, but that he was not asked; Iorgovan was the real master in the house and did as he pleased. Others knew that Iorgovan did not want to marry Simina; how could a man like him fall in love with a girl of the forest? But she had bewitched him with her spells, and tender-hearted Iorgovan could not get rid of her.

The priest knew that all this was not true. He shrugged his shoulders and said that he did not know anything. He told them all that they were right, in order to get rid of them.

Of one thing he was certain: if Neacsu had not died, Busuioc would not have given in to his son, and Iorgovan himself would never have insisted against his father's will. That's why, after Neacsu's death, the priest avoided speaking with Busuioc, Vica, or Iorgovan about Simina.

Busuioc felt that, and in the beginning he did not seem to mind. But he was accustomed to ask his brother-in-law's advice and so he got confused little by little.

"Well, speak up!" he said at last. "Haven't you anything to say?"

The priest looked at him smilingly. "Why do you ask me?" he answered. "As if you could do anything else but what your own mind tells you to do. When it's a question of your son's marriage, do what you think best."

"I take it upon myself," said Busuioc, and from then on his mind was made up.

As for Iorgovan, he was waiting. He was at war with himself, his mood and longings changing from hour to hour, from minute to minute. He remembered all that had happened, the words that they had spoken on that memorable night, Sofron's anger, Neacsu's dismay, and Simina's determination. He remembered his drunkenness and Neacsu's death. After all this, he could hardly look at Simina without hating her.

No! he could not hate her either. He was aware that if Simina were to remind him by a single sign of what had happened, he would either crawl at her feet as on that night or close his eyes and kill her. And yet, it was beyond him not to think of her.

Often, when he saw Sofron peacefully seeing to his work, he looked at him in shy wonder and he felt almost afraid of him.

When they left for Socodor, Iorgovan was not in a marrying mood. Busuioc felt it and would have liked to scold him. When they entered the priest's yard, Iorgovan began to tremble all over and when he saw Simina, everything became faint and he felt giddy.

Busuioc saw him and controlled himself with great difficulty. When the priest's wife took him aside to talk to him about Simina's relatives, he froze. "Tell Simina to come here!" he said firmly, walking about the room.

After a while, Simina entered and went up to him, hanging her head. "Simina," he said, carefully weighing his words so that she might not think him overly keen on becoming her father-in-law, "what have you decided? Are you going to stay here? Will you go up to your uncle or come and stay with us for good? You know how welcome you would be."

Simina lifted her head and with her left hand raised a few strands of hair from her face, then did not move for a while. She knew she could not stay with the priest any longer. However, she would be sorry to leave. "For the time being," she said with downcast eyes, "I'll go to my uncle's."

* * *

All Curtici knew why Busuioc had gone to Socodor, and so did Sofron. He had harnessed the horses and had handed the whip to Iorgovan. He had wished them good luck, and his eyes had followed them on their way. As a matter of fact he had known for a long time that things were coming to this; he was now used to the thought and saw no reason why he should go on worrying. However, when returning to the stables, his sight seemed to fail, and suddenly things became muddled in his head and heart. He would have liked to stop the course events were taking and to say: "Wait a while, I have to think things over." He dropped exhausted on a sack of corn and stayed thus for a long time.

If he had been a man of quick decision, he would not have tarried, but taken a horse from the stables, and dashed off to Socodor to get there before Busuioc. But his thoughts were too slow and whenever he wanted to rise, he remembered that he had once been shamed, dreadfully shamed, and remained where he was. And yet he loved her.

Looking around him, he left the stables and made for Socodor on foot, walking slowly, but steadily like a man who knows that he will be in time. And the whole distance from Curtici to Socodor, through yards, over fields of stubble and tilled fields, Sofron walked. But his mind had stopped, dwelling on the same thought—that it was impossible.

Simina sprang up, startled, when the priest's wife came to tell her that Sofron wanted to speak to her. Had she known what Sofron wanted, she would have let Simina go out alone to him, but the girl looked so upset that she thought it her duty not to leave her.

So they went in, the three of them. The priest's wife and Simina sat down while he remained standing near the door.

"Sit down, Sofron," said Simina, finally. Looking at Simina, he dared not utter the thoughts that had brought him there and tears streamed down his ruddy, weatherbeaten cheeks.

Simina felt her eyes drawn to his, and shivered when she sensed the fire burning in him. She narrowed her shoulders and drew back somewhat: she knew that now her tears would flow abundantly, stifling, smothering her. The priest's wife rose, looking amazed at the two of them.

"It is nothing," he said recovering his composure. "It caught me unawares but it will soon be over. I just wanted to tell you that everything is for the best," he went on with difficulty. "I am glad to hear that you'll be Iorgovan's wife."

Simina could not control her tears, and, for a while, they remained silent and motionless.

"No, Sofron," said Simina, recovering her usual calm. "That is over forever! He kept me away from my father on the day of his death; he keeps me away from you now, now that my life is hardest. Our ways have separated and they can never meet again in this earthly life. See here," she added after a while, "not for my sake, for I don't deserve it, but because you were fond of my father and he cared so much for you—if you only knew how much! See here," she said, "it's all the same to you, for you won't stay with Busuioc anyway. Settle down at Socodor so that dad will not be alone."

Speaking thus, she moved towards the door.

"Of course I'll come, there's no doubt about that," he answered and, following her, he seized the sleeve of her blouse and kissed the transparent tissue.

And Sofron was happy because now he had a place to go and could remain near Neacsu's grave at Socodor.

Busuioc would have liked to hurt Simina but he felt that he had not the means to reach her. Is money of such little consequence in this world? He was wealthy, yet what use was all his wealth now?

"It's all right," he told Vica on coming home.

"What do you mean, all right?" cried Vica. "You both look down and out."

"It's quite all right," said Busuioc again. "It couldn't be better. It had to be like this. Am I one of those who pick up members of their household from the gutter? She has her own relations; let her seek advice from them. Let her look after her dowry, so I need not be ashamed when I receive her into my house. I'll give her things, but let her ask for them at least."

Vica agreed. "If the poor are poor, they must at least give the rich the satisfaction of asking for what they want."

"Besides, somebody must give her away, I must take her from somebody, from somewhere," continued Busuioc. "For the present she's going to her uncle's at Cherechi. That's what I want her to do."

Vica declared herself satisfied, and, after a short while, the whole village knew what had been decided. The news soon reached Cherechi.

Simina heaved a sigh of relief. She understood why Busuioc had not told the truth even to his wife. By and by, everything would be forgotten; even the shame of refusal would not be felt for long. That was Busuioc's opinion and Simina's wish.

"That's how things are," she told those who were bothering her with questions, and to make it seem more probable, she started making her trousseau, but very leisurely—a small piece today, another the next, undoing everything after some days and beginning again. And if anyone attempted to hurry her, she said that she need not make haste as it might all come to nothing.

As if he could read her thoughts, Busuioc dropped a word here and there that there was no hurry. Who knows, maybe Iorgovan might change his mind. And after some weeks, it was generally known that Busuioc did not want it any longer and that Iorgovan did not insist either.

And though it was surprising, Iorgovan said much the same thing. Not that he had changed his mind. No, a man in love can't do that in a hurry, but in a hidden corner of his soul he was convinced that Simina would change her mind and even if he gave her up, she would not release him.

As for Sofron, he was in a complete daze, like a man who had been on the road in storm and rain the whole night. There were many who considered Sofron a stupid fellow, though nobody had ever seen him doing anything stupid. But he was slow, so slow that if somebody had taken him by surprise and asked him if he were a man or a woman, he would have floundered in his response. He would have wondered why he was asked that particular question, how he should interpret it, what he ought to answer, and finally he would have said: "Wait a bit. I'll have to think it over." . . . Nevertheless, he had done a foolish thing, a hopelessly foolish thing; he had committed an unforgivable baseness. "I am a villain," he told himself on returning from Socodor; and when Sofron, rightly or wrongly, had come to a conclusion, he stuck to it.

It was not right, he was not glad that Simina should marry Iorgovan, and yet he had told her that it was right and that he was glad of it. She hadn't given him time to think. What could he do if God had not endowed him with more brains, so that he lost his head the moment he saw Simina? But Simina had told him that what he had spoken about would never come true. She had said so. Why should he remember her words? He knew what he had said himself, what he was thinking, what he had in his mind and he remembered that he had to move to Socodor lest the dead man should remain alone.

At Curtici he felt lost. He dreaded being alone with his evil thoughts which, once conceived, haunted him day and night; and he was ashamed to look people in the face. When he saw Busuioc, his blood froze, and he avoided Iorgovan lest he should get hold of him and crush him.

He knew that he was not good enough for Simina, but Busuioc

should also have known that his house did not deserve Simina as a daughter-in-law; neither was Iorgovan fit to be her husband.

"And what do they care? It will last as long as it may," he told himself sometimes and then he wanted to shout: "Take me, tie me up and club me like a mad dog!"

But people began to speak about poor Simina, and how Busuioc did not want her and that Iorgovan insisted no longer. Sofron did not seem to understand. . . . He would not be too shy to speak to her now, he thought and he wanted to give her a piece of his mind as he was older and wiser than she was, and as he cared for her, oh! ever so much!

As it was understood that Sofron was to leave Curtici, it followed that he would sell his plot of ground. He had bought it a year and a half ago, and during that time he had grown accustomed to the idea that that was his plot, that his house was to be built on that place and that he would spend his life with his wife and children there. He could not leave the place without regret. . . .

True, Sofron never said that the place was not for sale, but when a purchaser turned up, he said that he would have to think it over. And he kept thinking it over. St. Dimitrie's day was drawing near, but he did not dream of leaving.

Two weeks before St. Dimitrie's day, coming home from the market via Socodor, Busuioc, putting two and two together from what he'd heard, came to know about all that had passed between Sofron and Simina.

On the way home and once there, walking from the door to the window, he tugged at his moustache. Now he could get at Simina.

Sofron's money was in his hands; not actually in his hands, for he had lent it to other people, but it was entirely up to him when the debt was to be paid. As a matter of fact, it was lent out till St. Dimitrie's day, and, though it would have been hard to get it back before that date, it was very easy to get the payment postponed.

He called Toader's Oanea, one of the borrowers, and put the thumb-screws on him. Borrowers are always short of money when you ask for your loan back, and Oanea moreover had lost an ox in the spring, so he solicited a postponement of a month or two.

"Willingly, even a year," replied Busuioc, "but you know the money is not mine. Speak to Sofron."

He knew that Sofron did not know how to insist upon payment and, without his money, he could not leave Curtici.

Sofron knew it himself, that's why he had given it to Busuioc, with whom it was safe, for the latter was rich enough to give it back to him and had enough influence to make debtors pay up. So Sofron thought hard when those who owed him money asked for a delay.

"My money is not with you, it is with Busuioc," he said at last. "I gave it to him and it's not my business what he did with it."

That's how it was, but if Sofron was right, the debtors were not stupid, and they had understood very well that Busuioc had sent them to Sofron because he wanted to keep his servant, a design with which they were in complete accord.

"If that is so, good luck to you; we don't owe you anything," they said and went about their business.

On St. Dimitrie's day, Sofron was as determined as ever to leave, but nothing had changed. He went to Busuioc for his wages.

Busuioc counted out the money due him to the last farthing, wished him good luck and success in everything, but did not say a word about the loans.

"He has very likely forgotten about it," said Sofron to himself, and stood about hoping that he might remember.

But Busuioc began to speak to him about other things and not about his money. At last, Sofron went away, but stopped before leaving the house; stopped again after shutting the door behind him, stayed on for a while and began to scratch behind his ear. "I shall have to think it over," he said to himself; "very likely he has not got it handy just now."

Then he began to think again. A day passed, then two, a week, and Busuioc did not return his money. He stayed on in the house and worked as usual though he was no paid servant any more. But he was ashamed to eat another's bread without doing anything for it. Not an evening passed without Sofron telling himself: "Tomorrow I'll speak to him." That's what he said, but he did not do it. Something was always cropping up: either Busuioc had people staying with him, or Vica had been quarrelsome during the morning, or a servant had broken a pitcher.

Busuioc expected that Sofron would finally come to him, felt slightly embarrassed when he saw him entering the house and wanted to tell him not to shut the door behind him. He seemed another man now, not the Sofron he knew, and the memory of that night when he had seen him walking up to Iorgovan flashed through his mind.

"I have come," said Sofron, "about the money I gave you in the autumn."

"Careful with your words," said Busuioc. "You did not give me any money. I don't need your money. I only found people to whom you lent it."

"Not at all!" replied the servant. "I gave you the money. When you engaged me, we settled it. I know how I sweated for it and I didn't want to give it to just anybody, so I looked for a rich and honest man who could give it back to me at any moment. 'See here,' I told you, 'take this money and return it to me next year with interest. If you agree, I'll work for you; if not, I shall look for another man who is ready to accept my offer.' Isn't that so?"

Busuioc wanted to throw him out, but he could not. Wealthy Busuioc could not throw out his servant who had grown impertinent. "It is so, Sofron, but still I have not taken your money; I have not used it. You know I haven't got it. If you want me to pay you out of my own purse, I will; if you'll wait, we'll take the matter to court and make the debtors pay up."

"Give it to me now," said Sofron, "because you can make them pay any time."

"Now, on the spot?" Busuioc asked laughing.

"On the spot," replied Sofron frowning.

"And if by any chance I won't or I can't?" inquired Busuioc.

"I see you don't want to or you can't, and I don't know why," said Sofron, troubled. He had not thought of that. But that was the point. How would he stand, if Busuioc did not or could not pay?

"Yet, you must give it to me," he continued. "It is impossible not to give it to me. I thought a long time before giving it to you and I told myself: 'If I give it to Busuioc, I need not worry. He will give it back to me.'"

"You're right, Sofron," said Busuioc, putting his hand on his shoulder and looking him straight in the eyes. "Don't worry. Your money couldn't be safer than with me. I shall give it to you, but you will have to wait a few days, maybe a week or two."

* * *

Simina seemed to know everything. Sofron had told her that he would move to Socodor and he had not, for he had not sufficient strength to go; he could not sell his bit of land, nor persuade Busuioc to let him have his money back. In short, he was not a man.

Neither did he want to move any longer, nor to see her or to know about her. He did not want anything. He was just existing, living his life without purpose, without caring for anything.

And who knows whether for all his mad worrying she cared about his going to Socodor or not? Perhaps she did not even know that he had not gone there. True she had asked him to come that day, but had she not said that she would not give up Iorgovan?

Why should he embitter his life for her sake?

For a long time he had promised himself not to think of Simina any more, but now he was quite determined to put her out of his mind for good.

Busuioc would have liked to see Simina, to know what she was saying and doing; Sofron also wanted to see her, but Iorgovan wanted to most of all. "She will be sorry one day for what she has done and she'll come back to me, repentant." That was Iorgovan's consolation. But as time went on, Iorgovan grew despondent and more impatient every day. He wanted to have some news, wanted something to happen, for his life had become aimless.

But Simina was the most despondent of them all. Her thoughts worried her in the daytime and her dreams at night. She now felt she was all alone in the wide world. Sofron had forsaken her too.

She seldom spent a night without seeing him in her dreams; Neacsu, too, either barefoot, or hungry, or thirsty, always angry, always reproaching her. In the mornings, she would weep for hours, give alms to the poor as well as her own food for the day and the last clothes she possessed.

Her father's curse was on her because she had been blind and had not listened to his advice, because she had left him in his hour of death, because she had laughed at the weakness of a man who had been so well beloved by her father. So she would sit by herself, thinking of the past and seeing everything in a new light.

In late autumn, one Sunday, when scarcely any leaves were left on the trees, she tied a kerchief round her head and went to the cemetery at Socodor. It was a journey of several hours and she walked deep in thought, wiping off a tear now and again. When she was among the graves, she broke into loud, painful sobs, threw herself on the ground and remained for a long time as in a trance. It was there that Father Ioan found her and, frightened by the change in her appearance, approved of her decision to remain in Socodor as a housekeeper in the household of a recently bereaved villager, Martin, caring for the latter's four motherless youngsters.

* * *

Busuioc was walking about in the house when Sofron entered unexpectedly and stopped in front of him. For a moment, they stood still, facing each other.

"I am going to Socodor," said Sofron, "and I'll be back either tomorrow or the day after for my money. I want to tell you now so that you should know."

Busuioc knew why he was going to Socodor and he was now ready to use all his influence to stop him. And Busuioc could do much. He had but to say that Sofron was a thief, that he had threatened him with his knife, and he would be sent to prison.

"I'll call the debtors and put the screws on them," he said.

Sofron advanced a step and gave him a long and sharp look. "Let's stop that game," he replied. "I'm a stupid fellow and don't know much, but I have made up my mind. Don't drive me to commit a sin.

My life is worthless to me, but you have a fortune and children. I am afraid of what I might do—you ought to be frightened too."

He turned around and left the room, not to breathe the same air as the man who was the cause of his misfortune.

Busuioc remained for a long time on the spot where Sofron had left him. Yes, he had a fortune and children. It was Thursday, and every Thursday Busuioc settled the accounts at the mill and sent the flour he had collected during the week to Arad for the Friday market. On the same day, all that was necessary for mill and household had to be bought. After he had filled his sacks, Iorgovan went to the mill.

At the mill, work was going on as usual. People were talking; one was filling sacks with flour, another unloading the wheat; others had brought their grain in baskets; and two or three of them waited their turn.

At the entrance, in the left corner, was a small table with an open ledger.

"Has Sofron left?" asked the miller, while Iorgovan tidied the table.

"He has," answered Iorgovan. He was in a hurry. In the evening, he had to be at Arad. He had lived at Arad for six years; he had plenty of friends and acquaintances there, whom he met every two or three weeks and who welcomed him gladly as he never came empty-handed.

Months had passed since his last drinking bout at the Curtici inn. The blood rose to his cheeks whenever he remembered it, and he had avoided his merry-making companions.

But now he looked around for some lively fellows again. In a café on the main street, he met his one-time landlord, Virgil Bargaut, a man of about twenty-three, short and plump, restless and badly dressed, a young wastrel, living from hand-to-mouth, earning his living by writing; here one day, there the next, and later nowhere.

"Let's go to the 'Devil's Mill,'" said Bargaut. "It's a decent pub, where people can do as they please without anyone gaping at them. Drinks, songs, cards, that sort of thing."

Iorgovan was not a drinker—a glass of wine went to his head and he became sullen. But he liked to see others drink till they could no longer stand on their feet. But now he was longing for noise, dancing and songs, broken bottles, spilt wine, quarrels and kisses . . . he wanted to see people giving way to wild revelry.

"Have you a suit for me?" he asked Bargaut after a while. "I can't go as I am. My peasant clothes are too conspicuous. A farmer can't do what you townspeople do every day of your life."

The priest had a hot temper but he was not rash in his actions.

Seeing Simina desolate, he felt remorse for not having done more for her at the right moment. He might have saved her from being abandoned by everybody. Simina had so unnerved him that he was ready to go to Busuioc to compel him to come again to woo her for his son.

"Why didn't you want to marry Iorgovan, girl?" he asked her when they had returned home and had been talking with his wife for some time.

"She was quite right," said his wife.

"I didn't say that I didn't want to," answered Simina. "I said it might be better to wait a bit."

"Well, but do you want him now?"

"No," she replied, "now less than ever."

The priest's wife knew why she hadn't wanted him then and why she didn't want him now. She remembered her look when she had faced Sofron.

"That's neither here nor there," she said. "Let's stop pretending. Simina is going to marry Sofron."

* * *

When he came to Socodor, a few days later, Sofron sought her out. They stood and faced each other as if they were facing disaster.

He stretched out his rough hand. "I am glad to see you. I thought I'd be sorry, but I'm glad."

"I don't know what to say," she said. "How is everybody—Vica, Busuioc, Iorgovan?"

"They're well," he replied. "Iorgovan has become quite reasonable; may God keep him so. I thought he might take a wrong turn. You remember that night. I was afraid."

"So was I, Sofron!" She went about her work as if she had been alone, and he sat down on a tub at the entrance, eyeing her.

"Simina!" he said in a loud voice after a while. "How thin you have become!"

She looked at him laughingly. "Because of you, Sofron," she answered as if she were joking. "You don't know how worried I've been since I realized that I shouldn't have asked you to move to Socodor."

Troubled, he cast down his eyes. "Why," he said, "you must have had a hard time. Knowing that you were alone, I couldn't help coming, and nothing could have prevented me, even if I had had to leave my own father unburied."

He got up, went to her and took her hands, looking at her.

Suddenly, tears filled Simina's eyes.

He stood in front of her not knowing what to do. "Why do you weep?" he asked, putting his hand on her shoulder and looking into her eyes.

"Have I no reason to weep? I have been weeping so much, Sofron, that it has become a habit, and often I find myself crying all of a sudden, without any reason, because my eyes are used to weeping."

"That is so," said Sofron, "tears will come and you can't help them."

Suddenly they were interrupted by the entrance of the priest followed by two gendarmes.

"We have been ordered to take him with us," said one of the gendarmes.

Sofron and Simina were both frightened.

"What is it, Sofron? What has happened?" snapped the priest.

"It is nothing," replied Sofron turning to Simina. "Don't get frightened. I served in the imperial army and justice will be done to me. I once punched the corporal so hard that I knocked out three of his teeth, and he was laid up for two weeks. The captain put me in chains but he told me that I had done right. If necessary, I shall go to the emperor himself. He may imprison me, but he will see that I get my money."

"What money?" asked the priest.

"My money, nine hundred silver pieces," answered Sofron, "which I entrusted to Busuioc. And now he wants to trick me out of them."

"Let's see whether he'll give them back or not," said the priest.

"Please, don't worry, Simina," said Sofron, going off with the priest and the gendarmes.

Simina's frightened eyes followed them. "It's my fault again," she cried in dismay. "Busuioc never forgets nor does he forgive. And Iorgovan," she said after a while, "how is he going to hurt me when his turn comes?"

Busuioc was stunned when he found the priest, his wife's brother, interfering in a matter that concerned only him and his servant. Moreover, he was ashamed to give in.

"I'm not giving him the money simply because I don't want to," he told the priest. "Let him go to law with me. I shall teach him to threaten me."

"And I tell you that I don't want a lawsuit," said Sofron. "Either I'll knife you or I'll set your house on fire. I shan't stay in prison forever."

"You'll come out of it today!" shouted the priest, "and the money is my affair. I'll see to it that he pays, and if you're worried about it, I'll give it to you tomorrow. We'll see who'll win. There's something here that doesn't smell right."

"We will see," shouted Busuioc. He was ready to risk his fortune out of sheer stubbornness.

In the evening, he waited for his son to return from Arad. But night came, and there was no Iorgovan. Vica, suspicious and anxious like all mothers, was full of all sorts of forebodings.

The farm hand had returned with the cart. He told them that Iorgovan had left him on Thursday evening and that he had not seen him since. He knew that he had been accompanied by a certain Bargaut. He himself had just left the sacks and come home.

Busuioc knew Bargaut. "It's nothing," he told Vica, "He's having himself a good time. He'll be back soon, though he'd do as well to stay where he is."

Yet, he was quite uneasy and would have given anything to send somebody on horseback after his son at Arad, to look for him and bring him back. He could not go himself. Iorgovan was his son and he could not shame him so.

Suddenly, he went out in despair and told a servant to ride to Socodor and tell the priest to come to Curtici early next morning. Then, thinking better of it, he said: "No, I'll go myself."

"Leave him alone," said the priest, "behave as if you didn't see, hear, or notice anything. He'll be back all right. Iorgovan is not the boy to go wrong."

On Saturday afternoon, Iorgovan turned up. He was ashamed to face the servants and neighbors. He would have liked his father to storm at him. He wanted to hang himself when his father did not ask him where he had been and what he had done, and did not even seem to be angry with him. He handed his father the money for the flour he had sold on the second day, and told him that the dealer had kept him waiting, and so he had been obliged to stay.

These were lies. It was not true that the dealer had kept him, and the money did not come from him either. He had borrowed it, because he had spent the money he had obtained for the flour. It was the first time he had borrowed money and, though the sum was a small one for a rich man's son, the debt weighed on his mind all the more as he did not want anybody to know about it and he had to repay it without fail by next Friday.

There was but one thing to do: cheat his father over the accounts at the mill. He would have got the sum for the asking; Busuioc would have given it willingly, but he did not want to upset him. One way or another, it was his father's money he would have to pay.

For once in his life, being in such a plight, he might do it. And on the following Thursday, he cheated his father over the accounts at the mill.

Busuioc trembled when he heard Iorgovan insist on going to Arad again, but he had not the strength to oppose him.

Iorgovan would have sworn on his life that he would return in good time, that he would not stay to talk to anybody and never get into debt again for the rest of his life. He alone knew how bitterly he had reproached himself during this last week. And he did return in time and without getting into debt.

But again he had changed his peasant clothes and spent a merry night, not with Bargaut, but with fellows he had never met before, and not in town, but at Schela, across the river Muras, where nobody knew him.

And this time Iorgovan joined in the dancing and singing. Nor did he feel such bitter remorse. He had had a good time, but after all with whom? With fellows he had never seen and would never see again. Good-for-nothings that he did not care one straw about!

Busuioc felt happier when he saw his boy returning promptly and not looking humiliated as on his return the week before. He was glad he had made his peace with the priest. He was afraid that Iorgovan might yield to temptation again and none but the priest could curb him. Yes! Busuioc would gladly have given Sofron twice his money now, just to keep on good terms with the priest. Whose fault was it if Iorgovan went astray?

"It's my fault, only mine," said Busuioc.

And Iorgovan was of the same opinion. That's what he had in mind when he robbed his father at the mill, when he drank and danced and sang and did things which would have disgusted him before. Every Friday, he showed less reserve at the orgies in which he took part. He even went dressed in his national costume. And then, he began to haunt the village inn as well.

When Busuioc heard how things were, he dashed off to the priest.

"The boy must marry," the priest said. "No matter whom, but marry he must." And perhaps the priest might have brought things to a head if they had gone as he expected them to.

Sofron had settled down at Socodor. He had bought a couple of oxen, a cart and a plough; he had rented some land and did his autumn ploughing. For the first time in his life he savored the sweetness of work done on his own land.

Nobody knew Sofron at Socodor. He had come only recently. But they knew the girl of the forest and that he was attached to her. They thought he might be a relative or a man from the same village. It was known that he often went to Martin's house where Simina was staying and that she tidied up for him and washed his linen as she did for Martin and the children. That's why people named him "the Forest Girl's Sofron."

Meanwhile, Iorgovan spent his time at the inn of Curtici.

"I say, Iorgovan," said the clerk, "do you remember the girl of the forest? She was a damned handsome wench."

Iorgovan gave him a long look. "I do, I certainly do!" he said. "And what is more, there is no other like her in the whole world."

"Do you happen to know that she is carrying on with Sofron now?" said the clerk. "A devil of a woman!"

Iorgovan rose to his feet, stared at him, and then he glanced at the table to find something hard and heavy. There was only the bottle of wine. He took it by its neck, lifted it and threw it at the clerk who sat dumbfounded opposite him.

"Carrying on, did you say? Simina is carrying on?" he shouted, and threw himself like a madman at the unfortunate man who fell to the floor, his face streaming with blood.

Everybody hurried to the table to separate the two. Seeing that people were crowding round him, Iorgovan pulled himself together, stopped, and looked around him.

"That will do!" he said. "Leave me alone, I'll go by myself wherever you want me to go."

"Home," said one of them.

"Home it is," answered Iorgovan.

When he came home, he confronted his father steadily, while the people who had come with him explained what had happened.

"What has become of you? What have you done, Iorgovan?" asked Busuioc when he was alone with him.

"I haven't done anything," answered his son. "You are responsible for everything." Having spoken, he left abruptly, to try to stifle the passion which had so suddenly flamed up in him, making him want to go far, far away, where nobody should ever find any trace of him.

Busuioc dashed off to the priest again.

"Now is the moment to leave him alone," said the priest, "and if he does not change his ways shortly, it will be pretty bad. We must arrange matters and close our eyes to what has happened."

The priest went to the clerk, who had taken to his bed, to smooth his ruffled feathers. Iorgovan was in despair. He could find no rest anywhere. There was one matter which hurt Iorgovan above all; the tension between him and his father. He could not forgive himself those rashly spoken words: "You are responsible for everything." He would have to add something to explain them, to tell his father all that was worrying him.

"We shall have to talk things over," they both thought whenever their eyes met. But neither was strong enough to begin.

On Thursday afternoon, five days after the scene at the inn, Iorgovan asked his father whether he should go to Arad or not.

"We'll be going Friday week," said the older man awkwardly.

Iorgovan would have liked to ask why, but he turned on his heels, walked straight out of the house, and made for the inn. He did it out of spite. He wanted to hurt his father.

When he entered the inn, he felt that everybody avoided him. Iorgovan slowly drank several glasses of wine; then, after sitting about for a while, he paid his bill and, towards dusk, made straight for the mill to close the accounts.

There were people at the mill as usual. Some of them were talking to the miller by the light of a lamp hanging on a nail over the small table in the corner. They rose when Iorgovan entered.

"Let's have a look round," said Iorgovan. "Dad says that we are not taking flour to the market tomorrow. I'll go on my own and if anything is needed, I had better know."

There were three lamps at the mill: one over the hopper, the other before the engine where the miller stood, and the third was hanging over the small table. On the right side of the mill, near those dangerous wheels, it was quite dark.

Seeing Iorgovan make for that part of the mill, the miller took the lamp from the wall and followed him to light his way.

Iorgovan examined the wheels, screws, and belt carefully, tapping them with the penholder he was holding in his hand. But over the wheels, he unexpectedly dropped his penholder. Then, saying things were all right, he declared himself satisfied and went back to the ledger on the small table.

The miller hung the lamp back on its nail. Iorgovan was looking for something on the table.

"My penholder," he said. "Ah, yes, I've forgotten it."

All was quiet for a while, except for the unceasing whirl of the wheels, the knocking of the hopper and the sound of Iorgovan's steps which were advancing straight towards the pillar to the right of the engine.

Suddenly, he screamed so that the whole mill trembled; pieces of broken glass fell on the ironwork of the engine and in an instant the mill was ablaze.

Rushing to the spot to help, the people found Iorgovan beneath the pillar wrapped in the flames which had caught his clothes in a twinkling.

The whole village gathered at Busuioc's house when people brought Iorgovan home, and nobody thought of extinguishing the fire which continued to burn at the end of the village, destroying the mill, the grain in the sacks, the flour in the hopper and the ledger with the mill accounts. "The wheels snatched him like Pupaza," said one of the men.

When the doctor came, Iorgovan lay on his back without moving, immobilized by his severe burns. The doctor examined him carefully and shrugged his shoulders. "It is pretty bad," he said, "but he is young and he may recover. We shall do everything that is possible."

"I'll give you my whole fortune," cried Busuioc, "if I can but see him go to the inn again!"

Iorgovan lifted his eyes to his father. "I don't want to any more," he murmured. "You'll see." After a while, he seized the doctor's hand, squeezed it desperately and looked at him intently.

"Patience," said the doctor, "you'll get over it."

"I am patient. Don't you see that I am not complaining?" answered Iorgovan. And Iorgovan was patient. For hours and hours, he lay motionless on his couch and, when anybody approached, his eyes smiled.

"Calm, absolute calm," the doctor ordered, and calm entered Iorgovan's heart, because physical pain rules all other feelings and remains the undisputed master of a human being.

On hearing the news about Iorgovan's misfortune, Simina jumped to her feet. "It is not true!" she said to herself. "He is lying again. He did it himself!" Worried by this thought, she hurried to Sofron.

"Go to him!" he said. "It will do him good to see you and to feel you near him."

Simina clenched her hands, remained for a while staring at him, then she covered her face with her hands and heaved a long, deep sigh.

"What is it?" he asked approaching her.

"Sofron," she said, again her usual quiet self, "Busuioc wants me again as a daughter-in-law; the priest's wife told me so the other day. I can't, I won't, my mind and heart won't allow me to refuse again. You see, Sofron, Iorgovan is my weakness. What can I do about it? I am as fond of him as if he were my child and—God forbid—I fear his death more than mine."

Sofron drew back a bit. "You must not go," he said. "You don't love him as I love you."

"I know that," she cried. "Don't I know that?"

"I shan't let you," he interrupted. "If I love you without possessing you, it is because I see it would be good neither for you nor for me. But I can't let you go to your own unhappiness. . . . Your life is yours; I don't care about his."

"And what do you want with me?" she asked obstinately.

"What do I want?" he answered. "I have been thinking about it. I think much and always about you. I have plenty of time. When I guide the plough along the furrow to make it straight and deep enough, I have nothing else to do but to think of you, because I could do my work blindfolded. I know what I feel, Simina, and it is impossible that you shouldn't know it too without caring for me at least as much as I care for my ox. It is mine, it draws well and knows me. It is aware of me, Simina, from a distance, and when I come to fetch it from its grazing, it turns around, raises its eyes and waits, looking at me till I have come. And if my ox doesn't want to do a thing, I can't do it gladly either. . . . Simina, it's better to be a beast than a human being."

Simina looked lost. She hung her head and began to weep. Then she caught his hand and kissed it several times. "I can't," she said. "What shall I do if I can't? Sofron, don't forsake me."

"Never," he said.

And Simina went to Curtici because she could not stay away. Busuioc was ready to give away his fortune to see his son about again, but he did not tell the doctor that Simina had come to nurse the patient. What did the doctor know? He might have said that it was not good for him to see her nor to be nursed by her.

When Simina entered the house, Iorgovan was on his back, quiet and motionless as usual. She drew near silently, trembling, and, when their eyes met, she stopped short under the spell of his gaze.

"Good Lord! Is that you, Simina?" he murmured. Then he concentrated all his strength, lifted both his arms towards her, caught her by her shoulders, drew her to him and kissed her. Then he held her at a distance so that he might look at her. She took his hand and put it down gently, sat on the bed near him, and for some time they neither spoke nor moved.

"And how is Sofron?" he asked after a while.

She started, rose a little and turned her head. "He is well, in good health," she answered.

Trembling, Iorgovan gathered his strength, lifted his arms once more to embrace her, then uttered a long moan. His arms fell back, and his breath stopped.

Simina stood up, stared awhile as if she were out of her mind, went to the door, and cried in a loud, but clear and steady voice:

"A candle!"

Barbu Delavrancea

(1858-1918)

Barbu Delavrancea is one of the foremost classical writers of Rumanian literature. He wrote novels and stories, contained in the volumes *Peace* (1883), *Sultanica* (1885), *The Minstrel* (1887), *The Parasites* (1893), *Between Life and Dream* (1893), and *Hagi Tudose* (1903), as well as the historical dramas, *The Sunset, The Tempest,* and *The Morning Star,* a trilogy written between 1909 and 1910 in which he evokes moments from the history of the Rumanian people.

Barbu Delavrancea played an important part in the development of Rumanian language and literature. Conscious of the genuine value of popular artistic creation, he was a constant researcher of Rumanian folklore, opening the gates of formal literature to the racy language of the Wallachian peasant, as the great storyteller Ion Creanga had done for the Moldavian vernacular.

Delavrancea is the creator, in Rumanian literature, of the poem in prose, as well as the founder of artistic and lyrical realism, a genre that later culminated in Mihail Sadoveanu's writings.

His colorful style is rich in picturesque images and metaphors.

Devil's Luck

"It's a question of luck."

"No, it isn't."

"Yes, it is, woman."

"No, it isn't!"

"Do you mean to say I don't work?"

"Yes, you do, enough for one; but we've nine mouths to feed and Plavita makes ten."

And Plavita lowed, and four small children began to clamor:

"I'm hungry!"

"I'm hungry too!"

"Me too!"

"Me too!"

The man emptied some corn flour from a napkin into the woman's kneading-trough.

"Shake it all out!"

"I have."

"First it was a full trough, then half a trough, then a quarter, and now you can lick its bottom. Nine mouths, always nine, and Plavita makes ten!"

And Plavita, as if she understood, lowed from outside while chewing a dry corncob, and the children started to wail.

"I'm hungry!"

"Me too!"

"And me too!"

The man stared, scratched his head, thrust the napkin into his shirt and walked out, saying:

"It's a question of luck, and I don't have any."

The woman called after him from the doorway:

"I tell you it isn't, man. If you work, you have luck; if you don't, you haven't."

And the man went off in search of work, but he kept thinking: "She says it isn't a question of luck, but it is. If it weren't, the world wouldn't be what it is. Didn't I plough and dig and hoe and weed like everybody else? Oh, yes, I did, but my plot turned out to be barren. Down came the hail; now I toil with my bare hands and nobody believes me; and when the time comes to measure my work, my pay gets less and less, the flour in the trough dwindles away, and the children get hungrier."

He went to the the leaseholder.

"There's no work, man."

He knocked at the priest's door.

"There's no work, man."

He called on the kulak.

"I've got enough hands."

He stopped at the innkeeper's.

"There's some digging that could be done for brandy."

"Can't you make it corn flour?"

"Nothing doing."

On his way home, the man could hear his children from afar:

"Mother, I haven't had enough!"

"Nor me!"

"Nor me!"

Nor had Plavita, lowing and stamping in the parched front yard that didn't have a single blade of green grass on it.

The woman stood in the doorway.

"Nothing in your napkin?"

"Nothing."

"The trough is empty."

"It's bad luck, woman."

"Lack of gumption, you mean."

The man mopped the sweat from his forehead with his shirt sleeve. She gazed at him; he gazed at her. She shook her head; he shook his; then he went to the back of the house, lay down, pillowed his head on his arm, and closed his eyes. Sleep, however, would not come. Beneath him, the hard, cold earth; above, darkness; in the house, the children going to sleep whimpering; in the yard, Plavita snorting from sheer hunger; he himself dogged by worry and bad luck. "What about tomorrow? Suppose I have nothing to empty into the trough? What am I to do tomorrow? God is above, on high, but His wife doesn't meet Him in the doorway, saying: 'Nine mouths, man, and Plavita makes ten!' God is above, but, if I don't get any work tomorrow, if I have no luck tomorrow either, I'll have a few drinks and go to market, and, well, if I go to market, let anything happen, just so long as I don't hear 'Mother, I'm hungry!' any more. I'll go to market and steal . . . steal whatever I can."

The man started. Where did that voice come from?

"How can you help it, if you've no luck?"

"Is it you, woman?"

"Yes, I thought you were asleep."

"Did you hear anything?"

"Hear what?"

"Nothing."

And the woman went into the house, and the man closed his eyes muttering:

"Come what may, I don't want to hear 'Mother, I'm hungry!' any more!"

Then somebody spoke again:

"How can you help it, if you've no luck!"

"Is it you, woman?"

Darkness. Silence.

"It wouldn't be the devil himself?"

And the man went to sleep, muttering:

"Come what may . . ."

It was scarcely daybreak when a childish voice piped out:

"Has the corn flour come, mother? I'm hungry!"

"And I haven't even started," said the man, jumping to his feet.

And he set out without looking back. When he was a good way off, he turned his head. The house seemed to be following on his heels, with a wide open mouth; the front door had swung back against the wall. Holy God, was the house pursuing him? He quickened his pace and sped on, faster and faster, till he reached the boyar's manor.

"Maybe tomorrow; there's no work today."

He went to the priest.

"Maybe the day after tomorrow; there's no work today."

"Tomorrow, the day after tomorrow," he said with a sigh, "but what of today? How am I to satisfy nine mouths, and Plavita makes ten? Well now, off to the innkeeper, to market, and, whatever happens, I won't come home empty-handed!"

At the pub he collected an advance payment for Plavita and sealed the bargain with five glasses of brandy which he gulped down one after the other. Then he hurried on to the market.

In the market he looked to the right and to the left; at the beans, at the bread, at the fish, at the smoked meat; but he never got a chance. The tradesmen kept a vigilant eye on their goods. And when he stopped opposite their stalls they would grin and ask him:

"What will you have, Mister Out-at-Elbows?"

After loitering about all day, he left.

"I've no luck, not even at stealing!"

As he was leaving the market, he saw a drunkard staggering along with his purse dangling behind him.

After looking around in every direction, the desperate man seized the purse, cut its strings, wrapped it up in his towel, thrust it into the front of his shirt and ran. When he had reached a wide, deserted field, he decided to see whether he had had any luck. He opened the towel, tugged at the opening of the purse, and out popped a little devil, with tiny tongues of fire shooting from its mouth and nostrils. In terror, the man slung the purse away and made off, crossing himself and spitting behind him. He had scarcely taken a few steps, when the towel inside his shirt began to swell. He pulled it out hurriedly, opened it, and was thunderstruck. There was the purse he had thrown away.

He opened the purse and out popped the devil, its tongue flickering like a tiny blue flame. He tied the mouth of the purse tight, put it down, took aim with his heel, and stamped on it violently. The purse burst like an ox bladder; a flame flickered under his sandal, then went out smelling of brimstone.

The man breathed again:

"That's why somebody said: 'Do not steal, or the devil will be after you.'"

He had hardly gone a dozen steps, when the towel swelled up again. This time he was all in a sweat. He pulled out the towel; felt it. The devil's purse was there again. He flung it away, towel and all, and took to his heels.

As soon as he got home, his children all rushed out to meet him:

"Dad, I'm hungry!"

"Me too!"

"Me too!"

The man looked inside his shirt, and turned pale. The purse was there, but no towel. While he was crossing himself, the woman asked:

"Why are you crossing yourself, man? Why are you looking inside your shirt? What have you brought the children?"

"Woman," said he, "Heat the oven, get it red hot; I'm going to bake four loaves of bread and a piglet."

He added in a whisper:

"I've got you now, Nick!"

The fire was roaring in the oven. The man kept crossing himself, while the children hopped merrily around the table, smacking their lips in anticipation and chanting one after another:

"Four loaves and a piglet!"

"Four loaves and a piglet!"

When the man saw that the oven was red hot, he asked for a shovel; then he drove everybody away. He put the purse on the shovel, pushed it gently to the far end of the oven, turned it upside down and withdrew it. Then he took the earthen lid, fitted it to the mouth of the oven and stepped aside, waiting to see what would happen.

Shortly after, there came a sharp report as of a gun. The lid of the oven flew up spinning: a blue tongue of flame licked the opening, flickered in the air, and vanished.

"The piglet's burst!" cried one of the children.

"No, it was a bread spirit!" volunteered another.

A smell of freshly baked bread pervaded the whole yard. The woman said to the man:

"We've let the oven get too hot. I'd better open the lid a little."

"Open it," said the man, mopping his perspiring face and trembling with fear.

The woman looked into the oven and said in amazement:

"You see, it was too quick!"

"What d' you mean, woman?"

"I mean the piglet and loaves are already baked."

"Baked?"

"Now what's the matter with you, man, asking questions like a frightened child?"

"Nothing! . . ."

And putting his hand to his chest, he felt the purse. A cold shiver ran through him from top to toe. Then, seeing the youngest child crouching at the oven and eagerly breathing in the hot smell, he looked at his wife and said:

"Come what may, woman. So the pig and the loaves are baked?"

"Why come what may? You can see they're baked."

She thrust the shovel into the oven and pulled out the pig and then the four loaves.

"Give me the towel to take out the tray."

"I've lost it, woman."

"How did you lose it?"

"You see, what's yours goes and what's the devil's remains."

"What on earth might that mean?"

The children filled their bellies and went to sleep on their backs, two on the porch and five in the house.

The man went to the back of the house, lay down, pillowed his head on one arm and fell asleep, dreaming of flocks of sheep and herds of cattle and horses, all of which were his. And he was telling his wife: "Now you see it's luck!" And she replied: "It's the devil's luck!"

The moon was a white paper disk. A glowing light had appeared in the east. The man woke up in fear, gripped by dire forebodings.

"I'll take another look at it," he thought, "grip the imp, and squeeze it till it bursts."

He took out the purse and looked into it. And what did he see? Instead of the demon, the glitter of gold coins. Startled and troubled, he flung a handful of coins to the east and another to the west, saying:

"To hell with you, devil's money!"

The words were scarcely out of his mouth when he saw white flocks in the east and black flocks in the west, emerging from the light and the mist like a vast expanse of rippling waters. Their bleating awakened the village. The flocks surrounded the house, the yard, the village, and still there was no end to them. And behold! a shepherd wearing long tresses and a bucket-shaped fur cap came up to him and said:

"Bless you, good master, they are all yours as far as the eye can see!"

"Mine? Impossible! I haven't got even a vessel to drink water from."

"They are yours," replied the shepherd, "for on his deathbed their owner said to us:

" 'Let some of you start from the east and others from the west, and at the house where the white flock shall meet the black flock, to that household you shall give them!' "

In his joy the man forgot everything and ran to his wife.

"Woman, all that you see is ours."

"Of all the devil's miracles!" said the woman.

"Whose miracles?"

That reminded the lucky man of the purse. He thought: "Now what can I do to get rid of it and still keep my flocks?" He looked inside his shirt. There nestled the purse, bulging with the golden coins he had scattered to the east and west. His fear was strong, but he was a man after all. "Suppose I take out some more before I get rid of it?" he thought. So he took out the money and flung one handful to the north and another to the south. And herds of cattle came pouring from the north, and herds of horses from the south.

When he had opened his eyes that morning, he hadn't had so much as a handful of corn flour; now, as night fell, he was the wealthiest man in the world.

"Thus are fortunes made: first you steal, then you associate with the devil," reflected the lucky man, and he broke into a cold sweat.

"Won't you come inside, man? I've made a fine bed for you with a soft pillow to rest your head on."

"No, woman."

"The evenings are chilly, the nights cold, the mornings frosty. Come inside, man."

"The sheep's breath is warm, and the rams' bells will wake me before the frost whitens the backs of the herds."

"Then I'll sleep with you outside, husband," said the woman merrily, pulling at his shirt sleeve.

"No, woman."

"Let me come, husband; we have only seven children to feed, next to nothing. Let me come and complete the even number; there's nothing on God's earth without its mate."

He refused. The woman retired despondently to the cottage, mumbling: "I won't rest, so help me God, until it's an even number. Better fourteen than seven!"

The lucky man went to the back of the house, lay down, pillowed his head on his arm, closed his eyes, and began to think of a plan to get rid of that thing in his bosom. He thought and thought, and presently he muttered:

"I shall dig a deep, deep pit."

And out of the darkness came a voice:

"Deep, deep."

"Is it you, woman?" asked the man starting in fear.

A little way off, the bells of the herd were tinkling.

"It's the cowbells," he thought.

He shut his eyes again.

"And after digging a deep, deep pit, I'll throw it right to the bottom, to the bottom, and throw earth on top of it, on top of it."

Out of the darkness came a voice:

"On top of it, on top of it . . ."

"Is it you, woman?" asked the man, jumping to his feet.

There was no reply. "Baa, baa," bleated the black flock. "It's the bleating of the sheep," he thought.

The lucky man took his spade, hoe, and shovel and went round to the back of the cow shed.

First he did some measuring; then he began to dig. All night he dug steadily, throwing up the earth. Up to his knees, his waist, his shoulder. Next morning, when the woman came looking for him, the pit was three hands above his head. Sweat streamed from him as from a squeezed sponge, dropping onto the moist earth, which he loosened in large shiny slices.

"What are you doing, man?" asked the woman in amazement.

"Digging a grave for the devil," he answered without looking up.

"You haven't slept all night."

"You're right; I haven't."

"Won't you go to bed?"

"I'm not sleepy."

"Won't you have a bite to eat?"

"I'm not hungry."

"What about a glass of wine?"

"I'm not thirsty."

"But what are you doing, man?"

"Digging a grave for the devil," he replied, nettled, and drove in his spade so deep that four inches of the shaft were buried in the earth.

The woman withdrew, crossing herself.

"Heaven save you from too much luck!"

Gradually the man dug his way down into the bowels of the earth.

Towards evening, the woman leaned over the edge of the pit and called:

"Man, is there nothing you want?"

"I want you to drive a stake into the ground on the spot where your right heel stands, tie a rope to the stake, lower the rope into the pit, and, by tomorrow morning at daybreak, roast a ram and get a cask of wine, for I'll eat the whole ram and drink all the wine in one draught."

His voice seemed to come from the bottom of a deep pit. The woman drove in a stake, tied a rope to it, kicked the rope into the pit, and went off to see about the wine and the ram.

Night had set in, and all was quiet. A shadow climbed out of the pit. The dogs began to howl. It was the lucky man. He got down on all fours and looked into the darkness of the pit. He hauled up the rope. He felt inside his shirt, threw the purse into the pit and listened: the coins tinkled.

Then he began to throw in the earth. From the bottom came a voice:

"Steady there, what's your grudge against your luck?"

Fear gripped the man. He went on throwing in the earth.

From the bottom came laughter:

"Ha, ha, beware of falling in yourself!"

The man fell on his back, picked himself up quickly, and set to work shovelling until all was quiet. By daybreak he had filled the pit to its brim. He laid his ear to this deep grave and heard a far-off sound of stifled weeping and laughter, as from another world.

Then he ran joyfully into the house.

"I'm hungry, thirsty, sleepy."

The woman brought in the mutton and the cask of wine.

"Eat, drink, and sleep, husband, but remember that seven mouths is next to nothing. I want an even number. Better fourteen than seven!"

He picked up a leg of mutton, raised it to his mouth, and stopped. He felt the purse inside his shirt. He sat frozen, the leg of mutton at his mouth.

"Won't you eat, man?" asked the woman, nudging him.

"I'm not hungry!"

"Won't you drink?"

"I'm not thirsty!"

"Lie down a bit."

"I'm not sleepy!"

"Devil's luck again!" said the woman, crossing herself.

"How do you know?" gasped the man, beside himself. And he rose from the table and left the house like a whirlwind.

Threading his way through his flocks of sheep and herds of cattle and horses, on the road to church, he said to himself: "Neither fire nor pit availed. I'll throw it into the altar. Maybe that'll make the gall in him burst." But when he put his hand on the church door, he stopped short, trembling. Who had grabbed him by the hair and pulled him back? He looked around on all sides. Nobody!

"Who is stopping me?" shouted the man, "*Him* in the purse or *Him* in the church?"

He turned and took to his heels, not knowing where to run. Hungry, thirsty, giddy from want of sleep, he wandered on, relentlessly hounded by the luck inside his shirt.

After a long while he came upon a beggar in the middle of the road.

"Old man," he said to the beggar, "watch what I'm going to do."

Raising his eyebrows with his hands, the old man watched intently. The lucky man took the purse out of his bosom, flung a gold coin to the east and another to the west. In a twinkling, a snow-white sheep appeared from the east, and a coal-black sheep from the west.

"Do you want me to give you this purse, old man?"

"Of course, little father, of course!"

The old man took the purse. He emptied the golden coins into his palm, flung a handful of them to the east and another to the west. Two flashes of lightning shaped like dragons appeared east and west and struck down the white and black sheep.

The frightened beggar crossed himself, pulled down the eyebrows over his eyes and said:

"Begone, fiend, and the holy cross strike you!"

"Old man," shouted the lucky one, "have you got the purse?"

"No, desolation be upon it!"

"It's inside my shirt," answered the lucky man, and began to run.

The soles of his feet had split from running, when he reached a cold stream. In his despair he ran straight on and dived in, head first. A few yards downstream the water tossed him up; he floated on like a swollen bladder.

"Now I cannot even drown myself!"

Exhausted, with bleeding feet, hounded by good fortune, he returned to the pub in his village. When he entered it, the men doffed their caps, the women curtsied, and an old man said:

"Health and good luck to you."

"Thank you for the health, but as for good luck—the devil with it!" he answered, and asked for a quart of wine.

No sooner was the vessel at his lips than he drank it off, heedless of the awe-struck gaze of those who sat watching the wealthiest man in the world. He asked for another quart and again drank it off at one draught.

"Give these people drink, as much as they want!" he ordered.

"Good luck to you!" said an old woman.

"The devil take the luck!" he shouted, staring at the woman with eyes so red that they seemed to drip blood.

And he drank and drank and drank. He could hardly stand upright.

He flung down his cap, shook off his cloak, pulled the purse from his bosom, loosened its mouth, and laid it on the counter. The golden coins sparkled like live things.

"There," he exclaimed with an uproarious peal of laughter, "let's drink it all up."

A young fellow came over to look at the coins.

"How beautifully they sparkle, like a maiden's eyes!"

"You're wrong," mumbled an old woman with a hunchback. "Money is the devil's eyes!"

"How do you know?" asked the lucky man, starting and setting down the wine vessel. "Give me brandy, a quart of brandy, for me and the old woman; she's the devil's mare!"

"How do you know?" said the hag, and a sharp tooth protruded from between her blackened lips, like a cat's claw.

And he drank and drank, and began to sing and whoop and dance, until suddenly he stopped and stared hard at the circle of people round him. His head was on fire.

"Good folks," he said, putting his hand to his belt, "mark my words! . . . Heaven preserve you from good fortune!"

"What a thing to say!" they chorused.

"Good folks, mark my words! If I tried to drown myself, I couldn't because I'd float like a bladder!"

"Nonsense!"

"Good folks, mark my words! If I tried to cut my throat, I couldn't because the knife wouldn't go in!"

"Nonsense!"

"You try it!" said the hunchbacked hag, leering from one ear to the other.

The man pulled the knife from his belt and stabbed himself in the throat.

It pierced his throat right through, as clean as a whistle! The blood gushed forth, and he collapsed like a log.

All froze to the spot. The door of the pub opened and shut without anybody going out. From outside came a high-pitched chuckle: "hee, hee, hee!" Then somebody asked:

"Where's the purse?"

All those present turned pale and began to cross themselves, whispering to each other in terror:

"Who was it laughed?"

"Where might the purse be?"

"It was here; now it's gone."

"And where's the hag?"

"Which hag?"

"That hunchbacked old woman with one sharp tooth!"

"I saw her," said a lad, and his teeth were chattering with fear; "she disappeared through that wall as if a whirlpool had sucked her in!"

An old man extracted the knife from the lucky man's throat.

"He's cold as ice."

"He's rid of his luck."

"Now, who will inherit his wealth?"

"Others."

"Don't you know," said an old man with a beard reaching to his waist, "don't you know that fortune never brings a man lasting happiness? Luck is of the devil; it comes to you only to profit others."

The woman mourned her dead husband. But with so many sheep and cows and horses, she soon found solace. And she never rested till her seven had become fourteen, for an odd number would never do; better fourteen than seven.

A. Bratescu-Voinesti

(1868-1946)

A. Bratescu-Voinesti's stories and short stories, grouped in two major volumes, *In the World of Justice* (1906) and *Darkness and Light* (1912), are peopled by heroes endowed with exemplary morality but quite unable to face life's vicissitudes. This lack of balance brings about true drama, the writer excelling in character depiction, adopting a calm, objective attitude, avoiding the melodramatic. His heroes, embodiments of virtue, are good, honest, generous to the point of naiveté; they show a total lack of energy and (if they belong to the declining aristocracy) seek refuge in the past when having to face life's meanness or the cold selfishness and greed of those around them, or else they isolate themselves in their inner worlds, resorting even to suicide, as does the hero in "Niculaita the Fibster." It is in depicting this process of inevitable inner breakdown that Bratescu-Voinesti's art lies. While he lacks the gifts of epic invention, or of poetry, he is capable of acute observation which he presents honestly and objectively albeit with gentleness.

Niculaita the Fibster

Niculaita Gropescu, son of Andrei Gropescu of the hamlet of Manga, which is part of the village of Magureni, was a sensible youngster, soft-spoken, with measured movements, but shy.

Throughout the primary school—he attended the school of Magureni—he always took first prize, which rejoiced and flattered his parents. Quite naturally, too, for it is no trifling thing to hear called out, "Niculae Gropescu, First Prize with Honors," in a school bedecked with flowers on Saint Peter's Day, nor to see the schoolmaster place the wreath of cowberry on his fine black hair, and the mayor give him a pile of books and stroke his cheek, and then to walk along the village street, you, the mother on one side, the father on the other, and between you two your son, with all the fellow villagers looking on and saying affectionately: "May you have joy of him, and may this be the beginning of greater things!"

When Niculaita had finished primary schooling, Mr. Irimescu, the schoolmaster, said it was a pity such a diligent boy should not go on with his learning; upon which Andrei Gropescu thought things over from Saint Peter's Day until September, and took counsel with all and sundry.

The schoolmaster had spoken as we have said; and Andrei Gropescu thought much the same thing at moments of fatigue and vexation when he realized that the proceeds of his work and that of Stana, his wife, did not go far in providing for a house burdened with four children: Niculaita, who was eleven, two three-year-old twin girls, and another boy still at the breast.

The big tenant farmer, Mr. Epaminonda, had told him that much learning rather poisoned a man's heart, that it was a costly affair and caused a fellow to look with disgust upon the tilling of the land; and he gave as an example Ghitica, son of the village priest, who had gone through six forms at the high school and ultimately came to be an erratic sort of fellow, a ne'er-do-well and the talk of the village. And so Andrei came to think along the same lines when his mind dwelt on his lack of means and the help Niculaita might be for him henceforth: another pair of arms. For although the boy was not very sturdy, he was very clever with his hands and had inherited from his grandfather, old Sandu Gropescu, an inclination for carpentry.

When the old man died, his tools had been taken up to the garret, but that "nosy little Niculaita," who on the old man's death was a little mite of four, had come across them one day; and for all his mother's scolding—"Come down at once, you little rascal, you; your father'll find you there and give you the thrashing of your life!"—the child, who but vaguely remembered the old man who had himself made the gate posts, would often run up into the garret to fiddle about with his grandfather's tools. And little by little, playing and passing the time as it were, he had made a few things: a stool, a rattle to scare the crows away with—the crows which were ruining the cherry tree up the slope—until one day, his father happening to lose the tail-piece of his cart, the boy had said: "I'll make you one exactly like it." And indeed the youngster set to work, and from old planks of wood in the courtyard he first made the upright bars, then those that run crosswise, and, after gluing them together, he produced such a tail-piece as caused his father and his mother, and also the neighbors, to cross themselves in wonder.

Yes, it was lack of means, the youngster's deftness in carpentry and the father's fear of losing this most valuable help that made him give way to the advice of Mr. Epaminonda and caused Niculaita to remain at home to till the land.

The lad did not regret it, for he liked to work on the land and more particularly carpentry. When in the fields, tending the oxen with other youngsters of his age, he would often play with them and carefully examine the herbs and insects. It was he who taught the others to get spiders and crickets out of holes by using a small bullet of wax attached to a thread of cotton.

The other boys would stay with him for a while and then leave him for their games; Niculaita would remain alone to watch the ants struggling with burdens four or five times bigger than themselves, or he would crawl noiselessly along the ground to watch a grasshopper and try to discover how it produced its lively chirp.

In this way the years went by, six in all, and the child became a youth of seventeen, good looking, of equable disposition, but shy. . . .

He was good at carpentry now. It was he who made the posts which lay in a heap under the shed, the posts for the front fence. With God's help, he would make that fence during the coming year. It was he again who had replaced the beam of the veranda which had rotted at one end. And his mother's spinning fork had also been decorated by him. And if you could only have seen the new wooden pail of Salomia, the daughter of Pirvu, the neighbor! He had bought it from the market, on Saint Eliah's Day and had adorned it with poker work. . . . It was simply wonderful!

As you see, he would have been the model of a happy young man if only a means had been devised of endowing him with all the happiness that was his due, and Niculaita himself had not felt the bitterness that springs from the untoward arrangement of things in our days. . . .

Niculaita's bitterness was also derived from his own inquisitive nature, different from that of the others. Ever since he was a child that bitterness had done him harm. How often had his father pulled him by the ear because he had wasted half the day looking at his mother's silkworms to see how they ate and wove their cocoons. A number of times he had been thrashed because, while busy watching some insect, the oxen he was supposed to tend had left the stubble field or the common and invaded the field of corn. How many times had he not been brought back to reality by the pain inflicted by a birch, with the admonition: "Are you with the spirits of the departed ones? Can't you see your oxen have got into my cornfield?"

But neither the sharp scolding of his parents, nor the thrashings he had got because of the fines imposed on his father could cure him.

All this Niculaita bore without much grieving. What he found more difficult to bear was the people's banter. For slowly, gradually, he had became a laughingstock.

Twice had he seen in the field a black-and-yellow striped bumblebee fight a spider bigger than itself, defeat it, and fly away with it between its legs. The fight had seemed a terribly fierce one to him and he had been so moved by it that he had told of it to others. "It might be . . ." some had answered. His father had replied reprovingly: "That is the sort of thing you gape at while I pay the fines, you young fool!" And the younger people said: "A fly to catch spiders! You do stretch it, you certainly do!"

Another time he had sprung up as if bitten by a snake and had called to some of the boys a little way off. When they had come up and asked what was up, he had told them in awe that he had seen a grasshopper—the kind they called "nun"—bristle up, buzz and take between its legs a grasshopper bigger than itself and begin to eat it.

"Where is it, old boy?"

"Over there."

"Where?"

"There, close to that thistle . . . a little more to the left."

The boys had bent down to look, and he also, but they had found no "nun." One of them had urged:

"Come on, boys. Let's hear the end of that story Marin was telling us about Frusina. You know what Niculaita is, don't you? And you, Niculaita, hadn't you better go to Father Alecu, to have a service read for you?"

"I'll swear I . . ."

"Don't swear for nothing."

One day, sitting on a stool cutting notches in a stick with his knife, Niculaita had seen their cat crouched in the dill border ready to spring upon some sparrows which, four or five steps away, were pecking at some spilled maize flour and chirping. Keeping the cat under careful observation, he had seen her open her mouth a little and had distinctly heard her make the same sound as the sparrows. It was as if she were trying to entice them, to bring them nearer to her hiding place. And, indeed, the sparrows had come towards her in their search for maize flour. He had seen the cat stretch her legs to the utmost and when she thought the sparrows near enough, she had suddenly pounced and caught one of them in her claws.

In the evening, standing by the gate, he had spoken of what he had seen and heard. Pirvu Miu, and his daughter Salomia, and Manda, Salomia's mother, and also old Grigore and another neighbor were all there.

"How is it that only *you* hear and see these things?" old man Grigore had asked with a smile. "Here am I, an old man going on seventy-four, and I have never heard a cat imitating a sparrow."

"I don't know about other cats; but ours does, Uncle Grigore. I've heard her, as plainly as I hear you."

"People'll soon be giving you a nickname, boy. Before you know where you are, someone'll call you "Niculaita the Fibster," and you'll always be known by that name."

Salomia began to laugh loudly and, as if not to forget, had repeated: "Niculaita the Fibster . . ."

After that he became henceforth for the whole village Niculaita the Fibster. And, of course, it grieved him when the boys called him that. Furthermore, when Ghitica, the priest's son, mocked him by asking, "What else have you seen, Niculaita, my lad?" amidst general laughter, he spoke about having seen a cricket catch a crow and eat it. Niculaita began to doubt his own senses. After all, Ghitica was a clever young man who had gone through six classes at high school!

As time went on, what with his parents' reproaches for the time spent uselessly—"mere foolishness and bats in the belfry"—what with the doubts of some and the mockery of others, the boy grew more silent, more withdrawn, more shy. . . .

But what grieved Niculaita most of all was the skeptical smile in Salomia's beautiful eyes; the boys he could easily shun. Or, when the villagers met in front of the inn, he could merely watch the dance, not join in it himself, and the boys wouldn't press him. And then again in the use of hoe and adze, he found a medicine against the bitter feelings caused by the people's mockery—a medicine that seemed to take away all his bitterness. The same medicine, however, seemed powerless to cure the grief caused by the mocking smile of the girl, a smile for which he had no need to go once a week to stand before the village inn for he had it close to him on the other side of the fence and at any hour of the day. Also on Sundays, more than that smile, there were the jokes and talk of Petrica, son of Stan Pasalan, who was only too evidently after Salomia.

One afternoon, some time after the incident with old Grigore, Niculaita went to see the schoolmaster at his home. He found him in the orchard picking plums. At first he was too shy to tell him the reason for his visit and started gathering plums with the other boys. Finally, however, afraid of staying too long, and availing himself of a moment when he was alone with the schoolmaster, he plucked up courage to say:

"Excuse me, Sir, you know a great many things. . . ."

"Well, what do you mean to say by that?" Irimescu asked as nothing else followed.

"You see . . . you know many things, Sir, having learned a lot.

Tell me, is it not true that a cat can imitate the chirping of sparrows?"

"The chirping of sparrows?"

"Yes, their chirping. Our cat does it in her throat. . . ."

The schoolmaster looked at him closely. Niculaita went on:

"I've been thinking you might have a book where it is written how cats can imitate the sparrows chirping. And in exchange I might help mend your fence . . . or do something else."

"I have no book where such nonsense is written, Niculaita!"

On his way back he felt really sorry, terribly sorry. . . . Oh, if only the schoolmaster had had a book like that. . . . If only he could have taken it to Salomia for her to read it with her own eyes. She might not laugh then as she had laughed at the gate, when old Grigore had given him that nickname—lovely laughter that had racked him with pain.

The next day, after working on a trellis, he had strewn some maize flour at the place where he had seen the sparrows before, and, having chased his sisters away, he brought the cat, sat his brother Ilie beside him to keep him quiet and, cutting notches in a stick, prepared himself to wait. Some sparrows shortly hopped along and the cat began imitating their chirping. Niculaita at once called to, or rather hissed at Salomia, who was shaking some bedclothes on the veranda.

The girl looked towards Niculaita who, lying motionless, whispered:

"Come to the fence . . . only quietly, quietly."

Salomia probably made too much noise because the sparrows flew away.

"You've frightened them away . . . but if you're not in a hurry, come in at the gate and stay for a bit. Look at the cat over there among the dill. . . . You'll hear her."

The girl was curious to hear the cat and came in. He gave her a stool while he himself sat at her side, one knee on the ground and holding his brother Ilie close to him. For a long time they remained so, near one another. Two or three sparrows came up, but the cat was dozing. . . . And as they sat next to each other, motionless, Niculaita smelled the scent of sweet basil and melilot being wafted from Salomia's golden hair and from her bosom, the bosom of a maiden of sixteen, a scent sweeter and more enticing than all the flowers he made with his notching, than all the insects he yearned to know about, and, wrapped in happiness, he stretched out his right hand and encircled her waist. Salomia who, while watching the cat had been thinking of Petrica, and how clever and strong he was, turned her head in surprise; then, removing his hand, began to laugh:

"So that's why you called me here, Fibster Niculaita," she said as she ran lightly back home.

It was after that that he had made the wooden pail for her and adorned it with a red-hot poker that burned like her faithless and scornful smile. Salomia in her turn gave him a waist band: it was no different from any other, but it seemed to Niculaita that it was beyond compare.

* * *

One day Niculaita went to town with a cartload of wood. His father had thought the oxen were not earning their feed now at the beginning of October. The maize they had reaped, little of it as there was, he had taken to town, and also the plums; and as to plowing, it was no use trying until God showed mercy and sent a little rain, for the earth was as hard as flint. . . .

So the man bought three cords of wood from Mr. Frim, who had a wood being cleared, and he planned from time to time to load the cart with wood—as much of it as the oxen could carry—and to go to market himself, or send Niculaita to sell it, and thus make a little money. The two of them had heaped a little over a cord onto the cart the night before, bound it with a chain as they usually did to keep it from falling off, and, when there were another two hours before daylight to go, Niculaita put on his sheepskin coat. His mother, from near the fireplace, called to him: "Close it at the neck; it's cold," and his father reminded him for the fourth time: "Don't sell for less than eleven *lei,* not a penny less than that, and take care no one cheats you, ninny that you are."

It was pitch dark but Niculaita had no sense of fear or of loneliness. Nearly all the way to town—some eight miles—he sat on top of the wood, whistling softly, his eyes on the stars that were all the brighter that night for the coldness of the autumn. He loved the stars and the late Isaia, the shepherd, had taught him the name of many. As he progressed eastward, he saw the new moon appear at the skyline and rise, to be followed by the morning star; next he saw a thin strip of red and the countenance of the sky opened more and more until the stars disappeared one after the other, among them the morning star and the crescent moon; and to the right of the place where the red strip had appeared, darts of gold—like the gold of Salomia's hair—began to appear.

When he reached the town the sun was high overhead. The innkeeper at the barrier asked him how much he wanted for his wood.

"Eleven *lei,*" Niculaita had answered.

And the innkeeper, who had no need of wood, having plenty, looked at the goods and said:

"It's worth the money, being sound pea-tree wood." And after eyeing the young man closely, he advised:

"Ask fifteen *lei* for it, youngster, so that you might have a margin to make a reduction from."

If Niculaita had taken that wood to the market three days earlier he would have sold it on the spot, for his lack of experience in trading would have been made up for by the bitter wind which had blown until the day before. That day, however, the warm sunshine, which caused him to discard his sheepskin coat, detracted from the value of his goods. One customer offered eight *lei*, another ten, and yet another ten *lei* and six *bani*. Niculaita, however, would not sell the wood and so went on and on through the town until midday.

"Are you a Turk by any chance not to come down in price?" a baker shouted at him, soon adding, however: "Come on into the courtyard."

"But it'll be eleven *lei*, Sir," Niculaita put in.

When he had unloaded the cart and set the logs close to one another to make a regular cord, the baker counted ten *lei* and a half in small change.

"We agreed on eleven *lei*, Sir."

"You are a Turk, aren't you? Either take it on my terms or load it back and away with you."

Niculaita returned the money and without any apparent annoyance began putting the wood back into the cart in orderly, leisurely fashion, just as he had loaded it in the forest the night before.

Perhaps it was the boy's calm that pleased the baker, for he began to laugh and taking eleven *lei*, handed the money to him, saying: "You must be Pacala* himself."

Niculaita thrust the money into his leather belt, yoked the oxen and started on his way home. He thought it would have been better if the money had been given him in rolls. For on his way back he might drop asleep in the cart on account of sleeping so little the night before, and his money might be lost. And so, as he walked along the street, he looked down to see whether he could spot a bit of paper to roll the money in. He was not long in looking: in front of the Law Courts he found half a sheet. He picked it up, slipped it into his shirt, and when he got out of town, climbed on to the cart, tore the paper in two, and again in two and, taking the money out of

---

* A character in Rumanian folk tales, the embodiment of foolish obstinacy.

his leather belt, made two rolls of it: one containing five *lei*, the other six. He put the money carefully back into his leather belt pocket which he closed firmly as he urged on his oxen.

Later when it grew cloudy and the wind began to blow, he put on his sheepskin coat. Putting it on, he felt something cold inside his shirt, and there was half a sheet of paper which he hadn't used but also hadn't thrown away. He got it out and looked at it. It was handwritten and as he could read, he read: "By virtue of article 327 which reads: 'He who finds anything not his own along highways and streets and who, being asked about it, denies having found such, is considered to have committed a misdemeanor and shall be punished with terms of imprisonment ranging from 15 days to 3 months.' "

"How strange!" Niculaita thought to himself. "If I find a gold piece on a highroad, doesn't it belong to me who have found it? I didn't steal it. I found it. And why should I give it to anyone else?" And then he read the paper over again, and having reached the point where it was stated "being asked about it" he quickly put his hand over his belt. The rolls of money were in their place. Light began to dawn in Niculaita's mind. The man who had lost that something had worked for it. Perhaps he had gone to the wood, as he himself had gone with his father, and a log had fallen over his leg, as had been the case with his father. Or the man might have gone about the town as he himself had gone that day. Or perhaps he had changed the money into a gold piece to make a present of it to a girl like Salomia to add to her necklace of gold pieces.

And remembering a saying of his father's to the effect that "nothing but dust comes of the money one hasn't worked for," he told himself just before falling asleep that were he to find a bag of money he would take it to the headman's office or to the head gendarme even if no one asked him.

Whoever could have known that this thought would turn into reality so soon? Four days after this he was put in exactly the circumstances he had thought of. They were all together in the maize field, cutting down the stalks, when his father said to him:

"We spoke about your mending the door of the loft, Niculaita, and you haven't done so. I should say you might make a new one in the four hours that are left until dark."

"All right, I will."

"There are enough of us here to get the work done and to load the carts before nightfall."

"You're right," he agreed again and made for home. In order to get there more quickly he took a short cut through the boyar's plum orchard, jumped the hedge behind the tall stone cross that stood by the side of the road, and reached the road to the left of it. And as he walked along the path parallel with the road he saw on the ground before him a black leather wallet. He picked it up, opened it, and saw banknotes in both parts, a great many of them, more than he and all his ancestors combined had seen. He looked around. There was no one about. Without giving the matter much thought, he went on again; but instead of making for home he cleared another hedge and struck for the gendarmery. And as he walked, he smiled at the thought that occurred to him. "If I didn't have it in my hand and I told people I had found a wallet full of money they would say I was lying." The grown-ups were all at their work; he met only children and so had no one to confide in. On reaching the gendarmery, he opened the door and found the head gendarme alone in the right-hand room. Sprawled on the bed, the head gendarme was reading a newspaper. From a back room came the gendarme's fancy wife. She must have been singing while at some work she was doing . . . "Cruel sighs tear my breast asunder. . . ."

"What is it?" the head gendarme asked as he looked up from his newspaper.

"What brings me here, Sir, is that on coming down the road—for father sent me home to mend the loft door—I cut across the boyar's plum orchard and jumped the hedge before the cross. And as I walked I saw something black on the ground. This is what I found: a wallet with lots of banknotes, and so I came to bring it to you, for whoever lost it must soon come to inquire after it."

The head gendarme eyed the youngster, then the money in the wallet, looking at both several times, and after a long interval of silence, asked:

"Was anyone with you?"

"No one."

"Did you tell anyone?"

"No one. I came down the path behind your house, straight here."

The head gendarme was silent for a while, then:

"Listen Niculaita, for that's your name I think."

"It is."

"Don't tell anyone until the owner comes himself, for someone may hear you describe the wallet and say he had lost it, though he hadn't. Don't tell even your mother and father until the owner comes to claim it, d'you hear?"

"I do!"

"It's a good thing you've brought it. Well done! You're an honest lad. And you must know I'll tell the owner to give you a handsome reward."

Niculaita made for the door but when he was on the threshold, the head gendarme, thinking of the report he was to draw up, asked him:

"What is your full name?"

"Niculae Gropescu."

"Can you read and write?"

"I can."

When he was alone again, the head gendarme took the bank-notes out of the wallet and counted them three times over; there were 5400 *lei* in hundred *lei* notes. Nothing more. He took out his tobacco case, rolled himself a cigarette, smoked it thoughtfully, crossed himself in sheer surprise and, before beginning to write, balanced himself on the chair leaning well back and called out, "Steluta!"

Steluta, however, was singing and consequently didn't hear him.

The head gendarme rose and called out in a louder voice from the threshold:

"Steluta!"

"Well?" Steluta said, looking up from the blouse she was making.

"Come here a moment."

When the head gendarme had told her the whole story and shown her the money, they both remained silent. . . . And then, Mrs. Steluta, her thoughts on the silk blouses, the jackets, and the hats she might have bought with so much money, said:

"Good heavens, why didn't I find it?"

And then she was silent again and her thoughts went to the airs the headman's wife and the Irimescu woman put on. They both looked down on her. Finally she asked:

"That's the one they call Niculaita the Fibster, isn't it?" And after another silence: "And you say no one saw him?"

The head gendarme looked her in the eyes and gave no answer.

In the meantime Niculaita had already set to work and, as he drew out the nails of the old door with the pliers, the thought came to him that he would have to tell his mother and father; that he simply had to.

"What are you doing, Niculaita?"

The youngster looked up, a smile of happiness lighting up his eyes on hearing the voice of Salomia. She had climbed onto a log and was resting her arms on the fence. The wind fluffed up her golden hair, and her eyes, as green as deep, limpid waters in the shade, smiled mockingly.

"I'm mending the door of the loft," Niculaita answered as he thought: "No, I won't tell her; she wouldn't believe me and she'll tell others just to make a laughingstock of me. Let her come to know about it from others when the owner comes along."

The owner had already come. He was over there in the village street in the midst of a crowd of women and children. The horseman who a little while ago had ridden at an amble was the owner.

Salomia, who from the log she had climbed could see the children running towards him, climbed down and rushed to the gate saying:

"I don't know what's happening down the road. But I see the children running like anything."

Niculaita ceased his work and went to the gate. A woman coming from the road made it clear to him:

"A tradesman who says he's lost a bag of money is asking if anyone has seen it."

Niculaita hurried to the spot, made his way through the childen and coming up to the tradesman, touched his arm as he asked:

"What was your bag like?"

"A wallet of black leather, scratched in one corner—a wallet which you can fold, with two pockets. . . ."

Niculaita said simply:

"I found it a little while ago by the big cross and took it to the head gendarme."

The tradesman was wild with joy and unable to speak. And as the women crossed themselves in wonder, he made towards the gendarmery together with the lad, a crowd of children following them.

* * *

There is unwonted animation at Magureni. People have gathered at the headman's office. . . . The attorney is expected momentarily to investigate the case on the spot. They are waiting eagerly for the authorities to clear up this intricate, puzzling affair. A strange thing! The day before yesterday, which was Tuesday, around the time of vespers, Mr. Nita Andreescu, who is felling the Colfescul wood, came to the village and asked all and sundry whether they hadn't found a wallet with 5400 lei *in it, saying he had lost it in the morning going down towards the valley. And as he was inquiring about it of some women of the Manga hamlet, up came Niculaita, son of Gropescu, the boy they call the Fibster, saying he had found it near the cross and had taken it to the gendarmery and given it to the head gendarme. But the head gendarme said he knew nothing about it. At a loss as to what to think, considering the boy's statement and the denial of the head gendarme, the owner has lodged a complaint with the court, and the public attorney should be here at any moment.*

Finally the attorney came, with the clerk of the court. The captain of gendarmes should have accompanied him but was away in Bucharest. The attorney went straight to the headman's office where the owner was waiting for him. He was annoyed: neither the head gendarme nor the boy who was said to have found the money was there. He gave orders for them to be brought at once; and in the meantime he made investigations, asking the headman's clerk, and the tax collector.

"I really don't know what to say, Sir," the headman said. "We've talked things over among ourselves ever since the day before yesterday. Can the head gendarme be lying? . . . Who knows? A great amount of money—5,400 *lei* . . . and money is the devil's own counsellor. . . . Who knows? And again I've been thinking one can't send the man to prison on the mere assertion of a scatterbrained youngster."

"How d'you mean scatterbrained?" the attorney asked.

The headman's clerk answered his question:

"You see, Sir, that boy is . . . how shall I put it . . . a little. . . ."

"What's his name?"

"Niculaita Gropescu, but people call him Niculaita the Fibster."

"Why do they call him that?"

"That's the nickname they've given him."

The attorney was more and more puzzled and impatient. He asked again:

"Who was sent after them?"

"A courier. But here's the head gendarme. You can question him if you like."

The door had opened and the head gendarme had come in. He took off his cap, holding it in his left hand, close to his sword. Then bringing his heels together with a jingling noise and looking the attorney straight in the eyes, he said:

"Good morning, Sir."

The attorney, the superior authority, examined him from top to toe and found him the same sturdy, dark-eyed, handsome young fellow he had known long ago and who now cut such a good figure in the uniform with the three stripes.

"What about that money, Albescu?" he asked him.

The gendarme smiled but not too broadly—Ah, Mistress Steluta, what a proficient teacher you are!—and answered:

"If you believe I could have done such a thing, Sir, and that there must be. . . ."

The attorney had come for an investigation and didn't want much talk. When the person under interrogation did not answer briefly and got too talkative, he cut him short. His two years' experience had taught him that this was the best system. Otherwise there'd be no end to it.

That is why he cut the head gendarme short and even informed him:

"You will please answer briefly. Where were you when the owner came to the gendarmery?"

"At my post."

"Call Andreescu in."

Andreescu, the owner, came in. The attorney asked him:

"Where did you find the gendarme when you came to the gendarmery?"

"You see, Sir. . . . After the boy asked me what the wallet was like, and I told him it was black and scratched in a corner. . . ."

"Ah! excuse me! In my office yesterday you told me it was the boy who had described the wallet to you. And now you're saying you told him. . . . Here is the report. . . ."

"You see, Sir. . . ."

"What am I to see? You will please answer briefly. Did *he* tell you what the wallet was like or did *you* tell him?"

"*I* told him."

The headman's clerk informed the attorney that the boy was there. The attorney, very eager to see the boy, told the owner and the gendarme to wait for him outside and gave orders for the boy to be brought in. The boy came in. A drawn face, with a wide forehead and two black eyes with a gleam in them as if from a fever. A neat-looking boy!

The courier explained the delay:

"He wouldn't come, Sir. I had great difficulty in bringing him."

"Why didn't you want to come, boy?"

Niculaita shrugged his shoulders . . . Ah! How many things had happened since Tuesday noon? Things which Niculaita could not speak of with any amount of coherence. Especially the things that happened within him. Trembling, gleaming things that shone and then disappeared, as fugitive as flashes of lightning.

. . . He had come to the gendarmery with the owner and other people following them, the headman among them or so it seemed to him. He had said with a smile: "The owner is here, Sir." But the gendarme had looked surprised and had asked: "What owner?" And Niculaita had opened his eyes to make sure he was really speaking to the head gendarme, and had said: "The owner of the wallet I found by the cross. . . . The one I brought you a little while ago."

And the head gendarme had said: "Are you dreaming?" And Niculaita had looked at the people around, and pinched himself to see if he were awake or dreaming, and had said again: "A little while ago when Mistress Steluta was singing on the veranda. . . ." And then the head gendarme had yelled: "Are you crazy, fellow?" At that moment he had felt as if something had burst within his head, and had spoken again, though without any thought of insulting anyone. He had said gently, as if on the point of running into some great danger: "A man should behave according to his words or speak according to his behavior, Sir." The head gendarme had then struck him over the mouth with his fist so that blood had flowed freely. . . . And then he knew no more until his mother and old Paraschiva came, old Paraschiva singing against the evil eye and giving him water to drink from a new pot. It was on the veranda of the house. Close by were Pirvu Miu and old Grigore, speaking to his father. . . . Old man Grigore had asked: "How was it he didn't say anything to you or his mother? How was it he didn't run over to tell you first?"

Pirvu had put in: "He didn't meet them, don't you see? But why didn't he tell my daughter? He spoke to her." And Pirvu had turned towards the fence and asked: "Isn't that so, Salomia?" Salomia, who was standing on the log on the other side of the fence, had looked frightened and answered: " 'Tis so." After which he himself had got up and had yelled as loud as he could: "I had it in these two hands. Let these hands dry up like wood if it wasn't so!" After that he had again lost consciousness. Vaguely he remembered that the headman and his clerk had come the day before and he had gone with them and shown where he had found the wallet, where he had jumped the hedge, which way he had gone and which way he had returned.

These things Niculaita had some idea of, for he had lived through them, seen them and heard them. But what he could not understand was the gradual loss of all sense of reality which the people's doubts and lack of confidence had brought him. And also the gendarme's indignation, for the gendarme simply could not contain himself. . . . For some hours now he hadn't been sure he had really found the money. Coming along in the company of the courier he had tried to gather his wits and remember how things had happened from the beginning.

"Can't you hear, boy? Why didn't you want to come?" the attorney asked for the second time.

"Oh, well! . . ."

"What d'you mean, 'Oh well'? You cause a complaint to be

made against a man; you cause me, an attorney, to come and investigate; I send for you, and you don't want to come. What do you mean by that?"

"Well . . ."

"What's your name?"

"Niculae Gropescu."

"Don't people call you Niculaita the Fibster?"

Niculaita hadn't thought of that. But it was so. People called him Niculaita the Fibster. You understand?

"Don't you hear what I said? Do people call you Niculaita the Fibster?"

"They might do so."

"What d'you mean 'they might'? They do call you that. Everybody says so. Now why do they call you that?"

"Oh, well!"

"Again the same answer! No matter. We'll leave it at that. Now tell me about the money."

The boy fought shy: he endeavored to clear his muddled brain. He wanted to begin from the beginning, as he had planned to do on his way here. He rubbed his forehead with his hand and swallowed hard. The attorney was waiting. . . .

"You see, Sir . . . when the baker gave me. . . ."

"What baker?"

"The baker I sold the wood to for eleven *lei* a week ago."

"What is all this about a baker? What's the baker got to do with it?"

"I'll tell you."

But Niculaita fell silent again, trying hard to collect his confused thoughts. The attorney looked intently at the boy's trembling hands, at his wild look; and, as he was a kind-hearted man full of compassion, and as he began to understand, he said gently after having sought the eyes of the headman and of his clerk:

"Go on."

"When the baker gave me the money. . . . That time when father sent me to the town with the wood. . . . And I saw the stars. . . ."

Niculaita stopped again.

"Go on," the attorney urged.

"At first he wanted to give me only ten *lei* and a half, but then. . . . It was Ghitica, the priest's son, who invented that nickname for me for he wouldn't believe that a bumblebee could carry away a spider. . . ."

The attorney was fully satisfied now. He no longer had any doubt. As plain as daylight. To save time he stopped the boy's story and told him to go and wait outside. When the boy had left, he said to the others:

"Poor boy."

"It's as I was telling you, Sir, isn't it?" the clerk said.

The attorney fell into a brown study. He thought hard. At the club last night where this case was spoken of, Mitica Ionescu, a lawyer, had said: "Perhaps the plaintiff hasn't lost anything; he's just preparing to be declared a bankrupt. . . ." The attorney knew quite a number of such cases. Only a few days ago there had been the Daradan case. . . . But where did the boy come in then? Oh, the boy had been told by a woman that a man had lost a wallet and was looking for it. This the owner had confessed to yesterday. And the description of the wallet was made by himself, as he had averred a little while ago. After thinking hard, the attorney asked the headman:

"How far is it to the Dalgeni Hospital?"

"Two and a half miles."

"Tell the coachman to harness the horses, and call a courier to take a letter to the doctor there. And let him impress on him that I am waiting for him here, and that he should come at once."

The attorney wrote quickly: "Dear Doctor. . . . Jump into the cab and come here immediately . . . a curious case of auto-suggestion, telepathy and pseudomania. As I do not want to assume full responsibility, I need the advice of a competent person like yourself. See you soon. Be sure to come. I have something very funny to tell you about Nineta."

The father was building up the heap of maize stalks. The mother was sweeping the yard, now and again casting a look at the veranda. Father Alecu was coming; the place must be clean. People had advised the parents to call in the priest and have a prayer read over the boy. Old Uta's charms were no good, her gentle words incensed the boy: "Niculaita dear, keep from thinking of that money. There might have been a charm . . . your imagination. Yes, charm, the devil take them. . . ."

Niculaita sat on the veranda, his head between his hands. With throbbing temples he was trying to understand why both the doctor and the attorney had put their hands inside his mouth.

But how was Niculaita to understand when none of the others there present could do so?

On receiving the attorney's letter, the doctor had taken the volume on legal medicine by Vilbert and all the way had read the chapter on cases of pseudomania so frequent with children. He had read that this was a mania that could be cured except when it was the first manifestation of progressive madness. . . . And having heard the boy as well as other people, including old Grigore, who had also come to the headman's office, he had reached a conclusion. There was no doubt that those were the early symptoms of insanity: confused speech, some temperature, hallucinations, strange animals, a cat supposed to have chirped—a typical case. . . . And so, having advised the boy's parents to deal gently with him, he had summoned the boy again, for he had remembered a final test: he made him open his mouth and, touching his palate with his forefinger, had said to the attorney: "Here, touch this with your finger, a little to the left. Don't you feel a protuberance on the palate?" "Yes," the attorney had answered, fully edified. This last proof, following the doctor's explanations illustrated by quotations from the author he had just read, had dispersed all doubt in the attorney's mind. As he got into the cab again he congratulated himself on the admirable idea he had had of sending for the doctor. However, touched by the obvious and rather noisy despair of the man who had lost the money, he had in a whisper admonished the headman, his clerk, and the head gendarme so that he might not be heard by the group of people standing a little to one side: "In any case," he had said, "Keep your eyes skinned. Watch whether anyone spends more than usual."

Niculaita was sitting on the veranda deep in thought, his head between his hands. Suddenly he jumped up. He remembered that the half sheet of paper which had served him to roll up his coins had been left in the pocket of his sheepskin coat. That, it seemed to him, would be the best proof of his really having found the money. He rushed into the room and rummaged through the pockets, looked and looked, and not finding the paper, he went out into the yard and began shouting at his sisters, and, catching hold of his brother Ilie, rapped him over the knuckles:

"Why did you go through my coat pockets? Why? Why do you poke your nose into my things?"

The child shrieked. The mother called her husband to help her and the two took Niculaita by the arm, one on each side. The youngster, however, swore at them, and with troubled eyes, tore himself away. From the veranda of the next house, Salomia looked on in horror, crossing herself.

That was the state in which Father Alecu found Niculaita. It was not the first time the priest had seen such things. He knew the power of prayer and so put his stole around his neck and began to read:

"Let us pray to the God, God of Gods and Lord of Lords, maker of the fiery hordes and builder of the bodiless powers, who is above whatever is in the heavens and on earth, and whom no man has seen or can see. . . ."

Niculaita sighed deeply and said in bitterness:

"Let me be."

His parents let him alone and Niculaita sat down quietly on the veranda. From where he was, only part of the priest's words came to him, the remainder was lost in a soft murmur: ". . . Curses on you, unclean spirit. With Sabaoth . . and with all . . . Adonai . . . Eloi . . . Curses on you . . . Those of Gomorrah . . . With brimstone did he burn. . . . Curses on you . . . Be in fear and go, go. . . ."

Niculaita could not sleep and so he went out into the yard. It was late. A chill wind was blowing, but the sky was as clear as glass. Beyond the tops of the plum trees in the boyar's orchard, the moon was disappearing. Was it the wind that caused the stars to twinkle so?

And as Niculaita was sitting by the neighbor's fence in the yard, the door of the neighboring cottage opened and a shadow came down the steps making towards him. It was Salomia. He would have known her had he been blind, merely by her steps. She passed between the house and the fence, making towards the orchard. She was but two steps away from him.

"Salomia!" he called out tenderly as if singing her name.

The girl gave a cry and hugged the wall of the house, looking at him in terror.

"Salomia, don't be afraid . . . no . . . I'm not mad, Salomia. And I wouldn't do you any harm, Salomia. . . ."

She looked at him with wide open eyes, without a shade of irony but full of terror, and said tremblingly:

"Go away, Niculaita, I'm afraid of you . . . I'm afraid."

And with that she ran into the orchard.

The two shadows which an hour later sat side by side whispering at the bottom of Pirvu Miu's orchard were Salomia and Petrica, son of Stan Pasalan.

"Don't," the girl said, "or I'll be cross with you. What d'you mean! You're holding me too tight. . . . I'm not of iron."

"No, you're not of iron; you're of flesh. Your little body is of flesh . . . and I want to fondle it, fondle it. But when I have you in my arms, it is as if I were afraid another would rob me of you, and then I clasp you tight, to make a little bundle of you and. . . ."

"Listen!"

"What is it?"

"Didn't you hear?"

"Hear what?"

"Someone sighing."

They both listened intently but could hear nothing but the wind.

"An illusion of yours."

It had been no illusion—women have better ears. The man who had sighed was now walking away quickly, driven by words that had come to him, words he had heard repeatedly. Where? At school? In church? Words that slumbered in some dark corner of the mind and which for some hours now had emerged and kept resounding in his ear: "Come unto me all ye that labor and are heavy-laden and I will give you rest."

The words called to him from the mound where the big cross stood. Reaching the cross he unwound his waist band, kissed it, and wept. Then he looked up and around. The stars were twinkling. A cold wind was blowing. There were no grasshoppers or crickets any more. The cold had killed them all. . . .

God speed you on your way, Niculaita, and may He forgive you. . . .

In a week's time, when beetles such as Niculaita had never seen will be eating his fine, black, inquiring eyes, people will think and speak about him according to their views.

Mr. Epaminonda, worthy descendant of Plato and Aristotle, will explain to the landowner who will have read in the papers about a boy having hanged himself on this estate:

"Yes, the lad of Andrei Gropescu. He was insane, poor boy. If you remember, a good-looking boy. Once, on Saint Peter's Day, when prizes were distributed . . . I was speaking to my wife. She believes it was his learning that sent him mad. Taken from one's father's bean plots, and made to learn a lot, is absolute poison for the blood. . . ."

And the landowner, after deep thinking, will answer: "That is so."

Salomia will feel lonely looking into the yard next to hers, where there will be no one with whom she might pass the time until her tryst with Petrica.

Andrei, Niculaita's father, looking at the heap of logs under the shed, will think sorrowfully of the trellis still unfinished and decide to take old Sandu's tools up to the garret.

And Niculaita's poor mother sitting on the veranda will strike her head with her clenched hands and moan:

"He was so kind and gentle and would hurt no one. . . . If I ever asked him to kill a fowl, he would tell me to give it to old man Grigore for he could not. What a rotten world. . . . !"

But she would not be right in describing the world as rotten any more than if she described herself as such. Is the world to blame for its rottenness? And besides the world may still be said to have improved in the last two thousand years. For if you are not like the others, people do not now cruelly nail you to a cross but (and especially if you are not a very great danger to them), without great wickedness and even with some compassion, cause you to work out your own crucifixion. And that is an improvement.

Gala Galaction

(1879-1961)

Gala Galaction (the pen name of Grigore Pisculescu) was one of the leading writers of Rumanian literature during the interwar period. He wrote several volumes of short stories, some depicting dramatic aspects of village life (*The Little Chapel in the Fields* [1914], *The Bells of the Neamtu Monastery* [1916]); some denouncing the degrading, dehumanizing influence of the lust for money (*Califar's Mill, Gloria Constantini*); others evoking moments from the heroic past of the people (*On the Shores of the Vodislava River, Deeds and Woes from the Time of the Rebellion, The Eagle's Eyrie*). Interested in problems of conscience (*From here to Cladova*), Galaction dedicated his work to the moral education of the reader in a spirit of deep humanitarianism. The same concern is manifest in his novels *Roxana* (1931), *Mehamud's Slippers* (1902), and *Doctor Typhoon* (1933).

His prose is conspicuous for its lyricism (at times pathetic), its commentary, its blending of the real and the fantastic, and its intense expression of love for humanity.

Galaction also wrote numerous essays, collected in the volume *A New World* (1919).

Califar's Mill

On the border of an ancient forest Califar's Mill stood mirrored in its own pond. It had stood so ever since the oldest men in the village, at the other end of the forest, could remember, and Califar had been called "Old Man Califar" since time immemorial. The old men of Alautesti could remember the hoary-haired miller, his piercing eyes peering intently from underneath his thick eyebrows, and his mill with its long overhanging eaves. The lads who were bold enough to cross the thick forest between Alautesti and the mill had seen him as he had been seen by the youths of eighty years ago. Beyond the mill lay Capristea's stony land, pitted with holes and covered with weeds; only the devil could plow such land with his horns.

At Alautesti, on stormy nights, the women, spinning and adding fresh wood to the fire, told how Califar had sold his soul to Satan in exchange for who knew how many centuries of life; that the Evil One had laid a snare across the millpond to catch Christian souls;

and that the miller bestowed the riches with which the devil had tempted our Lord upon anybody who sought them and came to ask for them. But the fiendish snare, they said, laid such a hold upon the soul of the man who coveted this devilish wealth that he went out of his mind. For the devil offered such a profusion of good things and tempted him with such delights that the unfortunate venturer, rolling on the ground like a dog stung by wasps and laughing like an idiot in his evilly-begotten joy, would roll down into the pond.

Califar's pond and mill, they said, were a creation of the Powers of Darkness. This pond, in which the mill had been mirrored for centuries, was like no other; no wave ever rippled its surface which lay, framed by reeds and willows, perfectly smooth, clear and icy, like a transparent block of salt. The dam at the side of mill, terrified Christians asserted, was made strong by the bones of those who, tempted by Satan's wealth, had come to Califar to ask for it. The mill, beneath its two-yard wide eaves, stood like a head ruminating wicked thoughts under a hat pulled down over its eyes. Nobody had ever seen it working. The miller only ground for his master, Old Nick —no one knew when. But they said that when Old Man Califar opened the dam, allowing the water to flow through the channel, it skirled like a bagpipe and hissed like a snake encircled by flames, while blood-red foam flowed from under the millstones. And still more legends were told: of those daring men from the village and elsewhere who had gone mad, turned into idiots by the Devil, and been swallowed up by the magic pond. Such tales were often told when Alautesti peasants gathered together. Then the faint-hearted huddled around the flickering stove, while the courageous stood upright, deep in thought, one hand thrust into sheepskin waistcoats as if ready for a great trial.

Stoicea was one of these brave young fellows, powerful as an oak, with arms of steel and as cunning as a fox. Born out of wedlock, he had neither father nor mother nor any other relatives to look after him. About one month after his wife's death, the old priest, Father Radu, now dead, had found him on the porch of the church and had taken the babe into his own empty house. But before the boy was six, Father Radu had followed his wife into the grave. Since then Stoicea had grown up on everybody's doorstep, a homeless bastard. Today, though, he was the valiant Stoicea. But who wants you for a son-in-law when you have been brought up on village charity, and you now tend the beasts of men who have marriageable daughters? Stoicea realized only too well that he would never grow prosperous in his own village; and for a long time his thoughts had wandered through the darkness of the forest towards Califar's mill.

"Why shouldn't I have a try after all? What do I own and what can I lose? No parents, no family, no one to care for me . . . I am quite alone in the whole, wide world. And I'm not a coward; I've never seen any ghosts or wolves during all these years, while looking after the village cattle at Saele, or near the old cemetery or in Pircalab's Field or anywhere else. Fancy going crazy and selling one's soul for such wonderful riches! Only let me feel them in my hand. I know how to deal with old man Califar and his master. I've made up my mind: tomorrow morning I'll leave the herd in the meadow and then hurry through the forest to Califar's mill."

And so he did. Next morning, when the sun, a flaming ball, circled and climbed Alautesti hill, Stoicea drove the cattle to the meadow, threw his cape over his shoulders, grasped his cudgel firmly and disappeared, whistling loudly, among the oaks.

There were no paths in the forest, yet he strode straight ahead. Whenever the wild vines hung too thickly and barred his path, he used his knife. He went steadily northward. He had been told that you could reach the mill in half a day if you walked straight to the north. Eventually, after a long wearisome journey he came to a glade, in the center of which stood an oak, stretching hoary, gnarled arms above a carpet of anemones. Tired, but soothed by the fragrance of the flowers, Stoicea loosened his belt, stretched his cape on the ground and laid himself down on it. The sun shone on the tips of his sandals. "When it reaches my eyes, it will wake me," he said, and slept soundly for as long as it takes a shadow to move down the length of a man. Then it was that he began to dream. In his dream, when the rays pricked his eyelids, he awoke. He rose refreshed and strode ever deeper into the dark forest pierced by the inverted flames cast by the sun. Long past midday he suddenly beheld between trees sloping downhill a razor-sharp glitter: Califar's pond. After more walking, he at last faced the mill itself, just a mill, like any other mill. But the pond below seemed to him too shiny and too icy. On the bridge the miller was roughing the millstone. He was a gray-bearded man, with eyebrows like dried moss and a nose like the beak of an owl.

"May your work prosper, Uncle Califar!"

"Thank you, my son. What wind blew you through the dark forest and brought you to my mill?"

"Uncle Califar, I've been told you are a wizard like no other and that whoever asks you to make him rich will receive what he asks. That's what I came for."

"All right my boy, I'll make you rich. Let me just finish roughing this stone. I've only got to strike it a few more times with the hammer. What's your name? And you must be hungry. Come and eat with me: I haven't eaten yet either. I've got some pike soup and nearly a cauldron of maize porridge. There you are, I've finished; while I get everything ready, go and have a wash; you're all covered with cobwebs from the forest. . . . There you are, up that ladder."

Stoicea went to the millpond and, leaning on his cudgel, stepped on the rotting ladder after testing it carefully with the end of his cudgel and with his sandal. "Old man Califar, why, he's a tottering old man. I could rid him of the days he still has to live with a single slap in his face!

". . . This pond that is never stirred by waves—what does it all mean? Just old wives' idle talk! Let's wash and forget all this childishness." After washing his hands, he hollowed the palms of his hands, plunged them into the icy pond and, pulling them out full of murmuring water, splashed his face. . . .

"Oh, what a long dream!" Stoicea leaped up from his cape and realized that he had been awakened by the cold drops of a torrential downpour coming unexpectedly from a treacherously clear sky. "Instead of the sun reaching my eyes and waking me up, here I am covered with a blanket of heavy, drenching rain. What shall I do now? I can't stay under this oak because there's the danger of lightning. Where shall I go? Forward, towards Califar's mill or back to the village? What time can it be? My, what a storm! One can hear the oldest trees in the forest breaking down. I'd better go back to the village and mark this day as one of the many I've lost."

But Stoicea, unable to find his own tracks in the forest, was soon lost. The more he tried to walk in the right direction, the more he wandered aimlessly among dense winding creepers, ditches where blasted trees lay prone, and holes from which white, tortured roots emerged like ribs protruding from a corpse. The wind, morever, came down viciously, roaring, smashing and howling against the oaks. Only a few large drops whistled between the leaves like bullets. Stoicea walked rapidly, anxious to see where the storm was leading him. He had been noticing for some time that a crowd of four-legged beasts: stags, deer, foxes, and even wolves, were hurriedly creeping along at his side, also going downhill, trying to hide among the bushes. The beasts fled huddled together, whining as if under the threat of an unseen whip. Hawks too fled before the tempest, rocked and tossed on their wings for a few moments, then plummeted to the ground like spent arrows. And then the beasts began to howl and whine most horribly. Wolves rushed down the slope like mad, trampling ruthlessly upon the smaller animals in their way, while stags leaped sideways stabbing at the bushes with their antlers. The storm, ever wilder, turned in a circle, blowing and croaking like a fiend above the forest that had suddenly grown thinner. Then the slope down which he had been swept willy-nilly by the storm with the desperate crowd of forest beasts, came to a sudden stop before a hill as white and as straight as a wall. The crowd of animals broke up into two or three groups, soon vanishing into the folds of the valley, while Stoicea hastened to take refuge in a cave at the foot of the hill.

"Where the devil can I be? I have never seen this place. I must have walked westward, in my bewilderment, and come near the edge of the mountains. I'm lucky to find some sort of shelter."

He had hardly finished his meditation when the tempest brought to his ears the sound of a horse neighing, the clattering of hoofs, and the scream of a woman. As he rushed out of the cave, a bay horse stopped suddenly in front of him, and a terrified girl leaped from the saddle into his arms shouting: "Oh, help me, good friend! A wounded bear is after me."

Indeed, the huge and terrifying beast was approaching, maddened by a gunshot wound and the crescendoing tumult of horn and baying hounds. Stoicea swiftly pushed the girl inside the limestone cavern, while the horse reared and vanished into the bushes. The young peasant waited for the beast to approach and then, with a tremendous blow, smashed in its head, so that its brains lay scattered on the ground.

"I'm deeply grateful to you. I'm Tecla, Boyar Rovin's daughter; your brave deed won't go unrewarded. I went out with my father, my brothers, and several servants, more to enjoy the ride than to hunt. The storm scattered us just when we met the bear, and so I lost my way and rode up here, with the bear upon my heels. But look, here are my people."

Horsemen could now be seen riding through the thickets and crowding along the valley; the hounds arrived first and howled around the dead monster, wagging their tails at their young mistress, then running back to the horsemen as if carrying the good news. Boyar Rovin and his sons with their retinue jumped off their horses, surrounded the girl and Stoicea, shook hands with the young hero and looked in deep amazement at the monster's scattered brains.

"Who are you and where are you from, brave young man? You've saved my daughter's life and shall be rewarded well for it. But wouldn't you like to enter my service? My house would be only too proud to receive such a valiant man!"

Stoicea accepted at once. Placing his sandal into the stirrup of a boyar's stallion, he leaned his cudgel against his shoulder, with its other end against the foaming mane of the steed. Soon he was riding with all the huntsmen across the fields of the Rovinesti estate.

though it was night before they reached the boyar's castle. . . . So, Stoicea, the cowherd from Alautesti, became within a few years the boyar's intimate, most trusted servant and chief steward of all his estates. And fortune was even kinder to him than he would ever have dared to dream, for the Lady Tecla fell deeply in love with him; and Boyar Rovin, somewhat reluctantly, gave her Stoicea for a husband and then presented his son-in-law with the largest of the estates belonging to the Rovin family.

So there was Stoicea given a boyar's rank by the ruling prince, held in high esteem by all and sundry, deeply loved by his wife, lucky in his children, the fruit of his soil and everything else just as in a fairy tale. Stoicea's boys grew up to become handsome men; his cows grazed in pastures that would take you more than three days to walk around; his sheep were so numerous that the fields seemed covered with snow as far as eye could reach. All his days were happy, full and clear, but they passed as quickly as a mountain stream or a dream. Very occasionally he remembered what he had been: "Am I Stoicea, the abandoned child that grew up at the doors of strangers? Was it I who decided one day to go to see miller Califar in the hope that he would make me rich?" But he did not have a lot of time to think about his past, for his days went by swift and serene.

One day, however, a messenger astride a horse foaming at the mouth entered Stoicea's courtyard. He came from Boyar Rovin, Stoicea's father-in-law.

"I kiss your hand! Your Honor's father-in-law advises you most urgently to take your wife and children and the belongings you value most and flee into the mountains, for two days ago a horde of Tartars invaded our country and are approaching like a hurricane."

Hardly had the messenger finished, when the servants, watchmen and shepherds of the estate came rushing into the courtyard, shouting in one voice: "The Tartars! The Tartars!" Boyar Stoicea, bareheaded as he was, went into the courtyard and ordered in a voice of thunder:

"Break the dam and flood the moat. Raise the drawbridge. Get into the house; some of you bolt the door leading to the servants' quarters and place logs, chests, and cupboards against it; others fetch from their place the powder barrels, bullets, guns, pistols and yataghans. And, if any Tartars dare to approach, shoot at them from the eaves and out of the windows, without cease!"

Boyar Stoicea then entered the house, through the great front doors as thick as a palm's breadth. He shut and bolted them and placed the iron bars across. Then he called his sons from the staircase: "Niculcea, Andrei, Zamfir! Bring me, dear boys, my curved dagger, my mace, and my pistol belt. I will watch here; you watch at the windows."

Seeing the Lady Tecla kissing her sons, and everyone running to defend the house against the impending menace, the boyar felt his heart grow heavy within him. But there was no time to lose. His orders had hardly been carried out, when, having examined with an eagle's eye every part of the house, from the attics down to the cellars, Stoicea suddenly saw, from the small window over the door, black groups of Tartars on the horizon, coming ever closer like the shadow of a cloud. Their horses leaped over the flooded ditches with the ease of grayhounds, and then, lo! they were already milling around the house. Through the narrow embrasures, from beneath the eaves and from the balconies the young noblemen and the servitors shot at the enemy. Boyar Stoicea satisfied himself that the entrance to the servants' quarters was so well reinforced from inside and defended by guns that it could not be forced by the enemy; but the main front door, which he was defending, gave him some anxiety, for the Tartars, who were sheltered from the bullets, were attacking it lustily. The blows of their axes rained down on the door like hail.

"The heathens will smash in the door, however thick it is. Come on, my sons, let's take the ladder and prop it against the door."

Boyar Stoicea rushed down the stairs, but as he reached the last step, a great blast of air struck his face, coming through the door, which shook with the blow of the Tartars' axes, throwing him back, while a mocking voice as harsh as an owl's froze the marrow in his bones:

"Why, here's a strong lad . . . a handful of water in his face, and he falls down before me like a gosling. . . ."

Stoicea stood up on trembling legs held wide apart . . . and stared around as if just awakened out of a deep sleep, as if crazy. . . .

"Where am I? What's happened to the Tartars?"

"What Tartars, my lad?"

"What is this place? Where is my house? My servants?"

"What house, what servants, lad?"

"Where is my wife Tecla, Boyar Rovin's daughter, my children, my estate, my fortune?"

"Come to your senses, young Stoicea. You are at Califar's mill; you came over from Alautesti, asking me to make you a rich man."

Stoicea listened with his mouth wide open, staring like an idiot; then, clutching his hair, he shook his head with both hands, as he would a pumpkin which had a wasp in it.

"Have you come to your senses? I'm Old Man Califar, and you are Stoicea from Alautesti. You came to me so that I might make you rich. Well, what d'you say . . . have I made you rich?"

"My Tecla, my children, my house, my fortune! Woe is me!"

"So there you are; all those things are the riches you asked for; I've fulfilled your wish."

Stoicea stood staring at the floor. At last he noticed his cudgel leaning against the stairs, felt that his cheeks were wet and collected his thoughts which had been scattered as by the devil's steed. During the few seconds he had thrown a handful of bewitched water in his face the devil had carried him on his horse for the span of a man's life; had made him wander in a raging storm, had made him meet Tecla and the Boyar Rovin, had made him marry, become a rich man and a boyar, and now had burst his dream like a bubble, destroying it all.

Stoicea leaned forward and grasped his cudgel.

The jeering miller was still sitting on the parapet of the bridge, like a huge gray owl.

"You devil, I want to go to hell tied to you with a bast-rope."

"What a kindness you would do me! It's three hundred years now that I have carried in my bones this accursed life. Alas, I cannot die unless I am murdered."

"Take it then"—and the wizard's brains bespattered the bridge. Stoicea walked to the dam and dived headlong into the transparent depths of the waters.

Ion Agirbiceanu

(1882-1963)

Ion Agirbiceanu rose to the forefront of Rumanian literature as a worthy successor to Slavici by his realistic portrayal of Rumanian society in Transylvania before the first World War and during the interwar period. His writings are essentially moralistic, untainted, however, by any exaggerated didacticism. He wrote several volumes of sketches and short stories (*From the Country* [1906], *Two Loves* [1910], *In Darkness* [1910], *Popa Man* [1920], *The Little Green Gig* [1921], *Disappointment* [1924]), novels (*The Archangels* [1914], his major work, *The Law of the Flesh* [1926], *The Law of Death* [1927], *The Sectarians* [1938]), and memoirs (*Collegian Long Ago* [1909], *Recollections* [1940]). His work is pervaded by a deep understanding and sympathy for the wretched and oppressed. His peasants are hard-working men, constantly harassed by troubles, stricken by poverty and ills. The intellectual milieu of the Transylvanian villages and towns is also submitted to a searching analysis in which he depicts "conscience cases," the struggle of man against his own vices or the temptations of the flesh.

"Fefeleaga," possibly his most vigorous short story, is one of the highlights of Rumanian short-story fiction.

Fefeleaga*

From early morning you can see her on the road, leading, or rather dragging, her horse by the bridle. She is a tall, bony woman; her pock-marked cheeks are deeply tanned by sun and wind. She takes long strides; her hard top-boots, which are strewn with dry humps on the surface, tramp noisily. The horse follows with outstretched neck, shuffling his bony shanks. Two pouches, split down the middle, are loaded on his deeply hollowed back. Two large brown patches appear beneath the bags when they are jolted. The horse is white, but beneath the bags the hair has been worn away; after the sore had healed those parts had become hard as a plow chain. He follows the woman as if lulled to sleep by the familiar tramp of her top-boots; his big head moves neither right nor left. The woman pays little

* An onomatopoetic word suggesting the slow movement of the woman and her horse as they worked with the loaded pouches on the beast's back.

attention to the horse; she walks on ahead, occasionally saying as if to herself: "Gee-ho, Bator!" Thus they both pass down the village streets, climb the slope up to Dealul Bailor, and disappear down the sharp slope on the other side. Here a narrow pathway leads down the boulder-strewn hillside, and the woman steadies the horse: "Hey, Bator! Whoa! You haven't got the Tartars chasing you!" The descent is a chaotic affair for Bator; his bones look as if they were about to break out of his skin. The pouches start hopping crazily up and down on his back, threatening to break loose from the little wooden saddle. Bator braces his hoofs firmly against the ground; his eyelids blink rapidly as if trying to revive long-extinguished lights.

At the bottom of the hill they stop near a heap of gravel. The woman takes a little wooden basin and uses it to load the bags on the horse's back. The horse sways gently to right or left as the woman fills the bags; when they are full, woman and horse start slowly uphill. On the way they meet youngsters perched atop of the bags on their ponies, whistling as they jog downhill. They too have come for gravel. They bid the woman good day as they pass. "Grow up and be happy," says the woman, tugging at the bridle. The younger horses emit occasional snorts and neighing calls, but Bator climbs with difficulty, his head drooping low: he hears nothing, not even the familiar tramp of his mistress's boots. He feels the ground with his hoofs; he knows when to expect the more difficult portions of the climb. On such occasions he braces himself, snorting noisily through his wide, hoary nostrils. "Whoa, there, Bator, poor old fellow! Let's take it easy; we haven't got the Tartars after us!" Gratefully the horse stops, puffing heavily as out of a pair of bellows. The woman rearranges the bags, replaces portions of the load which are threatening to spill over, and peers upward to see how much is left of the climb.

In this way, with frequent halts and promptings, they reach the crest. After that the way is easier. In the village she delivers the gravel to one homestead today, tomorrow to another; sometimes to the same one for weeks.

The woman's name is Maria, but people, scoffers as they are, call her Fefeleaga. The smaller fry of the village had always been accustomed to see her leading Bator by the bridle and bringing gravel. Maria had never wondered how much gold people made out of the gravel brought on Bator's back, but many times, with Bator hardly able to reach the top of the hill, she would say to herself: "The poor old chap must have humped enough gravel to make a hill as high as this one." For one load they paid her 10 *cruceri*. When the road was in good condition she could bring five or six loads a day. That might come to three *zloty* a week. And she would say to herself: "It's enough to live on."

Once she had been better off. When her husband Dinu was alive, people used to call her Maria Dinului, that is "Dinu's Maria"; she had worked with Bator beside her as she was still doing now. Dinu had worked in a mine, drilling the rock and blasting it with gunpowder or dynamite, like all miners. And Dinu also had made three or four *zloty* a week.

At the time they had five children, and a weedy lot they were. They had food enough, but they still looked poorly. Dinu coughed a lot; whenever he came from the mine, wet and muddy, he started coughing and abusing the children because he couldn't endure seeing them so skinny. The woman took their part, comforted them, kissed their roughened white, little cheeks, which were always peeling.

"Let them alone," she would say, "what can you be expecting of them now? When they start working they'll get stronger."

"Like hell they will! You'll never see 'em grow up." Dinu himself died before any of them. The woman mourned her loss, but she had no time to mourn for long, for the burial claimed every bit of money in the house. During his three days' rest until Dinu was buried, Bator nearly went stiff. Now the woman felt that this big white horse, so skinny you could count every bone in his body, was her only support. The village remained the same as in Dinu's lifetime. People went about their business as if nothing had happened. And when they saw Maria leading Bator by the bridle the day after she had buried her husband, some roguish fellow first remarked: "Here comes Fefeleaga." And "Fefeleaga" she remained.

But she never trusted her fellow men nor did she ask them for help. She had trusted but to a higher power and now, since Dinu's death, she only relied upon Bator. Ever since Dinu had closed his eyes and she had come out into the yard in grief, she had felt that henceforth she would rely not on the people who came to pay their respects to the dead, but on that big white horse, tethered to the gate post, stolidly chewing at his hay. As long as the dead man was still in the house, whenever Fefeleaga went into the yard it seemed to her that Bator, chewing away, was nodding his head and saying: "Yes, yes, yes. We'll do what we can."

And gradually, with her heavy top-boots tramping the village streets all day and leading Bator by the bridle, she began to forget Dinu. Not that she thought of another man. For a long time past everything had boiled down to a single essential: week after week, including Sundays, to puzzle out how to get enough food to go round in the household on the money available. She felt she could do it with Bator beside her. Maybe a long time ago she had had happier thoughts, and in her youth her heart had leapt to a ray of warmth. But once she had harnessed herself to work, which she saw she could not escape all her life, she realized that for a harassed woman like herself all such illusions of better times were plain nonsense and only served to make things even worse.

Two or three people had advised her to marry again. "What's the use of waiting? You'll grow old, and then nobody'll want you."

"They can go marry the devil's mother," said Fefeleaga, with a hostile glance at those well-meaning people. Then, chin on chest, she would jerk at the bridle: "Gee-up there, Bator, old fellow, gee-up," and went on her way thoughtfully. She didn't quite know what it was, but she had a bitter feeling. She couldn't escape the thought: "Why do men still go on living in this world?" She had never answered this question other than by shrugging her shoulders, so she felt annoyed that it recurred from time to time. Sometimes in the morning, while she was fastening the bags onto the horse's back, it occurred to her that Bator must be asking himself the same question and would have gazed at her inquiringly if he had not been blind.

After five years as a widow she was left with only two children, a boy and a girl. Three had died when about to reach their fifteenth year. It was as if on the threshold of this fifteenth year there were some high stile which made Fefeleaga's children trip and break their necks. The country folk were glad the Lord was taking some of the burden off her, but Fefeleaga wasn't glad at all. The boys were big enough but as they were always ill they could do no work. She managed to get one of them a job as a servant, but his master did not keep him long, saying he was too weak. Still Fefeleaga wasn't glad they died. She never told anybody whether she cared or not. Nor could people tell whether anybody had died in her house except from two signs: first, that two or three days before the death of a child Bator would be tethered to the gate post munching hay, and second, that a day after the burial Fefeleaga would start off before dawn down the village streets leading the horse by its bridle.

But with the dead still in the house she would often go into the yard and speak to the horse: "How are you getting on, poor old Bator?" And the bony horse would shake his big head, as if saying: "Why fuss? That's the way of the world."

And the horse was right! Such was the way of the world. Fefeleaga felt it sorely at the death of each child, with her house growing steadily emptier.

It was on Sundays that the bitterness would gather in her heart. It was then that she would collect her money for her week's work, and Bator's. The well-to-do, knowing she was alone in the world, did not pay regularly and did not even pay her in full; all of them owed Fefeleaga large arrears. They were sure she would come to work the following week, for she had to make use of Bator. They also reckoned that from one week to the other, Fefeleaga, being a woman, might forget. She did not forget but when she saw people were trying to deprive her of her modest due, she chose to say nothing. She never asked again; a contemptuous smile would pucker her whole face. And a smile seemed strange indeed on those earth-colored, pock-marked cheeks, which might have been likened to two small gray lumps of rock pitted by the falling of many large raindrops.

Since she collected her money on Sundays she seldom went to church. But the wealthy villagers did not go either. They stayed in the public house, drinking beer. Fefeleaga did not go to church, and yet when she saw those men spending on drink perhaps the very money they owed her, she despised them and in her bitterness felt herself better, a better Christian than they were. On very rare occasions, when someone or other would put her off for months and did not pay, she would tell him to his face: "What am I? Nothing at all. But nobody curses me, nobody calls on God to blast me, and the whole village curses you." Once she had said that she no longer wanted the money even if it had been thrice her due. She would go home, give the horse a handful of hay and say to him: "How's things with you, poor old Bator?" And the horse, his snout burrowing into the hay, would nod as if he were saying: "Yes, yes. That's what men are like."

Working all week in harmony with Bator as if the soul of her husband Dinu had passed into his shabby carcass, Fefeleaga did not notice how time passed. For her there was just one way of telling the time: the period that passed from the death of one child until the next passed away. There was just one girl left, and the last death in her house had occurred three years ago. Both woman and horse had grown old. The woman's hair was grayish like the wool of the sheep. Deep lines wrinkled her pock-marked face. Her chin was growing angular: it had begun to point towards her mouth which had fallen inwards. The horse was still scraggier. The two earth-colored patches under the bags had grown larger; the hair on his ribs and back was even thinner. His lower lip hung downward as if stretched by an invisible load.

The old women of the village were whispering among themselves about her. They had heard this and that; maybe a few spells should be tried, for it smacked of the Unclean that her children kept dying, and all at the same age.

But Fefeleaga did not believe in any devilish powers. Women crossed themselves at her lack of faith, but she answered sedately: "Oh, no, there is no devil. Wicked, dishonest men are devils."

She tried no spells or incantations. She did nothing of the sort, and four years, two months and thirteen days after the last death, her last girl passed away. She also was about to reach her fifteenth birthday. Nor had she been sickly any more than the others before her. The whitish powder which used to come off her face when she was a small child had gone. Her illness had lasted only a fortnight.

When this last girl died, Fefeleaga told nobody for a whole day. When the girl had breathed her last, Fefeleaga left the candle burning, went into the yard, untied Bator from the post, jerked at his bridle, led him into the barn full of hay and left him there untethered. She said nothing to him but accidentally glanced at his head. His eyelids were open, unblinking above the hollows of his eyes. Never had those two wounds seemed to her so frightening, as gaping as they did now. She went back into the house, sat down on the oaken bed and remained motionless in that position all day, like a wooden figure. She neither wept nor mourned. She did not kiss her child. She just sat there with her head buried in her horny palms, and the lump kept rising in her throat, with the thought: "What does man live for?" Now she did not shrug, but she could not unravel her thoughts to seek an answer. What she saw clearly was the life she had led tugging at a bridle, first with a black horse, then with Bator. She saw the high Dealul Bailor hill, with its sharp rocks jutting out like the teeth in a giant's jaw; she saw the beaten track and on the track she saw herself, Fefeleaga, leading Bator by the bridle. As in a dream she found herself counting the number of times she must have crossed that hill, how many loads of gravel she had brought in some forty-five years. Then her thoughts wandered over the Sundays of each year; on how many Sundays she had gone to church or stayed away; and when she stayed away, from whom she collected her money, and how much? With whom she had to haggle. Then she saw Bator again following behind her, his bones rattling with a noise like a loose horseshoe. She could see him struggling uphill with the load on his back, bracing his forelegs downhill. She could see him and hear the far-away voice of Fefeleaga encouraging him: "Easy, poor old Bator! Let's take it easy; we haven't got the Tartars after us!" Then gradually, with great difficulty she worked out the number of years between each death in her family, from her husband to the last girl. A weary succession of years. And how many journeys, Mother of God! If strung out in line they would reach the end of the world.

But now all this toil was over! Now she felt for the first time that she had nothing left to slave for. Not until the last of her children had died had she realized why she had kept it up. Now, with Paunita lying there with the wax candle flickering at her bedside, Fefeleaga realized that it was for the sake of her children that she had endured it all. She alone knew what she had endured! But it had not gone against the grain; she had worked gladly! For them; first for five of them, then for four, then for three, for two, and in the end for one. The void in her soul had gaped wider whenever one of them had died, but her will to work did not give in. Two small tears the size of pinheads wet her dry eyes.

That evening she went to the priest, to "do the last thing for the last soul in her household." Next morning she went to the barn, took Bator by the bridle and started off. The horse tugged in the direction of the two split pouches. But Fefeleaga stopped him. "No, Bator, no, poor old horse; from now on you won't carry any more gravel on your back." And she tugged him by the bridle towards the gate. The horse feeling himself without the bags, held back, stopping at the gate. "Gee-up dear! We're not going to work now. No! Now Fefeleaga's taking you to market to sell you, to buy a wreath and a white sheet, white as milk. Because now Paunita's dead too, old chap." And the tears started again from her dry eyes.

And, pulling at his bridle, and talking to him, she took him to town and sold him for an absurdly low price. The horse felt a stranger's hand taking him by the bridle, smelled the new master, and, turning his head towards Fefeleaga, neighed for the first time in many years. Tears started to the old woman's eyes a third time and in a flash she realized the sin she was committing in parting from this horse that had helped her during a lifetime. But in vain: she had no further use for Bator. He would have revived memories of the long succession of deaths, yes, deaths, for she realized she had worked for them, and she could not have endured it. She felt that her friendship for the horse, a friendship akin to the feeling for a human being, was due only to the help he had given her in looking after her children. Her love for that large, bony white horse was love for her children. And even now the last bit of help came from Bator. Without him Paunita would have had no painted coffin, no bridal wreath, no white winding sheets.

When Fefeleaga had bought what she wanted, the horse was tethered to a post, in a narrow street. She went up to him and stroked his neck. Again the horse neighed. "Bator, don't take on. You'll have a better time of it. Look, I'm going. I've got to go and dress up Paunita."

And with bowed back she tramped down the street in her heavy boots, in search of a conveyance to take home the finery bought with the price of Bator.

Matei I. Caragiale

(1885-1936)

Son of a great dramatist, Matei Caragiale acquires public notice by different, sometimes even contrary means. While I. L. Caragiale exposes hypocrisy by dealing ironically with "humbugs," his son evokes remote aristocratic origins, indulging in dreams of the past. His volume of verse, *Golden Eagles,* abounds in visions of an extinguished magnificence, of a faded-away glory, which reflect a remote, alluring grandeur. The novel *The Good-for-Nothing* (1928) sets face to face an exhausted, decrepit nobility and the rabble eager to get on in life. In an odd mixture of a peculiar kind, on the one hand refinement, on the other coarseness, Matei Caragiale distills strange essences meant to beguile those with excessively cultivated tastes. With him atmosphere and color stifle the epic thread of the narrative, the realistic observation sought by the ordinary reader. So hallucinatory seem the outlines of the environment depicted by the writer, so strange and unusual the heroes' attitudes, so learned and euphuistic the author's style, that the reader acquires an impression of unreality. In "Remember" the full liberation from whatever is ordinary takes place, and the writer enters the world of the miraculous once again under the spell of an aristocratic contemplation.

Remember*

Ceci est un fait-divers atroce
Les Mémoires du Bal-Mabille

There are dreams which we seem to have lived some day somewhere, very much as there are events we have lived through yet we wonder whether they were not dreams. That is precisely what I was thinking the other night when, rummaging through my papers in order to see what could be burned—papers may also be cumbersome—I found a letter which revived the memory of a queer occurrence, so queer that, had it taken place more than seven years ago, I should have been a prey to doubt, I should have felt inclined to think I only dreamt of it, or read about it, or simply heard the story in days of old.

* The original title is in English.

It was in 1907. I had been very ill in Bucharest and had afterwards returned to my home in Berlin. My recovery was rather slow and difficult, requiring very great care. Upon my departure, my physician advised me to avoid even the slightest agitation or distress. Poor doctor! I shrugged my shoulders with a smile and told him to set his mind at rest.

I saw Berlin again after two years of exile. I am extremely fond of Berlin; not even the saddest circumstances have ever spoilt my pleasure in seeing it again. I found it as I had left it: it was all in bloom. Yet never had it seemed to me so beautiful as in that year, at the beginning of June.

Unfortunately I was no longer able to explore and wander about as in bygone days. I found myself tiring too soon and fatigue could facilitate a relapse. Therefore, I resigned myself to staying indoors for some time. This was a sacrifice for which I was partly compensated by the beauty of the old music which I could hear being played in the house from morn till night. Pervaded by a sweet drowsiness I allowed my daydreams to emerge and to melt at will into the flood of sublime harmonies, while I stared out of the windows, with half-closed eyes, at the rainbows shimmering in the fluid spray of the fountain in the midst of the vast garden-square. The gentle breeze of twilight caused a trembling among the roses climbing all over the balcony of the house opposite, wafting their fragrance up to me. The evening was instilling animation into the shadows and the mirrors were thrilled by mysterious tremors. That was the hour to which I always looked forward in order to admire the most beautiful corner of the square—a patch of a grove left untouched in the midst of the town—a few old bushy and gloomy trees, worthy of begetting the masterpieces of the most famous artists.

I could even say that I used to meet the same bushy trees in a painting by Ruysdael to be found at Frederic's Museum, their shadow floating over a ruined castle by a waterfall. Never could I pass by that painting without dwelling upon it for quite a long time. While I was watching it, my thoughts would lose themselves endlessly in the small patch of purple sky whose horizon seemed infinite in depth. A heathen though devout love for old trees is an inborn thing with me, the lees of an age-old superstition. It is to those trees that I am indebted for noble thoughts and great inspiration, for I do not think there is any human verse or masterly song in the world which could move me more profoundly than the mysterious rustle aroused in the foliage by an evening wind. The painted trees, however, charmed me even more than the real ones, for that small melancholy landscape showed me a reflection of my own soul.

I was frequently at the museum. However deeply I was immersed in the contemplation of the pictures, I never overlooked the other visitors, who were sometimes rather interesting too. That is how I happened to notice the constant presence of a young man who was apt to attract anybody's eyes, particularly in that place. For one could say about him with full justification, that he seemed to have been wrested by some spell out of an old canvas. Can there be any rarer pleasure for those who have piously sipped at the mystery of the past than to meet an icon of forgotten centuries, in the flesh? Two years before I had seen a young lady copying "Maria Mancini" from Mignard's painting, in the French room of the museum. She was so strikingly like the model that one might have believed she was in front of a mirror drawing her own face with barely a few adornments.

There was the same resemblance between that young man and one of those lords whose looks, hands, and smiles were granted immortality by Van Dyke and, after him, by Van-der-Faes. I said "one of those lords," for they are mostly alike. In the past, within confined castes, every epoch imprinted the same mien, if not the same countenance too, upon the people closely and repeatedly related, who lived together and shared the same costumes and customs. On the other hand, it happens, in the most unexpected places and moments, that some beings arise whose true resemblance must be sought somewhere else, in other countries, in other nations, in other centuries. And yet one can hardly imagine that they could have the remotest kinship with those from whom they are separated by chasms of time and blood.

Any supposition about the descent of the above-mentioned youth was superfluous, yet I was remarking all sorts of things about his person, truly unique and strange, which strongly impressed themselves upon my memory. I had been intimidated by the cold pride displayed by the young man who strode alone through life in glorious beauty, careless, and erect. From the very outset I thought him one of those exceptional beings, estranged from mankind, by whom I was always keenly attracted. I saw him almost daily, as we also met outside the museum. During my walks about the town which I had timidly resumed, still fearing fatigue, I took long stops at a shop where people savored the masterpieces of a traditional Dutch spirits distillery. After Ruysdael, Brouwer, and Van-der-Hoogh, I could find no better place for collecting my thoughts than that narrow and rather dark room, which could have honored any dwelling of a burgomaster or head of a guild. It had rich paneling of smoked oak covering half the walls, while its protruding edge formed a broad shelf along the walls displaying Delft cups, chalices, and pitchers. What wonderful moments I spent there!

Next to me, on the only bench to be found in the hospitable room, rather lonely in the daytime, the young man with the face of an ancient picture, sipped at leisure the sweetest and most perfumed drinks. They were like molten gems, calling up exotic dreams and remote nostalgia, through spices of strong flavor from Java or the Antilles. In that spirits shop we no longer felt alien to each other and odd though it may seem later, when we became acquainted, we even confessed to each having been under the impression that we spent other hours together in a similar room.

It had never crossed my mind that we could become friends as I had thought him of a world entirely different from mine. It was quite obvious: a flower growing in the field is different from one growing in the garden. Whether it took centuries for a lofty race to produce in its twilight, the ideal aristocrat, or whether it was the result of chance, the young man's appearance approached perfection. It is also true that this ornament of mankind took some pains to enhance his beauty, for I have rarely seen even a woman pay so much attention to personal appearance. Should I have assumed this self-adornment to mark him as one of those perverse men of abnormal habits whose number seems to have increased everywhere in recent times? No, I did not feel like believing it. For though this painted Jezebel sometimes allowed a doubtful smile to play upon his lips, under the severe arch of the brows blackened with a pencil, his eyes had that innocent clearness which only shines under the lids of heroes and children.

He was very young too; he must have been about twenty. And what freakish behavior is forbidden at that age, especially to those born into the wealthy classes? The absence of worry for the morrow transforms the human brain, dulling the feeling of responsibility and fear. Wealth softens the conscience and intoxicates with a sweet uninterrupted drunkenness which urges one to court rare pleasures, to race after novel sensations. It is to that careless and wanton world, free from common prejudices, that my new acquaintance belonged. He must undoubtedly have lived in extremely easy circumstances, yet he seemed to live outside that world and, moreover, outside any world whatever. There were many other men like him in Berlin-W., but those men you could only seldom catch sight of, riding in the mist of the morning or flying quickly at night towards their florid luxuries. I could only picture this man renting a mansion on one of the streets which border upon the kingly Tiergarten, which is girded in the West with a wonderful string of villas, where wealth has been at least partially successful in reestablishing a paradise upon the earth. I therefore imagined him in the sumptuous solitude of rooms with a profusion of mirrors, reflecting the lavish abundance of rare flowers; I pictured him, with his slender fingers, turning over the leaves of books in expensive bindings. Wasn't the fragrance of passion he gave off sufficient to arouse the hallucination of such a décor, since it was so intoxicating that one could dream with wide awake eyes?

Aubrey de Vere. When I think of it. . . . One day we just started talking to each other as though we had always been acquainted. His Norman name—to this very day I'm not perfectly sure whether it was his true name—was not strange to me, as it had belonged to the wild earls of Oxford. After their line was extinct, it was picked up and joined to that of Beauclerc by the bastard Stuarts, the dukes of Saint Alban. If he actually descended from them, he would not have been more honored by them than he would have honored them. Although a true-blue Englishman, he usually spoke French, in a manner which I have but rarely had the pleasure to hear. In the grave tune of his supple and pure voice, French was more than a means of understanding; it was an instrument of seduction. Learning about his descent, I immediately understood everything he did; the tradition sealed by Brummell lived within Aubrey de Vere in the most splendid glory. In this way I found an explanation even for the pleasure he took in painting his face: weren't the first inhabitants of Albion recorded in history as given to painting their whole naked bodies blue? This color was particularly dear to my new friend; he wore it in his very being, in the eyes and under the very transparent skin of both hands loaded in turn with seven twinkling rings, all of the same kind—seven Ceylon sapphires. Together with the bracelet and the perfume, that unforgettable fragrance of red carnation, the rings were the only things to which he remained true, for otherwise, I do not remember having seen him even twice in the same clothes. But all this minute care he took in dressing and adorning himself was a mere detail out of a perfect ensemble of happy harmony. Aubrey de Vere had a wonderful mind and a sparkling wit; he would have been the pride of the most exclusive club and would not have felt out of his depth even in a gathering of scholars. For instance, when he confessed that he had his linen laundered in London, he added that in much the same way, in the 18th century, the Paris fops had theirs laundered in Flanders and the Bordeaux dandies in Curaçao. In the same way he could talk about everything with references to the past, with charming comparisons and details, whenever he happened to tell about his travels in the ancient realms of the East or among the forsaken islets of the quiet ocean where eternal spring prevails. The only thing I could learn about his life was this: he had seen much, wandering about seas and countries, and had read equally much, perhaps even too much for his years. It was also possible that he had mixed up what he had seen with what he had read, or to have viewed the things he had seen through the delusive window of his reading. In collusion with wealth, all this had somehow turned his head, although nature had originally endowed him with clear and cold reason. Thus, for example, I understood that he indulged in bold occult investigations, for which he had been born not only with a rare propensity but also with the most amazing training. He even seemed to have more connections with spirits than with the living, for his tales never even mentioned a human being.

On what occasion, under what circumstances had he made such wonderful trips at such an early age, he did not say; nor did he say who and what he was, what his place of origin was, whether he had any parents, relatives or friends, where he lived—nothing, absolutely nothing. It is no small wonder that, young as he was, he possessed enough self-control to be able to hide so much, without ever betraying himself. On the other hand, whereas he did not disclose anything, I myself questioned him even less; in fact, I suppose that was precisely the reason for our becoming friends. Had we continued to meet for a century, it would still have been easier for some revelation to escape his lips than for a question to escape mine. As a matter of fact, I was not particularly keen on learning anything: was it any business of mine? I happened to see him, without his being aware, choosing flowers worth 400 to 500 marks, carnations and rare orchids—real debauchery—and as I was very well acquainted with the florist's assistant it would have been a trifling matter for me to enter the shop after he had left and, while adorning my buttonhole, to learn where he sent those flowers. Thus, holding one end of the thread I could use that clue in order to push the investigation further. Yet why should I have done it? It was possible that the obstinate insistence with which he curtained off his very short past and his everyday life should have had some hidden cause or purpose. But there was so much pride in his look, permanently unconcerned with what happened on earth and seeming to lose itself elsewhere, beyond the distance of a dreamy world, that it could dispel any shadow of mistrust or doubt. Nevertheless, it had not escaped my notice that sometimes when he meant to add something, he suddenly changed his mind and stifled the words upon his very lips. At such times, did he actually blush under the paint on his face? Did his eyes actually cloud, as it appeared to me in a very short moment of disclosure, of some concealed confusion? I could not swear to it, but what I do know is that when he told a tale, his look deepened and riveted itself upon the rings which were never absent from his fingers. He stared at them long and tenderly, as if those gems had shrouded the mystery of his life, reflecting in their clear and blue ice, all his thoughts and recollections.

After some time, without our friendly relations becoming any closer, we saw more of each other, sometimes in the morning, most usually in the afternoon, yet never in the evening; never. Because of the heat, we had abandoned the Dutch tavern and used to meet at Grünewald, on the terrace of a coffeehouse on the outskirts of a pinetree grove—a terrace idyllically overrun by roses of all kinds and faces, the former of which in the breath of wind shed their petals in our glasses. He always arrived punctually. Once however, I waited for him in vain, up to dinnertime. Returning home, I found a letter in which he briefly apologized for having been unable to come. It was signed Sir Aubrey de Vere. I had a close look at the proud handwriting in large letter as well as at the blue wax seal: a sphinx lying down in the middle of the ribbon of a garter, like that encompassing the shield in the coat of arms of Great Britain. On the ribbon I could read the word "Remember" in English.

Heraldry being my hobby, I was not content with so little; I expected to see a genuine coat of arms, not a mere emblem. After that letter, Sir Aubrey never appeared again. No wonder then: a terrible, sultry dampness made the city seethe, like a huge hotbed of evil and wickedness. The only time one could go about was in the evening, but Sir Aubrey would never put in an appearance at such hours. The nights, however, were so beautiful that I could hardly find it in me to return home. While I rambled in this way, until all hours, once, towards midnight, I had a strange meeting in a lonely walk of the Tiergarten.

I passed by a tall woman with abundant red hair covered by a large hat with feathers, a lean, bony woman without the curves of hips or breasts, in a tight-fitting dress of black butterflies. She stalked rigidly like a corpse, seemingly pushed or drawn by an external force, alien to her own will, towards some mysterious goal in the dead of night. I don't know why I would not believe she was a woman like any other; no, from the very beginning I was reluctant to believe it—even before her large fixed eyes, which gave the impression of being turned inward, as well as the features of her heavily painted face seemed to remind me of. . . . But, was there any more room for doubt? How could I confine myself to a mere supposition when her hand with long fingers displayed seven grinning sapphires from Ceylon? I was left dumbfounded, the prey of a dim feeling in which was mixed amazement, disgust, as well as fear. Then, with my nostrils filled with the well-known fragrance, the fragrance of red carnations, I set out to follow her. Too late, however! I had lost trace of her. At the end of the walk, there were a few cabs; most probably she had climbed into one of them and had disappeared.

In view of my long stay in Berlin, it would have been childish to allow myself to be weighed down by amazement. I had seen so much! On the other hand, I felt goaded by a base curiosity, which made me lie in wait about the same place for several nights running. But there was nothing. In the meantime, the heat was growing fiercer; on the day preceding the night which I am about to describe, people had died in the street like so many flies.

It was a night of velvet and lead in which the soft breath of a scorching wind was vainly trying to dissipate the mist which had fallen thick upon the air. Short flashes of lightning flared upon the horizon; the wood and the sullen gardens kept silent as if benumbed by some ill-natured witchcraft; all about was the scent of mystery, of sin, of wild abandon. I experienced some difficulty in advancing through the darkness which padded the lonely alleys. Sometimes I was actually forced to stop, overcome by weakness. At the crossroads where Roland's Fountain is situated in Berlin, in the too crude light which, following the gloom out of which I had emerged, had pricked my eyes into blindness, I suddenly found myself face to face with Sir Aubrey, which, upon eyeing him more closely, gave me very little pleasure.

Not because this time he had actually overstepped any limit. Anyhow, that was no way to go about. The powder with which he had coated his cheeks was blue; his lips and nostrils he had painted violet; he had gilded his hair, sprinkling gold dust upon it; while his eyes he had circled with wide purplish-black rings which made him look like a chanteuse or ballerina. Otherwise, he was dressed impeccably, in a blue tailcoat, under the light evening cloak, with an orchid in his buttonhole, and, of course, the bracelet upon his wrist and the rings upon his fingers. But there was something changed in him. He was restless, agitated, to the same extent to which I was enervated and exhausted. Much against his habit, he spoke hurriedly and tremulously, begging me to remain with him—he, of all people, he, a member of that caste which, unwillingly, in spite of its extreme courtesy, usually makes it rather clear, that it is a substantial sacrifice for it to suffer anybody's company. Moreover, he had even taken me by the arm and had made me turn back. I felt him tremble in all his limbs, shaken by the ague, and saw his eyes now staring blankly, as glassy as those of the red-haired woman, now swimming in tears, languid, and lost. Very much as on that previous occasion I had been unwilling to believe that the apparition which had passed me in the park was a woman, this time it seemed to me that the human being who dragged me along in the darkness was not a man. We walked silently along the edge of the forest, I gloomily trying to hide as much as possible of my boredom, he smiling, gazing vacantly at his blue gems. It was to those mysterious souvenirs which he seemed to grant, passionately and yearningly, his last thought. We walked in silence until we reached the bridge over the canal, where the Electors' Road starts. He stopped, letting go my arm.

I now faced an entirely different human being, wholly unlike the man of a moment ago. Did those gems of his possess some hidden virtues? He had gradually recovered his usual self-possession; he had straightened his figure, his nose was pointing ahead, he was now erect, rigid and coldly proud, extremely proud. The features of his long face had sharpened; from the tender blue of flowers, the color of his eyes had changed to the harsh bluish glint of steel, while the smile playing upon his pursed lips had turned cruel. Pale as the moon, golden-haired, Sir Aubrey no longer had any natural trace in his appearance at that moment, looking rather like a seraph or archangel than like a human being. He remained speechless for a short time, peering into the darkness which he suddenly lashed with his white gloves as if trying to drive away a phantom.

"It's a strange night," he said gravely. "Such nights are more to be feared than drunkenness; the hot wind scatters evil fevers about. Stendhal writes that in Rome, when a certain wind blows in Transtevere, people are killed. . . ." And then he continued: "Most probably you too are enervated by the sultriness. Please do me the favor of having some refreshment: a trout or two and a bottle of rhenish, as a cordial. But before that please excuse me for a short while. . . ." And taking out his watch, a platinum flower dipped into a minute dew of blue gems, he resumed: "You will wait for me, won't you? I shall tarry a little, perhaps more than a quarter of an hour, but anyhow less than a half hour. Please take a short walk in the meantime; we shall meet again here on the bridge; the first to come will wait for the other."

He offered me his hand which was cold as ice, lifted his hand, and turned his back upon me. I took him at his word, retracing my steps towards the wood; close by there are the most beautiful trees one can imagine: giant, age-old trees, Druids so tall and leafy that to see them is to be in another world. I returned to the bridge after fifteen minutes. I did not find my companion. Because expectation, like any other evil, seems harder to bear in the beginning, I took a few steps down the embankment, without going too far away from our meeting place.

The embankment was desolate, the houses blind. All windows were black, yet some being open, one could vaguely catch sight within, of those sullen gleams of quicksilver which make the mirrors grin in the dark. Only one window upstairs was glowing in a cobweb of faint rays, the window of a room loaded with gilded ornaments, where a lamp held watch, placed on the edge of a cupboard. It was more a votive light than a lamp proper, hardly sifting the venom of a hazy light through a coat of green enamel, one of those lights which according to the traditions of the black art are propitious to the evil spirits roaming in the dead of night.

I stopped, and my eyes were glued for a long time upon that window. Oh, for the charm of lighted windows in an ocean of darkness, who would dare to sing about it after Barbey d'Aurevilly? Yet, in his immortal tale there is a crimson curtain; in other tales, written later and so soon forgotten, there are windows of I-don't-know-what color; in my window there was neither curtain, nor a glass pane, yet in that greenish mist, apart from the gilded ornaments and the mirrors which also seemed shrouded, there was nothing to be seen.

If there actually was any connection between that window—which as soon as I close my eyes, I immediately remember exactly as it was—and the happenings of that night, it is more than I know, yet I have a vague feeling that there was. I returned to the bridge with as little luck as the first time: my friend was nowhere in sight. Preparing for a longer wait, I leaned against the iron railing of the bridge, close to the bank. I bared my head which had started to ache and immersed impellent in the grandeur of the night.

I shall never forget it. It is true that I have not been fated to see as many as two such nights, though I am the one who prizes night more than anyone else, and who have always loved night more than one can ever love day, with relish and affection. My wild soul which by day seems to doze, shriveled up in a dim dissatisfaction, never starts living fully before the last flames of the sunset die out. As the veil of the evening closes in, I am reborn; I feel much more that I am myself, that I am mine. Had my material means permitted me to change things, I would have arranged never to set eyes on the light of day. Oh, if it had not been nighttime, I would not have waited for Sir Aubrey, not for the life of me! Frankly speaking, I was not very keen on meeting him again. I remained there because I would in no case have returned home; I would have lingered for as long a time, roving about those places where in the shade the rustle of the tall trees makes loneliness appear boundless.

Yet I could not forgive Sir Aubrey for having left me to wait, to wait for him while he was indulging in God knows what voluptuousness in the thrill of that hot night, maybe even bathed in that vague greenish light, in the arms of some woman whose beauty matched his own. I had another doubt: perhaps he had gone to prepare for some later meeting of an occult group of priests and had forgotten about the world of living beings. Anyhow, I had no reason to lose patience. I therefore resumed the thread of my thoughts, leaning upon the railings, the elbows upon the iron, the temples buried in my hands. Below me flowed the oily scales of that lazy water, over which a transparent deadly mist was gathering. The canal was sinister. What a difference! In the daytime, that district offered the mildest sight: the branches of the trees lining the banks, united fraternally towards the top, vaulted above the canal which mirrored their light and restless foliage of a fresh and tender greenness. Such is the road taken by the bodies of the drowned. In 1905, I remember, one gilded April morning, the waters bore an immaculate bride. As a matter of fact in Berlin one can hear a gay song: "A corpse floats on Landwehrkanal."

Chilling my forehead, a fresh breeze awakened me from my drowsiness. I did not realize how long I had remained glued to that place, without anybody disturbing me. I had most probably had a short nap—I do not remember having heard the Gedaechtniss clock strike the hours although it must have done so several times. When, in a sort of daze, I lifted my head from my hands and rubbed my eyes, the houses were looming dimly against the background of the sky now turning ashen. The wind was blowing harder, and colder at that, while the trees had started moaning. I covered my head, having found my hat at my feet—it had fallen without my knowledge—and then I took a few steps down the embankment to see that mysterious light again. It had been put out. I finally decided to bend my steps homewards, as heavy drops of rain had started falling and day was breaking.

Being a genuine nightbird I hate the dawn. Paying no attention to the fact that it would have been very bad for me to catch cold, instead of seeking some shelter, I hurried along the vacant streets, driven away by the dull light sifted from the scowling air, interwoven with the drops of water, occasionally lashed at furiously by the north wind. When I reached home, wet to the bone, I was seized with a terrible ache, which neverthless failed to prevent me from sleeping dreamlessly until noon.

The rains had set in, the rains which did not ease for a whole week, except for the short respites they granted themselves, only to start again with renewed strength. Whatever I was doing, my thoughts kept straying to the events of the recent nights. Whenever the postman came, I jumped to see whether I had any letter. Of course I was waiting for a note from Sir Aubrey—he was in duty bound to write—and I could find no explanation of the fact that the envelopes of my mail carried neither the proud handwriting nor the seal with the sphinx.

On the eve of a holiday, the bad weather eventually granted us a truce. Being still wary, I went for a walk only late in the day. The horizon was growing lighter, though in a way which looked like more rain. So blue was that mellow and soft evening, so fluid and deep was its blue that the city seemed sunk in the mysterious abyss of a sea. The streets swarmed with people: the happiness of being alive to enjoy the boon of life was written on every face, was reflected in every look, keen, almost inviting, lending particular brilliance to the beauty of women. My imagination carried me to the past. I was recalling the sight of what the great citadels of the ancients—Babylon, Palmyra, Alexandria, Byzantium—must have looked like on such evenings. Thus blending reality and dreams, I leisurely followed the stream of the crowd up to the bridge over the canal where, once upon a night, I had waited for hours to meet Sir Aubrey.

The beauty of the place was complete, perfected by the peerless whiteness of a few swans which seemed to float on purpose upon the water at that blue hour. I did not cross the bridge; I returned to a neighboring pub. While waiting for dinner to be served, a glance at a newspaper lying hard by put me abreast of the news which had been the rage of the city for two days.

At Charlottenburg, where the Spree recovers the water it lends to the canal, causing an eddy to swirl, a corpse had been recovered, bound tightly and wrapped in a cloak; it seemed to be that of a blond slender youth richly attired in an evening suit, well groomed and gloved, but barefooted.

The youth had been killed a short time before. His dead body showed a deep wound on the left side of his breast. The thrust had been so strong that the weapon, a thin double-edged blade, had broken, part of it remaining in the wound.

Searching had produced a small treasure in paper money as well as gold, to say nothing of the value of the jewels he had worn with reckless lavishness—all of them studded with Ceylon sapphires, only with Ceylon sapphires. On the other hand, no identification had been found that would disclose anything about the victim. There was nothing, nothing. The tab with the name of the tailor had been torn from his clothes, the watch had been deprived of the badge with the goldsmith's signature. There was no chance to identify the drowned man by his face, for it had been burned with some acid which had eaten deep into his skin as well as into his flesh, up to the bone.

It fell to the lot of Sir Aubrey de Vere to die like that. He could have found another end, or a later one at least after my departure, for of the two of us, I really don't know which was the more piteous in the beginning. . . . Is there any need for me to say all I underwent, all I experienced after I realized who the victim was? And yet that was nothing as compared to what I could have undergone. Remember?—why, I could not help it. A funk is said to be blue; I saw it in all colors of the rainbow. I went through hell from one end to the other, climbing down its bottomless chasms, climbing up the steepest crests, the horrible summits lost among the clouds of madness, and it is a matter of great wonder that I did not go mad altogether.

I had been the only person in whose company Sir Aubrey had been seen about the city in the daylight. At the Dutch tavern, at the Grünewald terrace, we must have been considered bosom friends. Nobody would have been willing to believe that, about the young man to whom I seemed so closely bound, I, poor man, knew least, perhaps less than nothing. Wouldn't that very thing provide more ground for the suspicion that I was privy to the killing of that unknown man? All around me I felt the diabolical police silently closing in upon me. I almost felt them seize me, victimize me. . . . I imagined myself lost forever, a new Lesurques, serving a sentence due in fact to I don't know whom. . . . I had gone so far as to think myself guilty. Wasn't I in fact guilty enough for merely having struck up a friendship with such a man as Sir Aubrey? It is then that I clearly realized the difficult position of a foreigner among foreigners. My first thought therefore was to leave Berlin at once, to fly to my homeland. I could not sleep all that night. This time I was oppressed by darkness, and I looked forward to the dawn as though to liberation. With the light, quiet and hope were reviving within me. I gave up the thought of leaving and unpacked my things; then in the evening I again packed them, again promising myself to leave in the morning without fail and it was the same for several days running, black days, too. When I remember them, I still shudder at the short echo of the remote though terrible fright at that time, when the meanest trifle caused my heart to flutter like a wounded bird.

Yet, like any other human feeling, except hatred, fear too abates and dies out in the long run. I think I should note at this moment that my profound agitation could not be noted from the outside; I had not changed my daily life in the least, and I felt no need to confess to anybody the fire which consumed my insides; nor did I think it fit to go tell the authorities what I knew, or rather what I did not know, about Sir Aubrey. Later on I went to the Dutch tavern and nobody asked me about my sometime companion, nobody asked me anything at the terrace in Grünewald. The same silence prevailed everywhere. I read all the newspapers and I was almost angry: there was not even a line recalling the terrible discovery in the river. Most probably the inquest had revealed nothing. The sphinx preserved its mystery untouched.

To my mind, the disappearance of Sir Aubrey, considered in itself, did not otherwise exceed the importance of any "common occurrence" mentioned in the news in brief. Was there any sense in bewailing a Marcellus in that unknown stranger? Merely because he was young and beautiful? Maybe in fact he had not been as young as he looked; there are people who beguile age, and as for beauty a certain explanation is not entirely superfluous. What I had found beautiful was not so much Sir Aubrey's appearance as his resemblance to some of those people who had been swallowed up by the sweeping squall of time. I had found him beautiful because I saw in him an icon of the past living again; I saw the dear past itself revived, the past which had set forever. That is why I resisted the temptation to join the other people who went to the morgue to see, under glass, the body of Aubrey de Vere; as the aspect which death imprints upon a man often wipes away that of the living man, it would have been a pity for that face to be spoiled in my remembrance. I wanted him to remain as I had known him, resembling so much those fine lords who had revelled so riotously at Whitehall with Killigrew and Rochester, with Barbara Villiers and Nell Gwyn and whom knight Lely depicted as smiling and proud, creatures wallowing in velvet clothes, in silks foaming with lace frills, florid with ribbons holding roses in their hands or fondling expensive dogs. Yet, more than his outward looks, from Aubrey de Vere I preserved, indelibly graven in my mind, certain interior movements which unexpectedly sparkled in his speech, some reflections which I have not heard from other people or read in any books. In his faraway travels, this odd being had managed to catch deep whispers from the thrill of groves to the ominous storms at sea, to penetrate inscrutable horizons which he treasured, reflected in his eyes as clear as the Ceylon sapphires, mysteries which are only revealed to the elect, which are vainly investigated, at great pains by those who lack the vocation, who wear and waste away their whole life, eyesight, and mind hanging upon the arid letters of books. And all—youth, beauty, wisdom—had been destined to end in the filthy water of a canal. . . .

At last the day of my departure came. Autumn had set in, but not the ruddy autumn of the south, the Bacchante girdled in a leopard skin, carrying clusters of grapes and other fruits in her auburn hair, but the pale, colorless autumn of the countries with rye and beer, with a dull sky, with a very low sun, creeping wanly on the horizon.

Of late I had again kept indoors. I read madly; I read because there was no more music in the house, while outside I had nothing to look at though I kept the window open until late. The waters of the fountain no longer played in the sunbeams; on the balcony of the house opposite ours, the roses had shed their petals and in the finest corner the axe had felled those old trees which had seemed to be painted by Ruysdael.

* * *

Seven years have elapsed since then. It seems as though it were yesterday or never. It seems it was yesterday because I have a good memory; it seems it was never because I lack the piety of remembrance. It has often happened to me to think of the murky tragedy, whose witness, unseen as well as blind, I may have been on that night of thrills and fevers. What it had actually been, what had actually happened, I never wondered. I was not anxious to know. On the contrary, the proof was offered the other day when, though enjoying an opportunity to learn, I did not want to.

In the bad weather, I had tarried until late in a Bucharest night-club and had come across an old schoolmate of mine; I had a remote memory of having seen him in Berlin, too; most probably he had attended some University courses. Being extremely talkative, and very humorous in a way, he dinned lots of things into my ears—countless trifles, sensational reports from the scandal-mongering papers, stories about the daughters and maidservants of various landladies—all sorts of edifying things in the manner of Hasdeu's *Little One.** What a difference between the way I had seen Berlin and the way it had been seen by the man now facing me, so smug in his cheap shamelessness! But why did that night conjure up, more vividly than ever, the memory of Sir Aubrey? Why did the vision of the nights spent in Berlin, with strange encounters, arise so strongly in my mind? Was it because of the bitter fumes of the brandy supplied by the same old and famous Dutch distillery? No, it was something else. More intoxicating than any drink was my awareness of the insistent, pervading fragrance of carnation emanating from a smart lady at the next table, the fragrance formerly given off by the young man with blue gems, the fragrance which once, towards midnight, had been left behind by the red-haired woman in a lonely walk of the Tiergarten. And upon my mind flashed that woman, that youth, the window with the dim greenish light, everything virtually as if spell-

* A story considered rather bold at the time, by the Rumanian encyclopedist, Bogdan Hasdeu (1836-1907).

bound. I no longer resisted a goading hitherto not experienced—that of telling somebody the story of Sir Aubrey de Vere.

I was listened to carefully. I only noticed how a faint smile occasionally overspread the lips of my acquaintance. When I concluded the story with the way the corpse had been recovered from the river, he asked me whether that was all. I said yes.

"Then let me tell you the sequel," he resumed, "it was quite a sensation. It's true it was soon hushed up, yet the truth could not be prevented from leaking out. You will learn terrible things. Just listen. . . ."

I cut him short:

"I want to learn nothing."

And as he was staring at me in wonder, unable to understand anything, I repeated my last word emphatically several times.

"It will seem strange to you," I continued, "but in my opinion, the beauty of a story lies only in its secret part; if you reveal it, I find it loses all its charm. Circumstances helped me to meet in actual life a fragment of a novel which should fulfill my desire for an endless mystery. Why then should I allow you to spoil it?"

Speaking like that I was not actually lying to him, but, behind this careless rejection for literary reasons, something loftier was hiding, a more noble way of thinking which alone made me decide to shut my friend's mouth; if I had told him about it, I doubt that he would have been able to understand me. In order not to spoil the serene icon of the external being treasured in my mind, I had avoided going to see the maimed face of the poor youth. I now refused to learn anything about him, lest it should be something which could defile his spiritual remembrance. Let that remembrance remain beautiful too, without a spot in its raiment of mystery and pride. Let Sir Aubrey de Vere remain entirely as I had enjoyed seeing him, just like that—what do I care for his actual appearance? I destroyed the only existing proof of my having known him. I burnt the letter in whose seal smiled the sphinx encompassed by the word "Remember." Remember? Why, of course, how could I forget?

Yet as the years obscure some of the older memories, making them float in a stream at the boundary between reality and fiction, if fate endows me with a long life, in the long run it will perhaps seem to me that all that occurred was just a dream or a story I read or heard somewhere, sometime, in the remote past.

Cezar Petrescu

(1892-1961)

Cezar Petrescu, a prolific prose writer, made a valuable contribution to the development of the contemporary Rumanian novel. He made his debut as a publicist and short-story writer. His printed works include about fifty volumes in addition to the large number of articles, chronicles, and notes, published in various newspapers and reviews of his time. His writing bears the stamp of his profession: Cezar Petrescu is pre-eminently a journalist whose style is characterized by a direct approach to reality, topicality of themes, wealth of incidents, and vivid versatility.

Petrescu published several volumes of short stories (*The Letter of a Yeoman, The Poplar Alley, The Dream-Man,* and others) and numerous novels (*Gathering Clouds, The Fantastic Symphony, Victory Road, King Dromichete's Treasure, Gone into the Unknown, Greta Garbo, Apostol, The Sobolia Shelter, John Poorman's War, The Tapir, Men of Yesterday, Men of Today*). He also wrote children's books (*Fram, the Polar Bear*). His work is a broad picture of Rumanian society of the first half of the 20th century. He was preparing to write a cycle of seven novels to evoke and analyze Rumanian society in the 19th century, in the form of a saga of the Vardar family, when his ambitious plans were cut short by his death. His literary models were Tolstoi, Balzac, and Zola, and in Rumanian literature, Mihail Sadoveanu.

My Friend Jan

Instead of a reply, my friend gave me a surprised and sympathetic look.

"What a simpleton!" he was about to say.

But as he was gobbling his food hurriedly he refrained, making instead an eloquent gesture of his hand armed with the knife. Then he thrust his fork into the chicken breast and ripped open the tender white flesh hostilely as he would the breast of a defeated opponent.

Around us the station refreshment room was booming. The waiters were hurrying among the tables; the din of the voices was cut by the shrill whistling of the engines; outside the blizzard was whirling enormous snow drifts at the white windows. A snow plow was hardly able to move along the line; in front of the platform it shut out the light of the windows, like some apocalyptic monster.

So I had long to wait, an hour, maybe two. I was terrified at the thought of the time that would pass so slowly, measured every five minutes by a desperate look at the dial of the watch, on which the hands seem to have stood still forever. But what a feverish din there was at all the neighboring tables. It was like the uproar at a fair or the bidding at an auction sale. The only thing missing was the accompaniment of drums. The railway line to Bucharest had been cleared; an express train was waiting, ready to start—we could hear the breath of the engine coming from its metal valves, and everywhere, at the tables, on the benches, in the corners, in front of the showcase filled with appetizers and mulled plum brandy, the last-minute advice could be heard:

"Hurry to the ministry before nine!

"Call on Horovitz; it falls due on Monday!

"Sixty-five thousand, not a penny less!

"Don't forget Mr. Tache's letter!

"Eight wagons . . .

"Make a note: circular no. 435/16 of September 7.

"Look him up at home or at Mrs. Vidopol's. . . ."

The voices crossed each other, grew louder and more hurried; they uttered figures and the names of VIP's in a lower tone, in whispers, to rise again aggressively, turning the bustle of the restaurant into an ever more heated noise, like that of a stock-exchange, a fair, an auction sale.

In a corner a woman wearing a shabby black coat was chewing, much against her liking, a horn-shaped roll with a dry interior.

My friend pushed away the plate he had emptied, drained off his glass of wine, and, choosing a cigarette bearing a gilt inscription from a flat silver cigarette case, turned again to me, now willing to answer: "The oaths we took in the trenches? Who on earth still remembers them today? What's the good of digging up ghosts?"

I looked him straight in the face, fully convinced that he would blush, that all the blood would rush to his face.

The last time we had met was five years ago, in uniforms caked with dry mud, our faces unshaven, our eyes glassy, on a rainy autumn afternoon in a mud hut on the bank of the Siret. A revolutionary wind was sweeping over us. We swore we would turn the world upside down, avenge the dead. From the acrid smoke of tobacco, black and moldy, we would imagine then, in the mud hovel, a purified world which we meant to set up as soon as we cast off our military uniforms. And among all of us, wretched reserve officers collected from all parts of the country, dull men harried by petty worries, all of us "heroes" against our will and quite unpremeditatedly, he was the fiercest, because he had also been the bravest.

That is why I expected he would blush under my gaze; I waited to stir up the remorse of the renegade, of those who disavow and capitulate.

My friend, however, chewed the gilt cardboard end of his cigarette, defying my gaze. I was the first to drop my eyes.

It was only after this victory that he asked me in a voice full of sarcastic reproof: "I hear you've taken up literature now. How much better it would suit you to look after a vineyard. Your vineyard is running wild, Sandu was telling me the other day!"

I felt I was blushing. And I couldn't remember the sharp retort I had prepared for him.

My companion took hold of my hand over the white tablecloth and pressed it gently, his voice suddenly tamer: "What poor devils we are. . . . We're to be pitied. D'you think we're any better or any worse than the others?"

I withdrew my hand from his flabby grip. What did that cheap melodramatic tone mean? He was a fellow in a hurry to rise in the world, that's all! Five years ago his eyes were consumed with an inner fire. Between the barbed wire of the trenches and the posts upset by the cannon balls he had appeared to me transfigured, and I feared he might do something rash. Had we not promised one another that we'd bring our grenades home with us? We did not know very well what we would do with them. We were not prepared to do anything; we had no plan, no solution ready. But many of us did return like that, to throw them away into some backwater, just as we had given up our great resolutions. My friend Jan had been the fiercest of them all.

And now there he sat in front of me, with ruddy cheeks, in a suit cut according to the latest fashion, his costly fur coat thrown over the back of a chair with the supreme negligence of a Croesus. From the very first quarter of an hour he had spoken to me only of "consolidated" shares, "premiums," "payments" and of "locked up bonds"—mysterious, puzzling terms which meant nothing to me except that he was stepping briskly along a road quite different from the former one. Why then this hypocrisy designed to arouse, like a beggar, a sympathy he did not deserve?

But my friend Jan went on with the thread of his story, undisturbed:

"I hesitated only once! Because of Private Ion Ion. . . . We had been home two years. Peace! Victory! Great Rumania! I can remember the day: the last day when I doubted myself and regretted having forgotten the sacred oaths we had taken in the trenches. Ha! Ha! The sacred oaths forgotten and our forgotten duties which you too have started writing about latterly! Everything has proved *I* was right, not you! Now I wouldn't blush even in front of Ion Ion. . . ."

He sat staring vacantly, perceiving in the void and in his memory something I did not know yet. Then with a bitter smile and a contraction of his lips, which I had never seen on his face before, he went on.

"He turned up one morning. I was in a hurry, and the phone had already rung three times impatiently. Just as I was going to put on my overcoat the maid reminded me, 'A man's been waiting for you for an hour. A peasant!'

"I told her to show him in. He looked rather like an apparition than a man. He was very thin, his eyes were sunken, and the skin on his face taut on his cheekbones, his nose pinched—a ghost. Still he clicked his heels with soldier-like energy.

" 'Your servant, sir! I see you no longer remember me.'

"He was right. I still could not remember him. But judging by his 'Your servant, sir' it immediately dawned on me he was some man of my former company. And, not wishing to dishearten him I hurried to answer with a lie: 'Why, I remember you quite well, my lad. The truth is, you've changed a bit. . . .'

"And I tried hard to imagine him dressed as a soldier. But the fellow shook his head; he seemed mistrustful and distressed. He had guessed I was lying.

" 'I see you've forgotten me, sir! I'm Ion Ion, orderly to poor Lieutenant Octav, may God rest his soul.'

"How could I help remembering now I had heard these words? Ion Ion had looked after us in the mud hut for a whole winter; he had become famous in the sector for the tea he made, the wine he mulled with pepper corns and cloves on bitterly cold nights, and for his dog-like devotion and fidelity to poor Octav. And all of a sudden what memories he brought back to my mind! The morning of the attack, the shell that smashed Octav's body to smithereens, scattering the pieces of flesh on the earth, the hot fragments of brain on my face, and the two fingers, white and drained of blood which I found later on in my greatcoat, when I recovered my senses! Everything had been so well buried away, so thoroughly forgotten, sealed up, since life had resumed its old course in the country's capital, since we had again bars, cafés, bands, splendid carriages and horses, motor cars and shop windows full of all kinds of early and expensive fruit and vegetables. Private Ion Ion was carrying me back three years. And the streets, the bars, the crammed shop windows, all the comfort around me in my own house, vanished all of a sudden.

"The memory of that hour alone was still alive. A wave of dark anxiety took possession of my soul.

"I made Private Ion Ion sit down on the edge of a chair and tell me about the troubles that had driven him to come and see me. Now I remembered well that that day we had thought he was killed and in the evening we put his name down on the list of the missing.

"But Private Ion Ion was not dead. It was only now that I learned what had happened. He had been hit and had fallen down near Octav. In the evening, when we had withdrawn into our trenches after unsuccessful counterattacks, he had come to, his eyes blurred. He felt the joints of his limbs. He was all right, he could move, none of his bones was broken, he had no deep wound through which his blood and his life might have oozed out. . . . All that had happened became quite clear to him now. The firing had ceased. The trenches, their barbed wire torn away, were not very far, and with a little luck he might be able to creep along in the night. First he thought of gathering the pieces of Octav's body, putting them in his greatcoat and bringing them to our trenches to be buried according to time-honored traditions. It was snowing; big flakes were falling slowly. He pressed his forehead against the cold snow to cool himself and pick up strength. He collected the letters found in the lieutenant's pocket, all the small trivial things which death suddenly makes so precious. He crept along on his elbows, from one fragment to another. . . . After that he could not remember anything. A bullet hit him. Maybe it was one from our trenches, maybe from the enemy. He awoke stupefied, much later, in a German ambulance. The first moment he felt glad: it was warm, the bed was soft, a light hand was carefully dressing his wound. The physician spoke to him in a friendly voice, in an unknown language. He did not understand him, but he could see, behind the thick-rimmed glasses, a gentle, kindly look, and all this filled him with wonder. He had expected less compassion. Had the war not accustomed him only to men insanely savage and cruel, to men lost to all sense of humanity? But the doctor and the hospital were but a rare and happy exception.

"The horror began again, for after the hospital came the camp. Days of fierce gnashing of teeth and slavery began. First they had to dig trenches, then mines, then to build new railways at the rear. For three years he was carried in cattle trucks from one line of trenches to another, from one end to the other of the enemy country. He suffered hunger, he was beaten with the rifle butt, he lived on scraps of refuse, lay on the frozen earth, his teeth chattering with the cold. His eyes sank in; his legs could hardly carry him. Exactly a week, at last, after the negotiations and arrangements of the peace treaty, after being examined by sundry control committees and commissions, a train had brought him home, together with other companions, now only skin and bone, after all their suffering and want. He had hurried home to see his wife, his children, and his cattle. And now he had come to bring me the lieutenant's wallet and letters which he had carried day after day, night after night, at his breast like so many invaluable talismans. He was not very clever; he could hardly read or write, and could not imagine where he could find the lieutenant's lady to deliver to her the things with his own hands. So he wanted me to do it for him.

"Private Ion Ion handed me the 'wallet' and the papers.

"It was a miserable brown pocketbook; its corners had become round with so many mishaps—a wretched talisman of leather discolored by sweat, its inner partitions in pieces, its monogram broken.

" 'I've got the other piece, too!' Private Ion Ion added, producing from a carefully folded handkerchief the other half of the broken silver initials.

"Private Ion Ion considered he had fulfilled his mission. He rose to leave. He stumbled over the carpets. He did not dare to hold out his hand to me.

"Left alone, I realized how futile all the hustle of my morning was. I disconnected the telephone, lest some call should tempt me. I needed to examine my heart.

"How soon had I forgotten poor Octav! And still, at the time, for months on end, the sight had appeared to me cruel and unforgettable. . . . I thought it would accompany me at every step, all my life.

"The night before he was killed, mangled by a shell, we had played cards in the hut, had sung and made merry with silly jokes. Then, with chins resting on the palm of our hands and with elbows on the table, we sat up late, making splendid and absurd plans for our country of tomorrow, the country we would build on returning home. How clearly I remembered now that table made of a door brought by Private Ion Ion, and supported by four stakes stuck in the beaten earthen floor of the hut. Of course none of us suspected what was in store for us the next day. War.

"For a fortnight the firing had ceased in our sector. We were even expecting to be sent to the rear for a rest and recovery. We were making plans. When we finished gambling, when the others had gone off to their dens, we sat and talked for a long time. Private Ion Ion had brought us some boiling hot tea. Tea made of carrots and tree leaves, wartime tea. Poor Octav again talked to me anxiously of his wife Lia, left in Bucharest, beyond the front line, from where he had had no news. He missed her so much. In their one year of married life they had never had any trouble. He knew she had no money now, maybe she had to suffer privations, maybe she was compelled to put up with the impudence and the swaggering airs of some *feldwebel,* according to the old law of wars, in all times. From the same pocketbook that Ion Ion had just brought me, he produced her photo, laid it on his knees, and looked at it for a long while, his chin firmly gripped in his fists, his eyes blurred by tears. . . . And the next day, the same fingers that had laid under my eyes the pale photo, the eyes moist with emotion, the brain in which so many thoughts, hopes, and wants had struggled—everything had been, all of a sudden, savagely torn to pieces, thrown down in the ground, mixed with the dust, changed into a ghastly heap of blood, cartilage and nerve, still according to the old law of wars in all times, beginning with Homer's *Iliad.* How could I forget? How could I go on laughing, talking, joking? How could I listen to bands playing? How could I let my eyes look greedily at a woman? How could I go on making plans, untroubled, as though nothing had happened, as though all my life I had never budged from my comfortable flat except to engage in the mean tricks and dodges of a lawyer's trade which brought me in the money to keep me in luxury for the two months' holiday I spent in summer, at the seaside or in the mountains.

"So, Private Ion Ion had been a man indeed, but I had not.

"For three long years, amid terrible sufferings, *he had not forgotten.* In his rags, he had carried in his bosom, like an extraordinarily valuable treasure, the last possessions of a man who had been my closest friend. No sooner had he come home, then he got on the train, maybe traveling on the top of a carriage, or had perhaps denied himself food to bring me those souvenirs he prized so highly. . . . So I was a beast, wasn't I? I remembered that in the early days of the war when we had not entered the trenches yet, the horse of one of the company's carts had been killed by a bomb dropped by a plane. We had had to take the horse out of the shafts in order to repair the broken wheels. Well, the other horse, untouched, had trotted away to the edge of the ditch and was grazing quietly as though nothing had happened. He had walked around his dead companion, without even turning to look at him for a moment and was nibbling at the grass, indifferently. And then I had been shocked! All the yarns about the horse being noble proved mere cock-and-bull stories, lies, rot. In my ridiculous fury I couldn't refrain from kicking the unfeeling brute. Was I now less of a brute than the wretched creature satisfying his hunger near his dead companion? Was there really any difference?

"Then I remembered that I had collected in a drawer a lot of sad souvenirs of the war. There lay the handkerchief with which I had wiped poor Octav's blood and brain off my face.

"I felt I had to see it again. I rummaged among the letters and buttons, the fragments of shell, the photo taken in the trenches. I found it. A dirty crumpled ball of linen with blackened stains of blood, of smoke and ashes.

"I felt I would have liked to press it to my lips, to ask forgiveness from Octav's memory. I unrolled it. The bits of brain, gray and dried up, looked like hateful dirt and refuse: it was all that was left of a poor decomposed brain. And suddenly some white moths which had made their nest there flew away through my fingers. I shuddered and dropped the handkerchief. How sad it all was!

"After a long time I put on my overcoat to carry out Private Ion Ion's mission. I took Octav's letters and pocketbook with me.

"On the way I tried to think of extenuating circumstances I might set forth with all my lawyer's tactfulness to explain to the widow why I had forgotten her for such a long time. And I felt another pang of conscience. That woman had suffered. I had found her so often with tearstained eyes; and she never tired asking me to describe every hour I had spent with Octav, until the very last! Every time I had called on her at the time, their house bore the signs of mourning. No doors were banged; the servants spoke in whispers; everybody walked on tiptoe; the curtains were always drawn. Lia was still wearing mourning and every time she seemed to me paler and more remote from the vain trifles of life. *She* did not forget. And such fidelity, continuing steadfastly beyond death, had touched me. . . . But gradually and instinctively I had from cowardice avoided the house more and more. Life had conquered me again. I needed laughter, smiles, mirth, plans I could speak of aloud; I felt strong and healthy. In the house with curtains always drawn and with the eternal memory of death I felt uncomfortable. Driven by a savage selfishness for which I often reproached myself mercilessly, I had gradually become a stranger to the 'sombre vault of memories' as I called Octav's house to myself. And how was I to tell Lia now, what words was I to use? What grief would the dead man's relics that I was carrying in my pocket revive? And how was I to discover in my heart and mind the wise precepts of life that would allay her pain?

"I opened the little gate of the iron fence with the same anguish I had felt on the morning when I had brought her the news, the first time. The curtains were no longer drawn.

"The appearance of the house seemed in a way to have revived and brightened up. It made me look around with justified surprise. I was even wondering if she had not moved.

"A bright-eyed young girl opened the door for me; that old woman with a funereal air who used to open it had vanished forever. In the vestibule I could hear the sound of a piano. When I took off my coat

I cast a look around with the same surprise. There was something changed inside too: flowers, brighter colors, more light. I could hardly recognize the place. And then only, and with great difficulty, did I begin to realize what was such a simple thing: life had conquered here too. Suddenly my task seemed to me more difficult: would I not cruelly and inopportunely revive a wound that was closing?

"Octav's widow received me with unfeigned joy.

"From the very first moment I couldn't take my eyes off her. How astoundingly she had changed. Her cheeks were pink, her lips were red, her eyes shone playfully. Something new and daring had transfigured her gloomy, mournful face which I had avoided instinctively for so long a time, taking a roundabout way in the street lest I should risk meeting her. Then I realized what made her look younger. She had changed the style of her hair—her hair was brushed up, showing her bare forehead; it was like a blind lifted up to let in floods of joyful light.

"I suddenly felt awkward, awkward in a way different from the guilty awkwardness I used to feel. I started with the usual small talk. I tried to slip in the words imperceptibly, slyly, to reach the object of my visit. But Lia asked me in a very simple and offhand way, what new plays were on; she wanted to know about a new singer from La Scala of Milan whose arrival had been announced, and about the horse races that were to begin on the first Sunday, next month.

"My eyes kept searching for Octav's portrait which I used to see multiplied, wherever my eyes turned to, on the walls, on the tables and little tables, over the piano closed forever. . . . The portrait had vanished. And just as I was about to disclose abruptly what had brought me there—to have done with it—the door at the far end of the room opened and in there came, walking steadily as if he were in his own house, a fair giant with a part accurately drawn like a line going to the crown of his head, with placid blue eyes, the eyes of a handsome and empty-minded animal.

"Lia jumped to her feet cheerfully, her cheeks afire. 'My husband! You will forgive us, won't you? We were so flurried, we forgot to send you an invitation. . . . As a matter of fact, we've been abroad. We got back only a week ago.'

"I sat gazing at her foolishly, foolishly and paralyzed.

"Luckily Octav's successor felt it his duty to carry on a polite conversation. He talked to me of the exceptionally fine weather, of the depression of the currency, then again of the horse races, the latest plays, the singer who was expected to arrive. The war and those killed in the war seemed never to have existed anywhere. . . .

"He talked moderately, seeming to pronounce final sentences; he informed me that he was keen only on sports and was expecting to get a new type of car from abroad, by special order.

" 'We'll start adventures that'll mark a decisive moment in the history of motoring in our country. What we need is courage; initiative. The country's become larger! There are heaps of picturesque spots that can vie with places abroad. All the same, the war has been of some use! We'll explore every highroad, every mountain, every pass in Great Rumania! Won't we Lia?'

"And he caressed the white hand and put it to his lips and gave it a long kiss as befits a couple who are prolonging their honeymoon.

"Then, before my eyes there suddenly rose the other man, his mangled flesh, the pieces of hot brain on my cheek, the two white bloodless fingers I found in the folds of my greatcoat at the time when Great Rumania was but a dream of the trenches . . . another kind of Great Rumania, in another kind of dream.

"There was no sense in fulfilling my mission now. I rose to leave. Lia asked me to her at-homes on Thursday, from four to seven.

"In the street I stopped undecided. The packet of letters in my pocket seemed to burn me. I thought for a moment of keeping them to put them among the distressing and reproachful treasures of my relics. Then I remembered Octav's sister. I remembered his old father who had mourned for him so long and whose eyes would fill with tears every time I pronounced his son's name.

"Surely *they* had not forgotten him. They would keep those sacred relics stained with the blood of a brother, with the blood of a son, more piously then I would.

"I found Octav's sister standing at the top of the stairs, buttoning her gloves, ready to go out.

" 'What a surprise! You've neglected us lately, Jan.'

"The top of the stairs was no place to talk. We walked down the steps together.

" 'Papa is at his club, for his usual game!' she explained. 'He's managed well this year! The price of wheat is tremendous and the crop has exceeded all expectations! All the same, the war has been of some use. There's another life in this Rumania, in this Great Rumania!'

"We walked side by side. She was lovely; she had grown taller, and slimmer. The passers-by turned to look at her; she walked with steady springy steps, with the enticing gait of a feline, delightful to the eye, but disquieting at the same time.

"After a few steps she spoke to me of the horse races, of the long expected singer, of the latest plays. It seemed to be contagious. Almost the same phrases! Almost the same words! Almost the same eagerness, the same tribute of gratitude to Great Rumania. She was cheerful, and her trilling laughter bubbled forth resonantly from her white throat, while she kept looking at her little shoes the color of gold, which, I gathered, she was wearing for the first time then.

"She stopped and, smoothing the lapel of my coat with a familiar gesture, she looked into my eyes cajolingly: 'Guess?'

"I didn't know what she meant.

"'Guess what the girlie's going to tell you?'

"I shrugged my shoulders. I looked at her, from top to toe and could not help admiring her slim waist, her large eyes shining with precocious sensuality, her tiny white teeth, as white as an advertisement for a miraculous tooth paste. How the girl had changed since she used to come and sit on my knees seven years ago, in Octav's study, and get me to teach her to color the maps in her exam copybooks, the map of little Rumania then! Now, Octav's sister was pouting, shocked that I had not been able to guess.

"'The girlie's getting engaged! A splendid fiancé. You'll love him, won't you? A handsome, athletic fiancé! The very image of Rudolph Valentino!'

"I parted with her abruptly, almost hostilely.

"I felt her eyes were following me, puzzled and distressed. She could not understand. How could she? She too had forgotten. They had all forgotten. The bundle of letters weighed heavier and heavier in my pocket.

"For a time I walked in the streets, aimlessly.

"People were bustling along. The streets were flooded with sunshine. Gipsy women were selling flowers freshly come out from under the snow. Carriages were driving to the Chaussée, at full trot. The town was brimming over with noise. It was one of those first warm spring days when women, in light natty seasonable clothes, worn for the first time, seemed to possess a youthfulness and beauty as inflammatory, destructive, and threatening as a public danger.

"I found myself counting them and identifying them: one had lost a brother, another her husband or her fiancé, there in the mire where flesh and arteries mixed with the earth. Everyone of them had forgotten, everyone of them had forgotten.

"At home I locked up Octav's letters in the drawer. I did not keep my promise to Private Ion Ion. Would you have done otherwise? Say, would you? You who haven't the pluck to scold me . . . But my train's leaving. So long!"

My friend put on his costly fur-lined coat; a waiter with bent back, a napkin over his arm, accompanied him to the door, fawningly.

A middleman ran after him as far as the train, hat in hand, begging something of him. The red lips of a woman smiled at him, fascinated by the strong, graceful, lithe appearance of the man who had been my companion in the trenches. I sat on, making bread pellets on the white table cloth, big pellets of the generous white bread of Great Rumania.

Was he only a cynic? Was he a sage? What could I reply from this bitter solitude?

Ion Marin Sadoveanu

(1893-1964)

A prominent figure in the literary and artistic life of Rumania, Ion Marin Sadoveanu distinguished himself as poet, prose writer, art critic and essayist, translator and publicist.

His novel *End of the Century in Bucharest* (1944) deals with the problem of the social climber—a theme with a rich tradition in Rumanian literature—painting with powerful realism the portrait of an unscrupulous upstart, Iancu Urmatecu, who works his way into the house of Baron Barbu, an old aristocrat, besotted by a life of idleness and dissipation, robs him of his fortune, and leads him to his ultimate ruin. The subtleness and critical spirit with which the author brings out the discrepancy between the new social position of the parvenu and his elemental makeup is a permanent source of humor and satire. The novel evokes picturesque aspects of the life, morals, and customs of Bucharest at the turn of the past century.

Ion Sintu, a vast fresco of Rumanian society at the beginning of the 20th century (1900-1916) is—unlike his previous novel, which was chiefly a character study—the testimonial of an honest-minded intellectual asserting a positive philosophy of life in conflict with the social realities of his time.

In his novel *The Sea-bull* (1963) the author evokes scenes from the slaves' struggle for freedom in the ancient city of Histria.

Ion Marin Sadoveanu is also the author of admirable translations from Shakespeare, Heine, Kleist, Stendhal, Ibsen, Thomas Mann, and numerous other authors.

Excerpt from *End of the Century in Bucharest*

Urmatecu's office led into a dark room facing the courtyard. Furniture of all kind was stacked into this storeroom. There were no two pieces that matched and yet each item had a value and a beauty of its own. They had been gathered—sometimes demanded—from various country squires; most of them, however, had come from Squire Barbu: the oak writing table, with four bear-heads with polished muzzles at the corners; the chairs of rosewood with little holes in the seat, and of rosewood too the tall cabinet desk with twelve draws, for files and documents, with the brass letters of the alphabet carefully inlaid. A green velvet sofa filled one empty corner, while hanging on the wall were blue maps indicating the plots of the Baron's estate. There was one single large portrait, in India ink, of Mistress Mita's father, Squire Grigore, with his long bushy whiskers and a small black bow tie, the wings tucked under the corners of the collar. Of all the forebears of the family he was the only one dressed in European clothes and hence the only one presentable to alien eyes. In his time he had not been just anybody; during the Russian occupation he had run a school and had set up a first-class choir that was hired to sing at all the great churches in Bucharest. He squandered his money lavishly on his lady loves and when, in the end, he was left in rather straitened circumstances with a houseful of children, it was Iancu—the orphan boy who had been picked up and brought up by Squire Grigore in his days of prosperity—who had come to his rescue. Soon after, Iancu married the Squire's eldest daughter, Mistress Mita.

For three years now Squire Grigore had been in a lunatic asylum. Iancu paid the hospital charges regularly, but never dared go to see him, for it upset him too badly. Mistress Mita would have the horses harnessed to the carriage once a month and would drive alone to see her father whom she unfailingly found standing at the window, recognizing no one, tearing his shirt to pieces, and staring afar at a distant mountain, which in his folly he beheld as a mountain of solid gold. Whenever Iancu's wife returned from the asylum and told the story of the patient's distressing state, Urmatecu felt a light shiver run up his spine, and he would raise his eyes in silence to the portrait of Squire Grigore, who from his nail on the wall watched and sponsored all the deals Iancu so shrewdly carried out. He often wondered what made Squire Grigore believe the mountain to be of solid gold! He could never find a clear answer. He thought it might be in atonement for the money he had squandered all his life, money wasted instead of earned. He was all the more inclined to accept this interpretation for his own experience of life and everything around him strengthened his faith in the wisdom of austerity and thrift and the folly of a dissolute life. Hadn't Squire Barbu and the others been wasting their fortune and hadn't their estates, stripped to pieces, gradually found their way into Urmatecu's storeroom? That's what he felt today. Tomorrow things might look hazier and the shadow of a doubt might work its way into the recesses of his conscience. And the struggle would begin again together with his doubts.

One thing, however, was clear in his mind: money and wealth were a serious affliction, whether they came or went, and lest he forget this truth he would peer into the shrewd pleasure-seeking eyes of Squire Grigore. Yet no one in the house ever suspected that Squire

Grigore's portrait was the image of Iancu's own deep-rooted foibles . . .

The fresh morning breeze, wafted through the windows that had just been closed, mingled with the warm air of the room. The autumn mists were slowly scattering under the challenge of daylight, when Iancu called for his morning cup of tea—containing more rum than tea—ordering it to be brought into his office. Lefterica was there already waiting for him with his wonted trustful mien. He glided about, like a shadow through the room, and then set about seeking out and classifying papers; every now and again with apparent pain he would raise his arm in a square angle and stroke his temples, running his pale nervous fingers through the hairs of his beard, which would quiver under their touch. He was a shy, silent man who, at the slow pace of a snail, fulfilled the post of quasi-secretary to his brother-in-law. The man had tackled all kinds of jobs everywhere about but had failed in all his attempts. He could not bear a voice raised at a faintly higher pitch, so much less could he endure reprimands cried out in a fiery tone. And his slowness had often caused him to hear words of abuse poured forth in wrath. Whenever such an incident occurred, without uttering a word, he would pick up his things with his doleful, slow gestures and walk out. After all these vain attempts elsewhere, Urmatecu decided to keep him around as his help. This was no paradise for Lefterica either! From morning till night all he heard from his brother-in-law was: "come on, blockhead," or "get a move, sluggard." But Lefterica turned a deaf ear to all these words of abuse. From the outset he had made up his mind to submit with a good grace to all that came from brother Iancu and ever since all had gone well! His chief virtue was his candor: he understood nothing unless the whole chain of reasoning was clearly and openly explained to him. He was utterly incapable of understanding the more distant effect of any event. Urmatecu had soon discovered Lefterica's childlike innocence and decided that his honesty and guilelessness was an asset worth preserving. As soon as he entered the room, Iancu, without a word of greeting, went straight to the draw whence he took out a pile of papers which he started examining. Letters, documents, unsealed envelopes of all kinds passed through his fingers. He hurriedly turned page after page, in obvious search for something, when suddenly he stopped in front of a square sheet of a schoolgirl's copybook, clumsily scribbled in violet ink. He gazed at it long, smiled, and then rather shyly said:

"I say, Dunderhead, just look at this paper. What do you make of it?" And he handed the paper to Lefterica.

The latter spelled out in Rumanian: "La poire et le couteau. La cruche, le vin et l'eau . . ." then, after a moment of reflection, sputtered out rapidly:

"It's something to do with wine."

When Urmatecu saw that Lefterica was unable to make out so simple a text, he burst forth with his customary arrogance:

"Damn it all! That I do not know French and am unable to read what my daughter writes is understandable! But that you, you who are younger and have been sent to all sorts of schools, are incapable, that is the limit!"

Then, holding out the sheet of paper, he gazed at it again with tender admiration.

"This is a leaf of a copybook of Amelica's, from the first year she entered the boarding school. I had to steal it from her; she wouldn't let me keep it. Quite a number of years have passed since. You can imagine how beautifully she must write now! If she only knew that I have her handwriting as a novice, by God, she would be in a rage!"

And for a few moments his thoughts wandered astray, roused by the tremulous handwriting of his cherished child. It was for him a source of endless comfort and joy to watch his daughter's unsteady steps rising into a world he credited with beauty and virtues that were forever beyond his reach. But Amelica, he was certain, with the education he was giving her, would become a lady; a lady who would be able to enjoy all the pleasures of life in a society he had never been able to enter. Until the day his daughter set out upon this path, until he was sure that the child that was the apple of his eye would bask in light, glamor, and wealth and would stir envy and jealousy around her, Urmatecu was willing to work as a galley slave. Through the folly and ineptitude of the boyars, he was paving his own and her way to fortune with hope in his heart—at times mingled with doubt for he was conscious of his shortcomings too. His mind, however, was more at rest now. He felt he needed no longer bow with humility to all, for now there was someone who was starting life as a native to this world he coveted. This world in his mind's eye was like a vast drawing room, brightly lit up, always ready for a glamorous ball. The people in this world of his fancy were so polite to one another, so exquisitely refined that when they had to impart their impressions however displeasing, the words flowed smoothly into the ears of smiling listeners. All one needed to preserve one's position in this world was money, money well husbanded, safely invested by a man wise and resourceful as he was. That's what the boyars lacked! He would take good care of Amelica, she need not worry; she would have all she needed all her life long! Awakening suddenly from his daydream, the man carefully folded the copybook leaf, slipped it into an envelope and thrust it among the papers, and went on searching for something else.

Here it was. An old letter, written laboriously with large and flowery letters. Of the entire text, the figures were the only lines drawn with self-assurance and alacrity, showing the author's familiarity with accounts rather than with letters. Urmatecu read it hurriedly again, as though fearing someone might snatch it out of his hand:

Iancu,
Ten thousand lei is a big sum, even for a solid merchant as I am. But if you say there's no other way out, I'm willing to pay up only to get out of the whole affair unscathed. Be sure you get a paper from the dead man's family —you know best how it must be done—lest I remain in the end without the money and wind up in jail in the bargain. I'll send you the money tonight. God help me! Ivanciu. 1883, February 23.

Urmatecu sipped some tea and beckoning to Lefterica to move closer, asked him:

"What about this paper? Have you seen this one before?"

Lefterica cast a glance at the letter.

"Why, of course."

"Do you remember the circumstances?"

"I should think so."

"Would you be able to tell the whole story as it happened then?"

"Yes, certainly! But it's quite an old story. It must have happened seven or eight years ago. I'd almost forgotten about it!"

"Shut up, stupid," and Iancu slipped the letter hastily into his pocket for Ivanciu himself had just walked into the room.

The newcomer seemed not to have spent a very restful night. An old merchant, he had learned to conceal his unrest and nervousness. And yet his anxiety, stronger than his will, was printed on his face. His small gray eyes kept shooting searching glances right and left as though he feared falling into some trap laid out for him. Iancu's threat the night before and, above all, the whole story with Father Gose's children, had left him sorely tired. He knew Urmatecu was a "madcap" as many of his friends called him and he was aware too (for he'd known him for years) that Iancu was shrewder and could work out schemes that his own duller brain was unable to fathom. For this reason, he regarded Iancu with mixed feelings of admiration and fear, which he concealed. He thus walked in slowly as if he had come from the next room, leaned his cherry-wood stick with its handle of polished chamois-horn against the wall corner and sitting down leisurely on a chair, said:

"Man, you are a caution, no doubt about that," and he gave a broad smile waiting to see what would happen next.

The other, accustomed to Ivanciu's cunning overtures, cut him short:

"So you've come? Well, this is the plot of land and these are its borders," and, moving over to the plan of the boyar's estates, traced a triangle outlined in white: "the Pietrosita orchard." Then turning to Lefterica: "Sit down and write!"

There followed a moment of silence. Urmatecu, who had rushed the matter and was ready to pass on to drafting the text of the deed, expected Ivanciu to flare up and ask to have everything explained. The purchaser, however, never said a word as though everything had been settled and no new circumstances could occur. Iancu was slightly irked. He was ready to fight it out, but was not willing to open fire. He would much rather have had Ivanciu protest and he retort, twisting the man's argument or stifling his wild outbursts, or, if Ivanciu should appeal to him in despair, generously purport to help him out and extort some extra money from him. But in face of this silent man who never said a word but kept smiling at him cordially, he was at a loss how to proceed. Lefterica had dipped his pen three times into the inkpot, staring blankly at a drop of ink that was sliding down the polished steel of his nib. Urmatecu paced the room for a brief moment and then suddenly stopped:

"Well, man, I hope you see what a true friend you've got? I even told a lie to the boyar, just for your sake."

Ivanciu nodded and chuckled.

"What did you say to my story," Iancu went on, "that you had a daughter to marry off! If it comes to marriageable daughters it's me who has one! Any day now a wooer may turn up and ask for her hand!" He brushed up the hair of his temples and lit a cigarette.

Ivanciu never breathed a word.

"You must admit, you yourself didn't expect the trick to work! I saw the look on your face: you were half scared and half ready to break into laughter. . . . The truth is I know how to deal with these people; I can twist them round my little finger, any day! And besides, when I decide to lend someone a helping hand, I don't do things by halves; I go the whole hog. I'm not the man to be baffled. . . ."

His head tilted over his left shoulder, Ivanciu opened his eyes wide and stared at Iancu with a look that could mean anything: expectation, admiration, approval, or entranced amazement. Iancu was completely in the dark. He was unable to sense whether he was on the right track; he had never seen Ivanciu in so placid a mood before. He paused for another minute and then resolutely started pouring forth. He analyzed every facet of his victory over Squire Barbu, pointing out his skill and his trustworthiness and friendship for Ivanciu, as well as his taking advantage of the boyar's good faith which bordered on naïvete.

And when, finally, he considered he had said all he had had to say, and that the coveted moment had come, he paused abruptly and cried:

"And now let's draw up the deed . . . at what price?"

"The price named by the Squire!" muttered Ivanciu, at last, almost in a whisper.

The two men exchanged brief, piercing looks, as they had never done before: Iancu with the air of a master stunned at the daring of his serf; Ivanciu with that of a rebel who, after enduring more than a man can bear, had mustered in a single glance a courage that he had never before dared to show.

Ivanciu appeared as a new man in Iancu's eyes. Another thought flashed across his mind: Perhaps the deal was of greater value than he had initially surmised. If the Bulgarian was so stubborn, he must know something. He must have something up his sleeve if he was so determined to let no one share the ownership of the Pietrosita orchard. As he realized that the battle would be grimmer than he had thought, Iancu paused a moment to muster his forces. Then, opening the window before which the first snowflakes were dancing, he drew a deep breath of cold air and then flung out a question, as though the room were crowded with people and he was addressing the entire audience:

"How long does it take a man to rot, fellows?"

Ivanciu sensed a vague danger. He was as nervous as if he had felt the muzzle of a dog ready to bite him. He breathed heavily and fidgeted on his seat. Lefterica, roused from his drowsiness, was glad to hear a word that was not about these endless bargains and sales that bored him to distraction. His brother-in-law's query was all the more interesting as, of all Mistress Tinca's children, including even the girls, Lefterica was the most conversant with all funeral rites and Christian customs. So, forsaking the drawing he had been engaged upon while he had been waiting to write—it was the same clumsy drawing of a bearded man, seen in profile, rigid as a poker and with a round hen's eye—he replied in an alert tone:

"I should say seven years!"

"Yes, I think you're right, about seven!" said Urmatecu, drawing a letter out of his pocket. "Corpses may rot in seven years, but facts don't rot. All they require to flare up again (and his gaze lingered heavily upon Ivanciu) and to burn as lively as if they were brand new . . . is a spark. . . ."

Ivanciu had expected this blow and yet not quite. During the sleepless night he had spent, he had recalled in passing the story, old but true, of the man he had killed by accident. Thanks to the statements of the dead man's brothers and the favorable witnesses who had testified that it had been the dead man's fault, Iancu had got him out of this mess. Iancu had never mentioned a word about it ever since. It was a matter long forgotten and, he thought, safely buried forever. They had crossed swords in other bargains too and though Iancu had always been insistent in his search for gain, there had always been a give and take and they had finally come to terms. He had never seen Iancu as ruthless as this time. He too began to wonder if this orchard in Pietrosita could be far more valuable than he had thought if Iancu were so fierce in his bargaining. What could this plot of land contain to make Iancu covet it! Unable to unravel the mystery, he was resolved to attempt the uttermost, when all at once Iancu brought up the question of the dead man and the letter. It was a stiff blow for the old merchant. It was not only the bitterness of having been beaten—for he had a soft spot in his heart for Iancu and accepted his superiority—there was also the uneasiness of feeling the ground slipping from under his feet and that he would be at the mercy of an implacable opponent. Nevertheless, he resolved to resist as long as he could. He knew he was playing a losing game; all he now hoped for was to cut his loss. So, prompted by no clear thought or stratagem but only by obstinacy and spite at having to share his profit, he retorted:

"Why, do you think there are no other lawyers to prove that the claim is foreclosed?"

Urmatecu kept silent, letting Ivanciu rejoice for a moment in his childish illusion. Then, in a quiet, almost friendly voice, he replied:

"My dear man, in such affairs an old witness is more precious than a new lawyer! Now then Lefterica, go ahead! Just tell this man your story," and he laughed.

If the ceiling had come down on his head, Lefterica could not have been more stunned. He was aware that this was one of those moments when a man has to pay for his present or past foolishness. The whole game, and all the words exchanged, appeared crystal clear now. He sat there apparently quiet, unable to foresee what was to follow but conscious that he was caught in a vise. Sent by Iancu to attend the cutting down of a forest contracted by Ivanciu, he had been present at that misfortune. He had been the principal eyewitness. He had thereupon told Iancu everything he had seen. The latter, succeeding in coming to terms with the dead forester's brothers, had not needed to make use of Lefterica's testimony which would have served to prove Ivanciu's innocence. But he was now expected to testify falsely.

A few moments elapsed while Lefterica, dazed, struggled to perform what was expected of him. The two men waited, their eyes riveted upon him. Drops of cold sweat broke forth upon his brow which he kept mopping and wiping with his coat sleeves. A deep gasp broke from his lips and after a few jerks, without uttering a word, he collapsed with his elbows on the table. Then, as the silence roared in his ears and a void took possession of his mind, in which the last gleam of hope had died away, he raised himself and, with his eyes brimming with tears, cast a beseeching look in turn at Iancu and at Ivanciu. Unable to articulate a sound, choking with emotion, with heavy, uncontrolled gestures, he seized the white sheet upon which he was to write the contract and on which he had scribbled his drawings, and started tearing it to pieces.

When Urmatecu saw him verging on idiocy, staring, tearing up the sheet of paper, he shuddered. He unwillingly lifted his eyes from the son to the father and peered at the portrait of Squire Grigore. He felt an icy chill run through his body and, laying his hand on Lefterica's arm, he tried to quiet and soothe him, and with almost brotherly tenderness, murmured:

"Stop it, Lefterica! Don't do that."

Ivanciu felt the warm spring of kindheartedness welling up in his opponent's words. He cast a long and grateful look at Lefterica, then rising to his feet he tapped Urmatecu on his shoulder, and muttered:

"Well, Iancu?"

Urmatecu stood for some moments with his hand on his brother-in-law's arm, his eyes fixed upon Squire Grigore's picture. (So, after all, the squire had not failed him. In response to his vague, almost childlike devotion, the old man had shown him the path and had stirred the human feelings that had to guide his actions.) Awakening from his trance he answered Ivanciu:

"Give me three thousand lei and we sign the deed!"

The purchaser was happy; his profit was still large enough.

"Done!" he replied promptly.

Happy to have escaped the ordeal and relieved to see Iancu and Ivanciu reconciled again, Lefterica burst into tears, sobbing like a child. Then, taking a fresh sheet of paper, over which he blew carefully, to remove the slightest speck of dust that might blot his writing, he sat down eagerly at the desk, and said:

"I'm ready!"

Ivanciu, with his hands thrust in his pockets and his glasses perched on his nose, was examining the plans and Iancu had just cleared his throat, when suddenly the door was flung open and Mistress Mita in the doorway cried out excitedly:

"The boyar's coming!"

Urmatecu had hardly had time to get Ivanciu and Lefterica out of the room when boyar Barbu walked in. He was wrapped up in a warm muffler, his top hat on his head, and Fantoche, his little pet dog, tucked inside his upturned fur collar. As soon as he set eyes upon him, Iancu racked his brain to make out what could have brought him to his place. Had he by any chance changed his mind about selling the land? No, there was no need to worry; he breathed relieved when he saw the anxious gaze in the boyar's face. He looked too harassed and his eyes kept blinking too restlessly for it to be a money matter. Urmatecu had been right!

With his small mincing steps, Squire Barbu walked up to him and, without any other introduction, said:

"I've come here Iancu, both to escape from her and to see her! She'll turn up, too, you may be sure of that! We'd better go into the front room. I should like to be nearer the street."

"Certainly, your Honor, of course!" and they made their way through the rooms that had not yet been tidied up, and reached the large drawing room next to the entrance. The window of this room overlooked the street that could be seen stretching forth to the right and to the left.

Squire Barbu seated himself in a large armchair and heaved a deep sigh:

"Oh, God, Iancu, believe me she is stark mad! Could I have a glass of water and a spoonful of Mistress Mita's orange marmalade?" After which he sat in expectation.

The scene was not new. Squire Barbu had again quarrelled with his lady love, Lady Natalia and, as was his wont, had raced to Urmatecu where they would continue to quarrel and then get reconciled. For over twenty years their love had remained as tempestuous as on the first day, except for one additional item: their quarrels caused by Squire Barbu's invariable and uncontrollable jealousy.

In his eyes, Lady Natalia was the same lovely and lovable girl she had been in Vienna where he had first met her. His eyes did not see her aging and he might even have been willing not to see her at all, provided she herself saw nobody else. A few houses further up on the same street, Podul Mogosoaiei, in a large one-story house with a huge garden where her ladyship lived, the baron had gathered everything that could keep a woman from boredom. True, he would sometimes for several days forget to call on her. But she had books, she had pictures, she had servants, she had dogs, and she had birds—so what else could she want? thought Squire Barbu. Her last fancy had been horses! From the outset the baron had disliked the idea. Horses meant driving out, not like dogs that you could take for a walk in the garden! But in the end he gave in and bought horses too.

"And what did her ladyship do, your Honor?" inquired Iancu, a smile playing in his moustache, when Squire Barbu mentioned the horses.

"Well, what do you expect she did! She had them harnessed to her carriage and came round to fetch me for a drive."

"And didn't you go?"

"What? I drive out with her? Am I mad! With everybody staring at us?"

Urmatecu broke into a hearty laugh. Suddenly the baron frowned. A wave of severity came down over his frail little body, stiffening his countenance. A steel spring seemed to coil up inside him, lending him an air of dignity and power. His eyes sparkled and in a deliberate, rare, icy voice he cried:

"Urmatecu! (This vocative, with a slightly haughty intonation was the height of sternness in the baron's tone.) Don't interfere in things you cannot understand!"

Iancu winced as if he had been rapped over his knuckles. "Another blunder!" he said to himself. "It's no joke moving in their world! The ground is terribly slippery!" But Iancu showed no offense. He had learned one lesson: they may come and intrude upon your privacy; you, however, must forbear. The mortification that tended to rise from the bottom of his heart abated only at the thought that his daughter Amelica would not have blundered but would have certainly known how to act in this circumstance too.

The distant rumble of a carriage could be heard approaching and then stopped before the gate. The baron slid hastily behind a curtain and with an excitement that lent his voice a passionate and youthful ring, cried:

"Look, Iancu, there she is!"

In the twinkling of an eye the cloud of his lordly pique had blown away and Iancu had become again the friend from whose mind and ability he expected precious aid in his plight.

The equipage standing in front of the gate was the acme of elegance: the carriage, with its red spokes, had the streamlined grace of the victorias built by Fritz, the famous coachmaker. You could almost feel with your eyes the softness of the velvet cushions. The horses were simply magnificent! As black as a raven, their manes and tails fluttering in the wind, their scared bloodshot eyes gazing around, white foam chewed with the bit, the horses kept stamping the ground with their sparkling hoofs beating a mincing tattoo of impatience and pent-up power. The waves of light shining in their brightly groomed hair glittered like natural jewels.

His forehead pressed against the windowpane to cool his feverish brow, the baron went suddenly ashen pale and, in a stifled voice, murmured, as if calling for mercy:

"Look at her, Iancu; she's with 'the Rake' again!"

Urmatecu leaned over the short gentleman, to get a clearer view of the scene. A smile curled his lips, and he might have laughed outright again had he not remembered the incident of a few minutes before. For years now nothing had changed in these scenes of jealousy. "The Rake" was no other than Squire Stefan, boyar Barbu's younger brother. A true lover of horses, as knowledgeable as a horse-dealer, Squire Stefan was a tall, handsome man with deep blue eyes, almond-shaped and as heavy-lashed as a woman's. With his beard peppered with a few glistening silver threads, his famous polka-dotted loosely tied necktie, his slender figure clothed in a tight-fitting, braided, black velvet riding-coat, his long slim legs in red highboots, he was to Squire Barbu, by his sole presence, an eyesore and a source of rage. The feeling of companionship between people of the same generation, his greater boldness and humor had contributed to foster his friendship with Lady Natalia. Urmatecu bore him sincere feelings of friendship and admiration. They had moreover in common the same passionate love for horses.

A time-worn jealousy, which he never confessed and of which he was truly ashamed, tortured the baron. It was for this reason that he had not forbidden this friendly relationship. He kept tormenting himself in silence, breaking out now and again with a word of abuse or a nickname. And when he felt that others saw through him, straight into his heart, he would claim that his words of abuse and disapproval were addressed to Stefan only for the dissolute and squandering life he lived. In point of fact the latter was neither more dissolute nor more wasteful than the baron himself. The only difference was that the one spent his young life joyfully, gaily, with revels, parties, and adventure, whereas the other led a life of despondency with the gloom of premature old age, compounded with a mixture of manias and uncontrolled fear. The baron was torn by the anguish that, of the two brothers, a woman's heart might sooner go out to the younger. This thought, though the product of his own fancy, was a constant source of distress and pain. Of course there was no reason for doubt in the present case. Lady Natalia was a woman above reproach, truly devoted to the baron, conscious of his tender heart and genuine delicacy.

Before the gate, Squire Stefan alertly jumped out of the carriage, and helped her ladyship to descend. They exchanged a few words and laughed heartily. He made a deep bow, kissed her hand, clicked his heels in military fashion and waited for her ladyship to reach the courtyard. Thereupon, casting a last appraising glance at the horses, he sauntered down the street whistling a tune.

For a jealous man every trifle, no matter how absurd, is decisive evidence; just as, when the rage caused by weakness and love has abated, the same trifle that may mean a lot, slips out of his mind and soul with the utmost ease. Thus was it that the baron suddenly felt more relieved on recording the trifling gestures that might have meant a lot or nothing. In the first place she had come. Secondly, on parting they had not stayed long nor close together in front of the gate; thirdly, while they were speaking, their eyes were constantly fixed upon the horses, and lastly, Stefan had refrained from coming up with her. Whereas, a few minutes before, Squire Barbu was like a drowning man who was calling out for help, now he was again master of the situation. The panting heart and stifling breath caused by his tenderness that he could ill control had abated. But his mind was still not quite at ease. He saw, pondered, hoped, but full relief he was unable to attain! A faint feeling of anger and bitterness still lingered in his heart. Urmatecu watched him for a while then hurried down the stairs to welcome her ladyship.

Sitting upright, his head thrust between his shoulders, and almost hidden in the huge fur collar, the baron strained his ear to hear the voice approaching from the adjoining room, rubbing the while the black cold nose of Fantoche with the tip of his finger.

The door was suddenly flung open and Lady Natalia, sensing the brewing storm, paused in the doorway and said in a dulcet voice:

"Thank you, Barbu, for the horses! Have you seen them?"

Ceremoniously, without uttering a word, however, the baron rose to his feet, kissed her hand and escorted her to her seat. Then, seating himself on another chair, he resumed his entertainment with his little dog.

Her ladyship's beauty shone more brightly in the full yet bleak daylight. The thin, finely shaped face, whose charm resided in the dainty line of the forehead prolonged by a straight nose, lit up by two large blue child's eyes, was framed in the shiny black hair that reached down to the eyebrows. Two curls descending from the middle part were faintly detectable under the little fur toque set high upon her forehead. When the silken folds of her marten fur-mantle fell, the figure of the woman, who refused to age, emerged in all its supple gracefulness under a tight dress of cherry-colored velvet, adorned with a long row of small gold buttons that ran from her bosom to her hips. The cool air she had brought in spread around; she was like the soul of a nosegay, in which the rich perfumes of her gown added a sweet and piercing odor to the fragrance of the autumn flowers.

There was a long moment of silence. Attempting to put an end to this heavy stillness, her ladyship peered around as if she were looking for something. Then, rising swiftly, she glided up to a grand piano standing in a corner, a piano that seemed still ill-matched with the objects around. You felt it was a stranger in Urmatecu's house: its owner, this shrewd businessman, was never its real master; his thoughts were exclusively taken up by his lustful interest in money and shrewd bargains.

* * *

As Lady Natalia sat down in front of the piano, she turned to Iancu and in a soft whispering voice asked:

"How's your daughter, Iancu?"

"Thank you, your Honor. She bids you humble grace!" replied the businessman, flattered to talk about his cherished pride.

Then her ladyship began to play. In incessant waves of music, her light fingers weaved the entrancing and sprightly waltzes of Johann Strauss. The piano rang out rich and full. To the marked and grave rhythm of the left hand, struck with exaggerated vigor, making it sound almost like a different instrument, her right hand traced ingenious spirited arabesques that soared away in bright and clear tunes. The specific undulations of the Viennese waltz, which had cradled her sun-flooded and carefree youth, was like a heart beating wildly in its crazy exuberance. You could feel that the woman who was playing had heard this waltz in Vienna; she had danced, had hoped, had loved, had dreamed to the rapturous rhythm of this great waltz, made up of dozens of exquisite shorter waltzes! Every now and again, as she let her fingers race along the keys, her ladyship would turn her head in the direction of the baron, with a smile and a glance that seemed to reach out to pick up one of the broken threads of their bond. Urmatecu, insensitive to the music, watched the scene with the eager interest of one who has nothing else to do. But the iciness of the baron's gestures soon began to thaw and gradually his gaze grew brighter. After staring long into the void, a smile curved his lips, tempering his stern look. He had always had a soft spot in his heart for waltzes under whose spell he had fallen long before he had met Natalia; ever since the days of his youth shared with the mother of his son, Bubi.

He had been a close friend of Strauss himself. He had admired him and looked upon him as a marvel. He'd have given his whole fortune just for a shred of the composer's talent. He had repeatedly struggled to unravel the mystery of this charm but had never succeeded. Both in his friendship for the man and in his love for his music, for years on end the baron had resigned himself to the role of expectant companion. They were together everywhere and at all times. And at every moment the baron expected Strauss to come forward with a new waltz. He waited for a name to be uttered, a few bars to be whistled, conscious that in one of the following nights in the gardens of the Prater, with their lights shining white through the green foliage, the surprise would come with the melodious chords of a new triumph.

The baron had never been really young. He had always fought shy of the pranks and antics of youth, afraid of the ridicule of such gestures that fitted his nature so ill. His youth had therefore been a struggle. His age and experience had now spared him the need of fighting to control his inner urges. But at the bottom of his heart there was still a smoldering fire that flared up at the tune of a waltz. What he appreciated most was this romantic blending of joyful youth with sentimental languor, but above all the sprightliness, the note of frolic and waggishness in every waltz and especially in those of his friend, Johann Strauss. Present in these gay waves of music was a twinkle of the eye, a hat cocked on one side, a bevy of young, winsome girls gliding swiftly by, leaving in their wake a lure and an urge to live and conquer. The waltzes had everything that the baron had never dared to show. If he were not to control his impulses, even now in his old age, he would have stood up, his arms akimbo, his nose tilted in the air, and would have swayed wildly to and fro to the beat of the waltz. . . . The notes struck at his heart sending a thrill of happiness through his whole body.

The great joys in life are gained from feelings that overflow the soul, without steps of transition. These feelings are rare and are the sole privilege of pure hearts. A new bracing state of mind all of a sudden takes hold of you. . . . It first sweeps away the memory of the past and a new moment begins. A man must have been spared the trial of fighting with the world and of searching into the deeper recesses of human beings and deeds, to be able to preserve this delicacy and purity of the heart, even beyond the age of maturity. Yes, the baron possessed these! So endowed, oblivious of place, circumstances, and time, which had all been swept away from his mind, the baron rose all of a sudden and, making his way to the door, cried out to her ladyship, as though she had been tarrying too long:

"Come on, Natalia!"

And Lady Natalia hastened after him, greeting Urmatecu in her stride with a smile. She had carried the day!

Iancu had hardly time enough to reach them at the gate to see them off. They both stepped into the same carriage and drove off. The puzzled merchant could not understand the baron's gesture; he could not grasp the change that had come over the baron. Gazing long after the receding carriage, he muttered under his breath an oath of admiration for this wondrous woman.

Camil Petrescu

(1894-1957)

Camil Petrescu is one of the most representative writers of Rumanian literature. His writings are saturated with ideological problems and bear the stamp of a deep-searching mind probing the complexities of modern social life. The central figure in most of his works is that of the intellectual, non-conformist and unadaptable, following his tragic destiny in a bourgeois society.

Camil Petrescu, making his debut as a poet, asserted himself soon after as a powerful prose writer and dramatist. His contribution to the theater is particularly significant.

He wrote war poems ("The Cycle of Death"), philosophical poems ("Transcendentalia") and erotic poetry ("A Sunlit Glade for Kicsikem").

Through his two novels, *The Last Night of Love, the First Night of War* (1930) and *Procust's Bed* (1933), Camil Petrescu may be included among the founders of the modern Rumanian novel, ranking as one of the outstanding analysts in Rumanian literature. The hero of his historical novel *A Man Amongst Men* (3 vol., 1955-1957), Nicolae Balcescu, the most prominent figure of the 1848 revolution in Wallachia, appears no longer as a solitary scholar or dreamer, tortured by the chimerical quest for the absolute, but as an intellectual dedicated to a social cause, whose efforts are integrated in the great struggle of the masses for a happier life.

In his theatrical productions Camil Petrescu remains the same subtle analyst as in his novels. His plays, *The Dance of the Elves, Venetian Act, Strong Souls,* are dramas of ideas, in which the heroes motivate their existence upon abstract notions that are opposed to the shallowness of bourgeois life. *Danton,* an evocation of an episode of the French Revolution, is one of Camil Petrescu's most brilliant plays. In his *Caragiale and His Time* the dramatist sets out not only to pay a tribute to Rumania's foremost playwright and humorist, but also to define the relationship of the artist with bourgeois society. The play *Balcescu,* written in 1949, recalls the figure of the noble-minded leader of the Wallachian revolution of 1848.

Camil Petrescu is also the author of interesting and challenging critical essays. He was also a brilliant publicist with notable and wide-ranging activity.

Excerpt from *A Man Amongst Men*

Balcescu, standing on his plank bed, watched the fire from behind the bars of the small upper window. Now and again he turned towards Farcasanu:

"It seems to be dying out," he said.

"I don't believe it'll reach as far as this, but we're confined here on account of it all the same. All the officers are."

When Sevastita, accompanied by Corporal Simion Firu, who was carrying the basket, appeared on the threshold, Balcescu stood as if petrified, staring at her.

Simion sin Firu, as he was listed in the registers, had early made up his mind about life in the barracks. He had been promoted to corporal and was very proud on that day to be the noncommissioned officer on duty in the barracks. In two years he had become imbued with the military spirit, and, when on duty as he was that day, he put the fear of God into the soldiers. Balcescu did not recognize him, of course, but he, Simion, well remembered the young Junker and his quarrel with the boyars at the Vadu Rau. He had been afraid of showing that he knew him, because he was not sure how his officers would take this and he certainly did not wish to anger them. But he had grown somewhat bolder on seeing Lieutenant Farcasanu often talking in a friendly way with the prisoner.

The young woman also stood motionless, as if rooted to the ground. Much shaken, she looked at her brother.

"It's the prisoner's sister, sir. She's got a pass from the Chancery of the *Spatar*, the *Agie* and the Great *Vornic*, and she's allowed to bring clothes and food. But I haven't looked in the basket. Will you examine it, sir?"

Farcasanu motioned him out of the room.

"All right, you can go now." Then, with a look at the basket: "I hope there are no firearms or forbidden books in it," he said in a friendly tone, then saluted and went out, leaving the two young people alone.

Sevastita flung her arms around her brother's neck.

"Nicolache . . . Nicolache . . . I haven't seen you since St. Simion's Day."

Balcescu gave her a happy look, but almost immediately asked why his mother hadn't come too.

Sevastita appeared embarrassed and flustered. She put down the basket she had meant to carry over to the bed and said:

"Mother? Oh, she's all right. . . . Everybody's all right—Maria, and Costache, and Barbu."

But mother, Sevastita, what's the matter with mother?" Nicolache asked again anxiously. "Why hasn't she come too?"

"Nicolache, you know how busy she is. But she's in good health. She insisted on my coming this time. How well she knows you!" She rummaged through her pockets and took out a letter. " 'Let me write to him,' she said, 'for Nicolache will get frightened if he doesn't see me or my handwriting.' "

He began anxiously reading the long letter, while Sevastita looked at him in childish admiration. After a while he said in tones of emotion:

"In Cyrillic letters, isn't it? She won't hear of the new alphabet."

Sevastita smiled as she explained:

"If you take a better look, you'll see a Latin M, beside the A's. She took a lot of trouble practicing for a few days, with her eyeglasses on her nose, and then she had enough of it and put my slate aside, for I was teaching her."

Balcescu, having hurriedly and nervously turned the letter over, looked up.

"I can't read it now. And I'm dying to hear everything. Though I'm afraid we shan't be able to say all we have to say . . . I can read the letter after you have gone. It's already late and I don't know how long you'll be allowed to stay."

Sevastita spoke of their adventures with childish gravity:

"If you knew what we've gone through to get here! And we left home at ten o'clock. . . . All the streets are blocked by soldiers. A fire has been burning in Lipscani Street for two days."

Balcescu showed her the fire through the little window, asking in bewilderment:

"Is Lipscani burning again? Is Bucharest burning?"

She gave him the explanations he wanted in a grave tone, putting the basket on the plank bed, preparatory to taking out the things it contained.

"Some people say the fire broke out around Serban Voda Inn and that the wind carried it this way. First it spread over Mogosoaia Street to the Meitani and Racovita mansions; then some outbuildings caught fire in the Corbeanu grounds and the fire also reached Brezoianu Street. Heaps of clothes and things can be seen in all the courtyards. All the water hoses have been taken into the neighboring streets, but they are not sufficient. Captain Costache ordered a large number of common people to be driven to the spot with whips so as to form about ten chains in the streets leading to the river, the pails being passed from hand to hand." Her eyes were sympathetic, but a youthful smile played about her lips. "There are perhaps a hundred pails, in each street. The passers-by are forced into the job, but many of them try to run away. They are drenched through and the water freezes on them, and their hands become frozen."

Balcescu was still puzzled and anxious.

"But how did you manage to get this pass? Everybody here tries to go one better than the others. They've become even stricter and harder since Ghica's flight. . . . They're afraid of an escape *en masse*."

The young woman smiled at him.

"It's again to poor Luxita Florescu that we owe this. She has knocked at every door untiringly. At a party, Luxita told the Great *Vornic* to his face that she knew in this cold weather you had nothing but rags to cover yourself with, and that you were left without food for days on end. And that, even though he is in power now, a curse would fall upon his head if anything happened to you."

Balcescu shrugged his shoulders in astonishment: he did not know the young woman who had befriended him.

"Luxita? Who's she?"

"Nicolache, this woman has been a guardian angel to you. She has done everything in her power." On her knees, Sevastita was opening the basket she had laid on the bed. But before getting out the things, she was distressed beyond measure to discover that the bed was made up of several planks, without any bedclothes.

"Nicolache, have you no sheets or blankets?"

The young man's eyes fell upon the bed with indifference, but after a time a smile came to his lips.

"I've got my coat. It's warm enough. . . ." It was obvious he was not telling the truth. "Anyway it's better here than at Margineni, though I think I'll be here only as long as the investigations continue. Afterwards they'll take me back to the other place."

She whispered faintly to him as if it were a secret:

"That was mere talk: it was Luxita's work again." Whereupon she drew a few things out of the basket. "Here are a couple of changes of linen," she said, "a pair of woolen stockings and a sheepskin coat. They'll be the right thing in this frost."

"Don't be so concerned about me; things are not so bad as they look. A man can endure discomforts. Just don't worry about me. What would you have? It's a prison after all!"

Sevastita took another parcel out of the basket.

"And here's some pastry," she went on, "that we made on the

quiet. It's Lent, you know, and mother would be angry about it. She sent you *halva** with hazelnuts, caramels, and almonds."

Balcescu was touched to see the big soup tureen.

"And I suppose she's sent me some rice pudding, thinking I'm still a child."

"Yes, but without milk, for it's Lent. Its made with sesame flour. She knows you like it so much . . . and some ham, though, only for after Lent. And these milk biscuits keep long, for they're made of very fine flour. Just dip them in water."

But Balcescu was still suspicious, still anxious. Putting the basket down on the floor near the bed, he said:

"Sevastita, I beg you to tell me the truth . . . why hasn't mother come? Why has she sent you? I'm terribly glad to see you, dear, but I shouldn't like to feel that you were here only because you were taking mother's place." And he added fearfully: "If she'd been in good health she wouldn't have allowed anyone to take her place."

"There! I'll tell you how it is, Nicolache . . ." But still she wavered. "I'll tell you exactly." She was trying to make things less difficult. "You know, when mother came to see you last autumn . . . you wouldn't hear of signing the petition of pardon addressed to the prince."

His face, already distorted with the strain of trying to dispel his fears, darkened. He took a few steps around the cell. Although he was cold, he refused to turn up his coat collar.

"It was the only thing to do, Sevastita." Some memory that weighed on his mind made him hang his head. "At the trial I was so terribly unhappy thinking of all you had done, using all your influence to make me out a minor . . . that I lost my head. But ever since I've been in prison, I've felt ashamed of what I said there." He became thoughtful, his eyes grew sombre. "All of us behaved basely . . . shaking off every responsibility in a shameful way, laying the guilt at another's door. Dumitru Filipescu alone acted uprightly, taking the blame upon himself . . . and now his legs are rotting in water, at Snagov." After a time he asked in a whisper, taking her hand: "Is mother grieved?"

"Nicolache, you shouldn't have refused to sign the petition. Mother has looked so ill ever since. She has been talking to people about you and knocking at every door for a year, though often they remained closed and the people didn't care. On St. Alexander's Day Luxita induced her grandmother, Anica Florescu, to see her brother, Prince Alecu Ghica, about you. For half an hour the old lady used

* Turkish sweetmeat.

every persuasion she knew; then, finally, for the sake of his name day, the prince softened. He said the forms should be drawn up and a petition of pardon signed by you should be brought to him by Luxita within a week. Mother thought she'd go wild with happiness. She couldn't sleep until she came to see you . . . And then, you wouldn't even hear about the petition."

"My heart aches at the thought of mother's suffering, little sister. I realize that she can't understand. But you must understand that I couldn't bring myself to ask to be pardoned by a despot who had signed our sentence in so cowardly a way. Prison life has opened my eyes, the eyes of my mind. Today I believe that if human dignity cannot resist certain temptations, there should be another name for man."

Sevastita was moved and pensive. Her hand, with its long fingers, went to her cheek. . . . She hesitated.

"Nicolache. . . ."

He misunderstood her emotion and, taking her hand with brotherly affection, said to her:

"Of course you understand me. You're nearer to me than any other human being on earth. Mother is a saint, little sister, but she belongs to another age; she's forgotten her youth. Now she can only think about family troubles and is overcome by them. She's angry with me and won't see me."

The young woman interrupted him nervously.

"No, no! Don't say that. You're quite wrong. She's not cross with you, poor dear." And she smiled, melting into tenderness at the thought of their mother. "Were she allowed, she would sleep at your door. There's another reason why she sent me."

He frowned and gave her a puzzled look:

"I don't understand . . ." he said and looked inquiringly at her.

Again she hesitated. It was hard to explain the matter, and embarrassing too.

"It's so difficult to say . . ." she said. And as a refuge she began fidgeting with the strings of her hood.

"Tell me," he said, puzzled even more and trying to read meaning into her prolonged silence.

Smiling tenderly, she sought her words:

"You see, Nicolache, you don't believe in certain things. And I am not very good at talking."

Drawing closer his threadbare coat—now actually torn in places—for a cold shiver had run through him, he urged her to continue.

"Go on, Sevastita, tell me . . ." And then, taken by a fit of coughing, he explained with care: "I caught cold last night. . . ."

Sevastita, hearing his racking cough, looked searchingly at him, but at the tender thought of her mother her face became smiling again.

"You see, on Christmas Eve mother had a dream."

So that was it! It was plain to him now and he too smiled, asking with tender irony:

"And are we to take dreams into account now, Sevastita, my dear?"

The young girl also seemed to think this interpretation of dreams a weakness on their mother's part, but she loved her as she was and defended her as best she could.

"You know how mother is. . . . Well, she says the Holy Virgin appeared to her in a dream and spoke to her thus: 'Zinca, let your youngest daughter go and persuade her brother to sign the petition of pardon.' She woke up immediately after and hasn't had a quiet moment since." Sevastita would have liked to say more, but she was uncertain of herself and hesitated. Then, her face buried in the collar of her cloak, she resumed: "And Luxita too thinks it would be far easier now that Bibescu is reigning. That's why mother sent me, saying she was sure I'd induce you to sign the petition. And that's why she hasn't come. 'Go, my little girl,' she said to me, 'for you've got a child's heart . . . and a special grace from the Holy Virgin. You'll persuade him . . . he won't refuse you.'"

He gave a sigh of relief, now sympathizing with his mother.

"How childish to believe in dreams," he said. "But I'm no longer anxious now, Sevastita dear," and he kissed her as if in gratitude. Then his face became overcast again. "But surely you yourself don't believe in such things? Nor could you expect me to sink to such depths of degradation as to ask the prince's pardon and wait for his answer."

There followed a prolonged, stubborn silence on her part, after which she drew the petition from her muff.

"Nicolache, there's another prince now, not the one who sentenced you." She showed him the sheet of paper, her eyes pleading for his signature.

He looked at her in amazement, as if she had become a stranger, then drawing near laid his hands on her shoulders:

"Are you really asking me to do this thing?"

His surprise made him cough again—and even choke.

Suddenly the young woman's face betrayed her emotion, showing how deeply she had been stirred.

"You've suffered so much, we've all suffered so much. Mother, your brothers . . . and we, your two sisters, all implore you." Out of the basket she took a small inkpot and a pen, her pleading look insisting.

He seemed to waver, as if his armor had been pierced.

Emboldened by this wavering, Sevastita knelt by the poor wooden chair and, pen in hand, drew him down beside her. "You must sign," she whispered. She had opened the petition, spreading it on the chair, and, as they knelt side by side, she handed him the pen.

Bending over the chair, Balcescu began to read absent-mindedly, emphasizing the words here and there. It almost seemed as if the young woman had convinced him. "Your Highness, ardently pleading for mercy, I kneel at Your Highness's feet . . ." Kneel! . . . he was surprised to find himself kneeling indeed and suddenly he rose in disgust, shuddering at what he was being asked to do. Tearing the sheet of paper to pieces, his voice rose in anger springing from the very roots of his being:

"No despot will ever find me kneeling at his feet. I'd sooner spend my life in the salt mine."

Sevastita also rose, dumfounded, feeling her cause was lost and that she could never succeed, even though she thought he was wrong.

"But, Nicolache," she persisted, "you know that's the way one phrases these things. It is almost, how shall I put it, a common rule. It doesn't mean that you actually kneel before anyone. It's just a way of writing it." She would have liked to tell him that this was the way everyone wrote, but stopped, for she knew it would rouse him still further.

"I cannot plead with any despot. I hate them all. Truth, justice, the people's happiness should not depend on a single man, whoever he is." He coughed again and, putting his handkerchief to his lips, found fit to repeat: "I caught cold last night."

Grieved, Sevastita looked vaguely into the distance as if listening to the thoughts within her. Somehow her brother seemed to be different from what he had been. Even the fact that, whereas before she had always seen him clean-shaven, he now wore a short black beard, helped to emphasize this difference.

"The people's happiness, you say? What about our happiness? The happiness of our own downtrodden family should come before the people's happiness." She began to weep softly. "And all this for a mere flourish of the pen. How can you give such importance to a trifle like this? You were ready to sign. . . ."

Her grief touched him deeply, bringing him to the verge of surrender, but suddenly he remembered what Lacusteanu had told him about his friend at Snagov and he whispered in heartbroken tones:

"Dimitru Filipescu is rotting away, his legs in water. . . ."

"And what good will it do if you also perish?"

On his feet, Balcescu became himself again. His momentary weakness had passed and he now remained lost in thought. When he spoke it was quietly and with determination:

"Listen, Sevastita, these people, my comrades, rarely asked my opinion and that riles me to this day whenever I remember it. They took decisions without me, without even asking me. They considered me of no importance, perhaps too young. I might have had a great deal to say, but they made me keep silent, some of them talking to me conceitedly, others injudiciously. But this sentence—I realize it only now—has bound us all into one sheaf and their fate has become my own. I cannot be the only one to escape prison." His pale hand grasped his coat collar resolutely, as if to protect himself from the cold within him. He kept a long silence, an awkward silence, making a change of mind impossible. Sevastita seemed to feel her defeat and became downcast. Through the small window the crimson light of the burning skies increased. The young woman insisted no longer and, drawing a small item from the basket—an icon carefully wrapped in a towel—looked long at it, overcome with emotion. Then, shrugging her shoulders and shaking her head, at a loss as to what to say, she breathed:

"He is too stubborn, Holy Mother of God." She gave a deep sigh, trying to catch his eyes. Then, with a sorrowful smile, added: "And you were ready to sign . . . poor mother. . . ." Suddenly the young woman remembered her mother, waiting on the bench in that bitter frost. The sound of stamping feet came from outside, then a noise at the door. With an embarrassed gesture, Farcasanu appeared on the threshold, his sword under his arm:

"I'm sorry, but I must remind you that in ten minutes' time. . . ."

"Yes, sir," the young woman murmured dejectedly.

"My dear young lady," the officer resumed in a hesitating tone, yet as if eager to know something, "may I take the liberty of asking whether you are not the fiancée of a fellow officer, Oprea Nedelescu?"

Sevastita was embarrassed. Her childlike face seemed slightly distorted.

"Yes . . . No . . . Y-es. . . ."

"I was on duty at the Palace when you were both presented to the prince."

Sevastita's embarrassment was now at its height. She stammered out a broken sentence:

"Yes . . . I was betrothed to him, but . . . our betrothal has been broken."

The officer made a gallant bow.

"I regret having missed the occasion of forming the guard of honor."

Sevastita, breathless with amazement, took a step towards him, her hood falling upon her shoulders.

"Would my brother have been allowed to attend the wedding?"

"Oh, no! what I meant to say was a guard of honor for the bridegroom, our fellow officer Nedelescu." He also was embarrassed now. "But who knows? Perhaps if we had taken him on parole, even your brother might have been allowed to attend for an hour or two." Sevastita gave a start: exalted, a mad hope taking possession of her, she grabbed the lapel of his coat.

"Could Nicolache come home under your escort, sir?"

He realized that he had been misunderstood and retreated in haste.

"No, I didn't mean that."

Her eyes bright with hope and her voice warm and imploring, Sevastita seemed ready to kneel at his feet.

"Let us take Nicolache home for an hour tonight, sir. To allow him to get some hot tea. . . . He's caught cold . . . and then my mother would see him."

Farcasanu was horrified; he was no longer listening as he backed towards the door.

"No, no, such a thing is not possible."

Balcescu, who had been dumfounded to hear that his sister's engagement had been broken off, now came up to her, his countenance glowering.

"Why aren't you getting married?"

It was plain that within him anxiety mingled with passion.

She was silent for a long time, humiliated by this troublesome occurrence.

"Tell me, Sevastita," her brother insisted.

"He broke the engagement . . ." she said hanging her head. "And when everybody knew we were preparing for the wedding."

"Good God, how was he able to do such a thing? Ruin your reputation in this way? What did Scarlat say? And Costache? Didn't they break his sword when they met him in the street?"

Sevastita turned her head away in sadness and dejection.

"It's better ended so."

Anxiously, Balcescu took her arm, insisting stubbornly, full of suspicion.

"Sevastita, what reason did he give? What made him capable of such a low-down trick?"

"Don't bother about it. It isn't worth it. Pretexts are easy to find."

Never before had he felt the duties of a brother to such an extent: a brother bound hand and foot, with the walls pressing in upon him, a helpless prisoner. He clenched his fists in despair.

"This loneliness, oh, my God! What a wall it raises between me and the world. I feel like a poor blind mole. How could I know what has been happening beyond these walls," he repeated. He longed to bang on the door, to run amuck.

A shrewd suspicion that here must have been a great misfortune gnawed at his heart. He felt a sense of responsibility that had long been overlooked and implored her with bitterness.

"I'm your brother, little sister. We've always been great friends. Tell me everything." His voice was friendly but urgent. He came to her, tensely expectant. "Tell me everything."

Sevastita wavered, tortured by irresolution. She wanted to spare him and asked herself whether she should tell him or not. Finally, in her grief, she decided to keep nothing back, for she realized that to be involved in lies would make matters worse.

"His father came and brought back his ring, saying that he could not have his son ruin his career by marrying me. An officer married to the sister of one condemned for high treason, he claimed, would draw the prince's ill will upon him."

It was all plain now. His whole being reverted from the path of gnawing suspicion. The blame lay not with this delicate being that faced him, but with himself. It was only now that he discovered how much evil he had innocently caused, merely by proceeding stubbornly along the road which he considered right, without ever asking his family whether they agreed with him, although they too had to suffer the consequences of his deeds. He leaned against the wall, overcome with fatigue, and very nearly collapsed under the strain. Now at last the full meaning of the word—family—so often pronounced without much heed, struck him. . . . He had thought that the blows had fallen on him alone, that the grief of his family was merely sentimental sorrow and love. But he realized now that a fighter does not sacrifice himself alone. He had not asked the girl her opinion when he went to visit Dumitru Filipescu. He now realized that he had exposed her to blows he had not imagined would ever fall on her. Nor had he ever asked his mother, and his mother was the very heart of the family through which the knife had been driven. Dazed, he leaned against the wall. Horrified by the effect of her confession, the young woman tried to minimize her sorrow, to make him forget his conscience-stricken grief.

"I've told you these were mere pretexts. Just fabrications. . . ." But it was beyond her power to conceal her sorrow, and she collapsed on the bed. Balcescu came to her and stroked her hands, her cheeks.

"You've suffered through me, little sister, forgive me."

"No . . . you . . . why should you ask forgiveness?" Silent and thoughtful for a moment, she suddenly broke down, sorely stricken, as she remembered what she would have liked to forget:

"He was a coward, a coward . . . a miserable coward."

Her voice was expressionless in her sorrow and humiliation.

Overcome with the sense of his guilt and utterly dismayed, he could only stroke her cheeks.

"Sevastita, it was your first love. It might have been so beautiful."

The girl put her hands to her sorrowful face and looked up at him. Little, tearful stars twinkled in her hazel eyes, while her lips trembled, but after a moment she mastered herself and, with a smile that might have fluttered from another world, and with absolute composure, she spoke of that unforgettable moment when she had felt her heartstrings snap like the strings of a violin.

"When he came to Bucharest for Christmas, he told our cousin Caliopi, during a dance, that he had realized in good time he was no longer in love with me . . . and didn't wish us both to be unhappy in later life." For a few seconds, this memory was again like a knife in her heart; then, reverting to her natural state of gentle calm, she added: "He left Bucharest without giving an explanation, without writing a line. . . ." This last bitter thought caused her self-control to give way and she broke down again, collapsing on the plank bed.

Shattered by the depth of the sorrow that consumed her, a sorrow she had tried to conceal from the world, her brother asked:

"And did you love him?" He would have liked to add: "So much?" But he realized how senseless it was.

Although she was looking at him, she seemed neither to see nor hear him.

"His father brought back his ring." Again her eyes filled at the memory. "He used to say he'd lay down his life for me." Half-sitting, half-reclining on the bed, her sorrow seemed all-consuming: she might have been a flaming sheet of paper.

His heart bled for her. Going up to her, he took her cheeks in his hands and raised her face towards his.

"Why didn't he realize all this earlier—before the engagement, or at least at the time of the trial—that I was a traitor?"

The storm of memory had blown over now and the cold within her had frozen her sorrow. The young woman rose, fully mistress of herself.

"A coward. . . . He lost his head when he saw he had been transferred to Bucharest."

Boundless sorrow had taken possession of her brother, who now understood his great guilt towards her. He took a few steps through the cell feverishly, stopped close to her as she stood by the poor unpainted chair, her hands in her muff.

"Forgive me, Sevastita." His voice trembled.

Sevastita looked harassed as if communing with her distressing thoughts, with her own unfathomed self.

"Whatever flowers might be brought me now would only be for the grave of my love. I know now what love is—a well with but little pure water at the bottom. I'll never fall in love again."

There was deadly determination on her young face, with its pale eyes looking into the distance.

Balcescu was at a loss what to say, overcome by the sorrow she could not conceal fully and which revealed itself to him.

"Sevastita, you're a mere child. . . . What can you know?"

She suddenly turned round and faced him with savage determination.

"I will never be in love again," she said, her eyes now fixed upon the floor.

Balcescu was disconsolate. He again walked up and down the cell, his blame in the matter torturing him. He would have liked to speak to her, but found he could hardly open his mouth because of the strain and worry. The words stuck in his throat. A fit of coughing seized him and, turning away quietly to avoid her eyes, he hastily pressed his handkerchief to his lips.

When the awful fit passed, Sevastita, who had been anxiously watching him, went up to him and took his cheeks between her hands, catching sight of the bloodstained handkerchief.

Seeing his awful secret betrayed, he looked at her helplessly; his lips, framed by his young beard, twisted in pain.

"You know . . . I think. . . ." But he was unable to finish his sentence, unable to find the right words. His eyes had a perplexed look. He had wished to keep his secret, a horrible secret, to himself forever.

Sevastita, too, as if the blow had been struck directly at her, looked around for support, then suddenly remembered her mother waiting on the bench in the cold and, overwhelmed by the thought that she might find out, said:

"Don't let mother hear about it." Whereupon it was as if a shadow, a mellow light, had come between them. She took her own handkerchief from her muff and wiped his face, as she gently helped him towards the bed.

"They've murdered you, my poor brother."

Balcescu gave a nervous start, an imploring look in his black eyes.

"Nobody must know. . . ."

Quietly making a gift of her life, her clear, tear-suffused eyes sought his and a look of intense love enwrapped him.

"I'll be your sister, your sister until I die. . . ." Then, trying to recapture a lighter spirit, stroking him gently, she said: "And you'll get better, too. But you must ask to be removed from here and taken to the hospital at once."

Balcescu, shaking with fever, his shoulders bent, his elbows resting on his knees, spoke desperately, his words seeming to come from great depths.

"No, no . . . the beasts would get off too cheaply then. I don't need their pity. They've left me with only a short span of life, perhaps, but they'll pay for it as they would for three lives. . . ." He drew close to her, his cheek against hers and said under his breath, as if he were revealing a secret:

"Sevastita, I can't sleep at nights; so I make my plans and my accounts. I'm twenty-three now. I'd like to live another ten years to overthrow this rotten structure of theirs, as the plow-share turns up the earth of a field overgrown with weeds."

And with a thirst for life that was like a desperate prayer, a prayer that came from the depths of his soul, but stifled by a stubbornness that grew unwittingly, he repeated:

"Ten years . . . only ten years . . ."

A terrible silence prevailed in the cell.

Sevastita looked at him anxiously, sympathetically, and said gently:

"So much hatred is not good, brother."

But Balcescu heeded her not, savagely isolating himself with his thoughts, bent on one purpose:

"No Rumanian should experience what Dumitru Filipescu, I and the others are experiencing . . . never again should the Rumanian people endure what they are enduring now."

* * *

All this time, on the bench by the gate of the dilapidated mansions near Dura's Lake, Zinca sat waiting, frozen to the bone though she had wrapped a thick woollen shawl over the sheepskin jacket. The weather had changed, the sky was now cloudy, and a light snow was falling. A guard came up to her.

"What are you waiting for, my good woman? The fire has been put out. Everybody has gone."

Zinca was so frozen that she found it difficult to speak. She explained things that held no meaning for him:

"Sevastita is coming . . . with a petition he's signed."

She huddled up towards the end of the bench. It was growing dark, and big, slow snowflakes were falling from a sky of lead.

* * *

There was silence now in the prison cell, the silence of downcast people. More than an hour had gone by. Sevastita continued to stroke her brother lightly: his forehead, his cheeks, his hair. They no longer heard the curses of Corporal Simion Firu, the noncommissioned officer on duty, swearing at the soldiers who brought in snow on their boots, dirtying the brick floor of the passage. "Damn you and those who brought you into the world."

But finally Farcasanu entered the cell. He was obviously disturbed, in a state of uncertainty, unable to express himself.

"Do you still want to go home?" the officer asked again nervously.

Sevastita, who had thought he was annoyed by her long stay or by something that had occurred on account of her, did not seem to understand him. But Balcescu did, and looked at him as if petrified.

"What?"

"Do you still want to go home?" the officer asked again nervously.

Sevastita now realized that he had taken his courage in both hands and was ready to accompany them home. Her face flushed, she came up to him on an impulse that showed her gratitude.

"Oh, could you really accompany us, sir?"

With the frown of a conspirator, Farcasanu quickly produced a fur cap.

"Put on your coat, this cap and get ready to leave. . . ."

But Balcescu remained motionless.

"I can't accept that, sir. You're risking your career and your freedom."

Sevastita, however, was bent on the plan being carried out. "Nothing would happen," she thought.

"We'll be back so soon—this very night. We must go, come Nicolache, put on your coat."

But he refused to put on his coat.

"No. I have no right to accept such a sacrifice."

Farcasanu suddenly smiled, as if it were beyond him to continue the game.

"There's no risk for me. A friend of yours has brought an order from the Chancery. . . . You've been reprieved. . . . The Moor, that's what he calls himself." Whereupon he opened the door wide to reveal the man on the threshold. "Come in, sir," he said happily.

Sevastita rushed to the door, amazed to recognize Alecu Golescu, overflowing with joy at bringing the glad news.

"You're free, my boy, absolutely free."

Balcescu, however, still suspicious, asked, without moving a step: "Am I the only one to be reprieved?"

"No! you've all been reprieved. For the last three days there's been a rumor that Dumitru Filipescu is on his deathbed. Crowds have gathered before the Palace, asking for your release. And Bibescu gave in. A sledge has already left to bring Dumitru Filipescu over from Snagov, and others have gone to Telega.

Sevastita sank to her knees, powerless, with a look in her eyes that seemed to come from another world. She took out of her muff the little icon she had brought to adorn the cell.

"I'm not worthy of this gift, Holy Mother of God, I'm not worthy!"

* * *

Still wondering anxiously whether Sevastita would induce Nicolache to sign, Zinca continued to wait on the bench in the Podul de Pamint Street.

In the slowly gathering dusk she finally caught sight of the young woman climbing the slope across the road. She sought to rise from the bench, trembling with the hope that she might bring the signed petition. But before she had time to get to her feet, she saw a vision, in the shape of Nicolache, following Sevastita. And as the vision drew nearer, she knew it to be Nicolache himself, whom she had never expected to see. Not knowing whether to believe her eyes, she remained as if petrified, her sight dimmed with tears. Then, shivering violently, unable to say a word, she collapsed in the frozen snow.

The two young people rushed towards her. Balcescu lifted her gently, holding her in his arms, surprised, shattered and bewildered to see her before him.

"Is it here you have been waiting?"

Zinca came to herself, but, still unable to speak, could only clumsily kiss his cheek, feeling he was too remote for her to reach. . . . While Nicolache, as if he were making an overwhelming discovery and was afraid to touch her, could only murmur again:

"Mother, is it here you have been waiting, oh, mother?"

Zaharia Stancu

(b. 1902)

Zaharia Stancu, Member of the Academy of the Socialist Republic of Rumania and vice president of the Writers' Union, is one of the most representative writers of contemporary Rumanian literature.

He made his literary debut in the interwar period, with poetry (*Simple Poems* [1925], *White* [1937], *The Red Tree* [1940], *The Magic Herb* [1941], *The Years of Smoke* [1944]), novels (*Typhoon* [1937], *Men in Tophat* [1941]), and numerous essays and lampoons.

With his novel *Barefoot,* published in 1948, Zaharia Stancu inaugurated a cycle of autobiographical novels, representing a vast fresco of social life in Rumania during the first half of our century. In this cycle, the author has brought out up to the present such works as *The Hounds* (1952), *The Roots Are Bitter* (5 volumes, beginning in 1958), *Courting Death* (1962), and *The Crazy Forest* (1963).

As a novelist, Zaharia Stancu is conspicuous for the acuity of his social observation and the power of his expression combined with the tender lyricism of his recollections. His prose is essentially lyrical in structure.

A large number of Zaharia Stancu's novels translated into foreign languages are already an integral part of world literature.

Lilac Time

Panting and leaning upon a stick, I mounted the embankment of the railway line and climbed up the hill. Leaning upon the stick and panting, I descended the slope again.

"You are breathing heavily," says Cuculet, "as if you had been pulling at the yoke."

"Yes," I answer, "I am rather out of breath. I have indeed pulled at many yokes."

"As for me, I feel as brisk as a lark. I never tire, no matter how far I wander."

"I never tired either when I was your age."

"Was that a long time ago?"

"Rather."

"When I'm as old as you are, will you still be of this world?"

"No, Cuculet, I'll not be of this world any longer."

The lad sighs. Then, he says in a whisper:

"I'm sorry."

"What are you sorry about?"

"I don't know; I can't explain. But I feel a sort of regret."

"I don't," I reply. "I feel no regret. I have lived my life and done what I could."

At the gate my relations bid my sister and me good night.

"We shall be seeing you tomorrow. . . ."

"No, not tomorrow," my sister says. "Haven't you noticed he's not feeling quite himself? So, better let him rest tomorrow."

"As you say. . . ."

They scatter, each one to his home. Cuculet pushes off too, with small, firm steps, his cocked fur cap shoved to the back of his head, his staff under his arm. He tramps along as if the whole world were his. Perhaps it is.

Above the village, in the heavens, the stars glitter.

"Just have something to eat and go to bed," says my sister to me. "You must be tired after the journey!"

"The journey . . . is it only the journey?"

On the porch, near the door, there's a woman leaning against the wall. She stands motionless, like a statue of stone, waiting. My sister asks her:

"Is that you, Filimona?"

"Yes, it's me . . . I've come to. . . ."

"Oh, yes, but you'd better come tomorrow . . . or no, not tomorrow. The day after tomorrow. My brother. . . ."

I tell my sister:

"Let her stay . . . since she has come. . . . Let her come in. I won't be able to fall asleep before morning anyhow. For quite a number of years my eyes haven't been able to shut before the early morning."

"Someone may have cast a curse upon you and chased your sleep away," says Filimona.

"Maybe."

"It's not me. Honest. I've never cursed you or wished you evil."

I lay my stick in a corner, take off my hat, drop my overcoat, and sit down on the edge of the bed. The room is warm and brightly lit. Filimona sits down on a chair too. She has some old army boots on her feet, and a black skirt. Black too is the shawl that is thrown over her head and shoulders.

My sister gives her a sullen look. If she weren't afraid to annoy me, she'd tell her to go. Filimona says to me:

"If then, long ago, there had been as much light in the house as now, you'd have stayed up all night reading. In the summer nights with a full moon you used to read in the moonlight."

"True. I used to read by moonlight. My eyes were good then."

"Aren't they good any more?"

"No. Not really. I have to help them with glasses."

A train booms past. The house quivers. The windows tremble for a couple of seconds. My sister says:

"I'm going to get the supper ready. My husband will soon be back from his work."

I remain alone with Filimona. My eyes are riveted upon the boots she's got on.

"You're looking at the boots? I wear them in winter. I got them from my youngest son, Floricel. You see . . . the other two, it was not I who buried them. One got killed off God knows where, in Russia. The other died in Hungary. Floricel was sent home without his legs. As a matter of fact, he was not sent home. They called me to Turnu, at the hospital, to see him and carry him away. I went with the ox wagon. I filled it with grass and set off. I unyoked the oxen near the hospital building and went in. There was a huge yard in front of the hospital! In the yard, under the acacia trees, some benches. On the benches some convalescent soldiers had come out like beetles to bask in the sun.

" 'Who are you looking for, mother?'

" 'For my youngest son, soldier.'

" 'What's his name, mother?'

" 'Floricel Lazu.'

" 'Ah, Lazu! You'll find him in the big ward.'

" 'Which way is it?'

" 'Just a moment, mother, I'll show you the way.'

"He rose from the bench and, limping along, the soldier led me to the room.

" 'That's the ward . . . go in and you'll find him in there.'

"I did find him. As white as a sheet, lying in a bed.

" 'Are you all right, my boy?'

" 'Quite all right.'

"He was covered with a blanket. A young doctor came up.

" 'Are you Lazu's mother?'

" 'Yes, I'm his mother.'

" 'Well, woman, you can take him home. Have you come with a wagon? With a cart?'

" 'With the wagon.'

" 'Very good then. Go and yoke the oxen, and we'll have him carried to the wagon.'

"I hitched the oxen to the yoke. A hospital attendant came carrying him on his back and laid him in the wagon, on the grass. Another man brought a bundle with his things.

" 'Have you put my boots into the bundle, Oprea?' asked my boy.

" 'Yes, I've packed them up too. . . . You could have left them to me though. You don't need them any more, anyhow.'

" 'I should like to give them to mother, to wear them . . . so as not to walk barefoot in the mud.'

"I brought him home. At the hospital they had given him two short wooden strap-boards. He propped his hands on them, and crawled along, leaping like a grasshopper. I was happy to have him back, even just a stump as he was. Oh, Lord Almighty, what a strange creature man is! . . . A cripple though he was, he was young and lusty. He got entangled with Mielu's widow, my daughter-in-law.

" 'It's a sin, Floricel, my boy. She was your brother's wife. She's got children with him. Three children, my boy.'

" 'It is no sin, mother. My brother is dead; he knows nothing more about it.'

" 'But the whole village is laughing at you, Floricel my boy.'

" 'Laughing? They ought to cry, not laugh.'

"What was I to do? I bore the shame. He then took to drinking. He would pick up any money he found at home and crawl along to the pub. There he would swill until he got drunk. Then he would start squabbling with the people. And squabble with the gendarmes too.

" 'Blue-bottles,' he would cry to them. 'You are young, lusty men. Why don't you go to the front too and have your legs chopped off by the Russian guns!'

"One evening he did not return home. I waited for him. I went to look for him. I found him in the morning among the brambles in the copse. His head was bashed in with a club. My daughter-in-law, Mielu's widow, ran away. I've been told she's got engaged as a servant with a rich family in Bucharest. She left the children behind, for me to bring up. I brought them up, with great trouble."

My brother-in-law, Saminta, the smithy, arrives. His face is sallow, his eyes blue, his moustache clipped short; his hands are large and his fingers thick.

"Welcome to our home, brother-in-law."

"Well met," I reply.

"Aren't you coming to supper?" asks my sister.

"No, I don't feel hungry. I'd rather stay and chat with Filimona. . . ."

"Chatting with Filimona and smoking all the time. . . . How can you be hungry?"

"Yes, I do smoke rather a lot. I can't seem to break the habit."

I look at Filimona. Filimona looks at me. Her hands have grown coarse and callous. Her brow is wrinkled. Her cheeks are sunken. Her lips are still full though. The wind has colored them blue.

"It's rather warm."

She takes the shawl off her head. She lays it on the back of her chair. Her head is covered with a kerchief. A black kerchief.

"Yes, it is rather warm," I reply.

"And you've filled the room with smoke."

"True, I have filled the room with smoke."

"Do you remember, then, after the war, you came home for a week?"

"Yes, I remember."

"It was springtime. The lilac was in blossom."

"Yes, indeed, I remember the lilac was in blossom, Fili."

"When you went away, you never wrote me."

"It's true, I never wrote you."

"Not a single line."

"Yes, Fili, not a single line."

"I fell ill after that. Oh, no, not because you hadn't written to me. Believe me, I quite understood that there, in that city of stone, you had no time to write."

"I really had no time, Fili."

"I don't know what I was suffering from. I felt as though I was no longer part of this world. I felt like running wild. Do you remember Bondar?"

"Which one?"

"Bondar, the gendarme corporal."

"A tall, pale-faced chap?"

"Yes, that's the one. He was just about to get his discharge. He was a native of a village somewhere near Pitesti. He told me he would marry me. He asked me to go with him. I did. I was sick of living in these parts. I couldn't bear to see the fields or the hills any longer. Even our houses . . . I could not stand the sight any more. I quietly packed up my gear in a bundle, and one evening I left with him, by train. After midnight we reached Pitesti.

" 'It's here we get off,' he told me. 'We will spend the night at the hotel.'

" 'But you won't touch me.'

" 'No, I won't touch you. Tomorrow we shall be going on home, and we'll get married.'

"He took me to a hotel, a sort of squalid shed, near the railway station . . . O Lord . . . what I was to see and endure! Oh, God! I wish I had died then.

"Unfortunately, Fili, man does not die when he wishes. Every one dies when his hour of death arrives."

"Some do die when they wish. They put an end to themselves. It's no great trouble after all! Just a noose round one's neck and that's all. The idea had crossed my mind. But I was afraid. And besides, it was not becoming! Strangers coming upon you and seeing you dangling from a nail, your tongue hanging out. . . ."

"No, Fili, indeed it's not becoming."

"Death does come, in the end, by itself."

"It does come, Fili. To every one. . . ."

She weighs my words. Her face grows sad. I hear her whisper.

"But, you, why are you so sad? I heard you've made good in life, and you've made a name for yourself. What is wrong with you?"

I light another cigarette. How many have I smoked?

I draw the hot, bitter smoke deep into my chest. I laugh. I roar with laughter. I rise to my feet and pace the room, my hands clasped behind my back. My sister comes in with a tray in her hand.

"I am glad to hear you laughing. God knows what deviltries this crazy creature has been telling you. . . ."

Filimona joins in the laughter and says:

"I've told him some of the jokes that are being told in our parts."

"I can imagine," says my sister. And she adds: "I've brought you something to eat. And a bottle of wine. To get merry . . . the two of you, as far as I know, were once quite fond of each other."

"Nonsense!" says Filimona. "Just stories. . . ."

My sister walks out. Her smithy is waiting for her in the next room. We have a bite of some cold meat with sweet, home-made bread. We have a drop of wine. Filimona wipes her mouth with her hand.

"I say," she tells me, "do you know it's the first time we two have dined together?"

"I never thought of that. Yes, indeed, Fili, you're right."

I fill Filimona's glass. I fill mine too.

"Cheerio, Fili, good luck!"

"Good luck to you!"

I find myself tossing down the glass of wine and I hear myself saying:

"Let's have another, Fili. . . ."

The walls of the room seem to rock a little. From the icon, St. George stares out at me. The Holy Virgin stares at me too. So does the Infant in her arms.

"You asked me, Fili, if there's anything wrong with me. If I have everything I wish? Yes, I have everything I wish. I am happy . . . happy. . . ."

Filimona cuts in sharply: "You don't look it! You don't look it in the least."

"Maybe," I say. "Maybe I don't look it. But, believe me, I'm happy, really happy."

"There at the hotel, Bondar ordered salami and sausages, and wine. I ate with him. I drank with him. You know how raw I was then."

"I know, Fili."

"And, drunk as he was, he took advantage of me. I woke up in the morning. I was all alone. He had gone. With all my things too. I went to the porter and asked him:

" 'Haven't you seen my man, the one I came with last night?'

" 'Yes, my girl, I have seen him. He paid the bill, and went his way.'

" 'And what will become of me, now?'

" 'Where are you from?'

" 'From' . . . and I broke into tears.

" 'Don't cry,' said the porter. 'Crying does no good.'

" 'What shall I do? What will become of me?'

" 'This has happened to other girls too. And you can do what the other girls did. We'll talk to the landlord, Mr. Fotache. Here he is.'

"A bald-pated, paunchy man was just coming down the stairs. He had a long, drooping mustache.

" 'What's the matter with the girl?'

" 'Why, sir, a rascal brought her in with him last night and this morning pushed off and left her behind. I would suggest . . . she stay on. . . .'

"Mr. Fotache weighed me up, pursed his lips, and uttered:

" 'Hem, Hem! She's got a good figure. She's quite fresh-looking. Trimmed up, she might be pleasing.'

"I burst into tears again.

" 'Call Madam Clara,' Mr. Fotache ordered the porter.

"Madam Clara was a lean, dry sort of creature, with a long pointed nose.

" 'Do you think she's worth keeping?' asked Mr. Fotache.

" 'Quite fine stuff! The only thing, Mr. Fotache, is that I'll have to waste some time on her. I'm afraid she's rather green and as you know, our customers are rather particular . . . Squire Georgel, Squire Costachel, to say nothing of that rotter of a prefect.'

" 'I could wash the stairs,' I said. 'Clear the rooms, sweep the yard.'

" 'We have no yard,' replied Mr. Fotache.

"Oh, Lord! . . . Need I tell you all I went through?"

"No, Fili, there's no need for you to tell me all you went through."

The walls have ceased to rock. St. George no longer stares at me.

Neither does the Holy Mother, nor the buxom babe that She holds in Her arms.

"One month later I succeeded in running away. I plucked up my courage and returned home.

" 'You've made yourself a laughingstock,' said my mother. 'We are the talk of the village. Who will marry you now?'

" 'There might still be a kind Christian heart somewhere.'

"And was there any?"

"A few weeks later, Onu Lazu, halfwit, asked me to be his wife. And I took him.

" 'You are no longer a maiden,' he told me when he had taken me home.

" 'True, I'm a maiden no more. . . .'

" 'Why is that?'

" 'You know too well! Bondar. . . .'

" 'Was it only Bondar?'

"I made no reply. He rushed upon me and hit me. He beat me to jelly. I lived with him for five years. Do you hear? Five years. And in those five years I suffered him three times. I bore him three boys. God called Onu Lazu to Himself. After that. . . ."

She falls silent. She gazes at me with her large, dry, black eyes, sunken in their orbits. She picks up a piece of meat. Bites into it. Then bites off a crust of sweet bread.

"The roast is tasty and good," she says. "The bread is good too. Your sister is quite a good hand at baking bread."

"Yes, she is," I answer. "But the wheat must have been well grounded too. And the oven properly heated."

"Yes," says Filimona, "to make tasty bread everything must be carefully worked out. But what about you. . . . Tell me how you have fared."

"I have fared very well," I answer. "Very well indeed. Haven't you heard about it?"

"Of course, I have. People get to know everything."

"Don't you see how fine I look?"

"Yes, I see. I have been looking at you all the while. I see you have to lean upon a stick."

"Yes, I do lean upon a stick. Now and again. When I feel tired."

With a light step, my sister glides in.

"I have brought you another bottle of wine. I see you want to go on chatting."

"Yes, we do," I reply.

"Well then, I'll say good night. Samintha says we had better turn in."

"Good night."

We drink. One glass after another. Filimona says:

"Cheerio! Good luck to you."

I rise and we clink glasses.

"Good luck to you, Fili."

"My luck! I don't wish my enemies the luck I have had."

Another train rolls by. The windows tremble once again.

"Midnight," says Filimona.

I glance at my watch.

"Midnight, Fili."

"Midnight only caught us chatting once."

"Only once, Fili."

"I'll be going now. I expect you want to turn in too."

"I'll see you home first, Fili."

"Why, I know the way. But if you like. . . ."

She picks up the shawl. Raises it over her head, wraps it around her shoulders.

Leaning upon my stick, I hobble along the village lane with Filimona beside me. The sky is as dark and steep as ever. The stars are still all alight. Filimona guesses my thought.

"Yes, indeed. . . . The same sky above. The same stars. The same as then. And do you realize, man? Under our soles the same earth."

"The sky, Fili, never grows old."

"The earth, man, never grows old either."

We pass by a large, newly erected building. The moon beams upon its windows and lights them up. I ask:

"Whose house is this, Fili? I don't remember it."

"It's not a house. It's a school. Of course you can't remember it. It was built last year."

We reach a large yard. In the middle of the yard the same house with its sugar-loaf roof.

"This is the house Tracalie lived in," I say.

"Tracalie! Haven't you forgotten him?"

"No."

"Now it's a man called Lungu, from Stanicut, who lives here. He married Tracalie's younger daughter."

"And Tracalie himself?"

"He? He's under the hill, near the old church."

A dog awakes. Jumps across the fence. Barks at us. Prowls around us. I ward him off with my stick.

"Get away!" Filimona shouts at him.

The mongrel recognizes her voice. He quiets down and slinks off to his couch.

"Here we are," she says.

"Is this the gate?"

"Yes . . . the same gate."

The moon has risen and climbed up to the top of the heaven. The air is blue-gray. My head is burning. I clasp my temples in my fists. And press as hard as I can. I say:

"Fili, I believe the lilac is in blossom."

"Yes, it is in blossom," she replies. "The lilac broke into blossom last night. Is it only now that you have noticed that?"

"Only now, Fili."

I fold her in my arms. She presses her body against mine.

I raise her face and bite deep and eagerly into her fleshy, dry, bitter lips.

The sky begins to rock. The stars sway. The moon swings. The earth reels.

Filimona breaks herself loose. I hear her voice whisper:

"You silly fool! What good is it now? There's no sense in it."

"True, Fili, there's no sense in it. . . . "

The gate opens. And closes.

I wander aimlessly through the village. The dogs don't know me. They bark at me. Some of them jump at me.

I stop. I stop and ward them off with my stick.

Alexandru Sahia

(1908-1937)

An original writer, concerned with the pressing problems of his time, Alexandru Sahia, dying at an early age, had cut short a literary career that evinced vigor, a challenging spirit, and genuine artistic gifts.

He is the author of profoundly realistic short stories and sketches, written in an epic vein, with a penetrating insight into the realities of life. He, in turn, evoked the tragic experience of war ("Father's Return from the War," "In the Blood-Soaked Fields of Marasesti") and the hard life of the industrial workers ("The Living Factory," "Revolt in the Port"). He condemned racial discrimination ("Spring Execution," "Race-free Unemployment"), and depicted with a powerful brush the hapless existence of the poor peasants ("Rain in June").

Alexandru Sahia also was active as a publicist.

Rain in June

The June sun was burning and, here and there, the grass had already withered away. The land had dried up, and the wheat was thin, with starved ears. Thousands of blue cornflowers and stork's-bills brightened the burnt furrows.

About the middle of May there had been a few short showers, but not a drop of rain had fallen since.

For that reason the plains of the Baragan looked mournful. The waters of the Ialomita wound along, tamely, between dry banks, crawling towards the Danube.

Now and again came the dull neighing of some horse in the sweltering heat and drought. The sky was glassy and blue. There was a single cloud in the distance, rising from the marshes, where the Baragan plains ended.

Petre Magaun had stopped working. He straightened his back, and his bones cracked. A light wind blew from the east, lifting his shirt from his back, soaked with sweat as it was. The palm of his right hand was green from the paint of the sickle handle. He plunged the tool into a sheaf, then, with both hands, rooted up a bunch of knotgrass. He rubbed it between his palms and then crushed it. But the green color had gotten into the skin and would not come off. The sweat trickled its way down from his forehead onto his cheeks, then under his chin, then dripped onto the front of his linen shirt.

Petre Magaun was tall and gaunt, long-necked like an ostrich. He had girt himself round the waist with a piece of rope and he was barefoot. He always worked with his trousers turned up to his knees, so that anyone could see there was no flesh on his right leg: it had been taken off by a piece of shell in the war. That's why his right leg looked like a worm-eaten log.

Working by his side was Ana, her belly bulging out and almost touching her chin. She could hardly move and looked like an overfed duck. She walked with her feet wide apart, groaning under her breath.

Ana too was barefoot. She had wide feet deeply chapped; her toes stuck out sideways, like spindles. With her left hand she carefully clutched a handful of wheat stalks, while with her right she slowly cut them, closing her eyes with the sharp movement. It was the ninth month of her pregnancy, the month of childbirth.

She had tied a yellow kerchief round her head and over her mouth. She could not bear the dust shaken from the straw or which rose from the ground.

Every now and then she lay down face upwards on the stubble, like an overdriven beast. Then her eyes were wet, and her belly a shapeless bulge.

Petre Magaun looked at his wife intently. She seemed horribly big and as she bent reaping, her nose and whole face disappeared, buried in her belly. When she had cut a few handfuls she wiped her eyes with a corner of her kerchief, so that Petre thought she was crying.

He spoke:

"Are you crying, Ana?"

Ana did not answer.

"You're not crying, are you?"

Ana propped her hands on her knees, drew them slowly up her thighs, then along her hips; and with each movement she stuck out her belly a little more. She loosened her kerchief, turning its corners upon the top of her head.

She answered, breathing heavily:

"Why should I cry?"

"I thought you were crying."

"It's just a bit hard; though why it should be so, I don't know. As if it were the first time I was like that."

Lisandru Lucea's ox, tethered though he was, came capering up to the furrow and was almost into the wheatfield.

Magaun rushed at him, cursing and striking him with the hook of the sickle.

"Damn you, you bloody beast, couldn't you have found somewhere else? As if I had a hundred acres. I've only got this patch. . . ."

The voice of Lisandru Lucea, who was also reaping a few fields away, was suddenly heard:

"I say, man, don't hit my ox. Drive it back here to me!"

All was still again.

Petre Magaun reaped with a sort of fury, catching handfuls of wheatstalks in his large paw. Meanwhile Ana hardly moved. She was far behind. When he had gone too far ahead, Petre came back to help her, bringing her up even with him.

They were both silent. Often, when the sickle stuck in the brambles, Petre burst out swearing. Ana still remained silent.

She turned towards him and drew a deep sigh, in order to get some relief. Her eyes were inordinately large and sad.

A heavy stillness hung over the plains. One could almost see it in the air, trembling in the sun. The earth exuded a fiery heat, which was why the stalks broke easily. The cornstalks had turned yellow before their time, twisted up into dry funnels.

Yet the peasants were working. One could see their backs, as they advanced on all fours over the fields. They reaped. Often, from time to time, they raised themselves and looked up at the sky. The robins struck the drooping ears with their wings.

Towards the marshes a white patch of cloud was shaping; several trails of smoke were already dying away.

The drought spread like an infection, catching at everything.

You could feel it in the blue, glassy sky, in the bellowing of the beasts, in every stalk and stem, in the dried-up earth. It grew deaf and oppressive; like death, it swallowed up water and life.

Petre Magaun looked at her and saw her belly rise and fall, rhythmically. He thought: "Ana here, what a life! To bear them one after the other, like a bitch, just anyhow!"

Then he asked:

"How long is it now until your time?"

"My word, Petre, I wish I knew. I don't think it's time yet. Maybe another week."

She smiled as she lay there, her eyes upon the sky.

"Then get up, Ana, and let's finish."

Ana rose. She was no longer even reaping. Rather she tangled the wheat ears, leaving a wake of stalks behind her.

Petre patiently picked them up when he bound the sheaves. At last he said:

"You might go to the cart, Ana. You'll get some rest there. It's shady there and cool; I can see this is too much for you. I don't mind myself, but you mustn't have your child out here. The whole village would talk."

"Oh, the village—as if I were the only woman with child to be taken in the field. The men may laugh, but we have them wherever it takes us. It's God's will, not man's."

She wiped her face with the corner of her yellow kerchief, then carefully straightened her apron over her belly and made for the cart.

Under her feet the earth was burning. She too was tall, almost as tall as Magaun. She walked with long steps, but, because of her pregnancy, walked unevenly. Along with her walked her shadow, appallingly long and misshapen. It touched the ends of the stubble, darkening it for a minute.

She was soon stretched out under the cart. But there was not much shade. Half her body from the waist down was still in the sun.

The sharp pains of approaching childbirth shot through her body, warning her that it might happen at any moment. It had happened this way before, but only once. They had been harvesting corn in the autumn and it had been drizzling.

The pains always frightened her. She didn't wish it to happen just then. Cold sweat cooled her loins. Desperately, with her left hand, she hung on to the cart wheel, while with her right hand she clung to the stubble, uprooting it.

She lay quite still, her eyes fixed on the sky, almost breathless.

Up there, where the sky really begins, there were two skylarks chasing each other, no bigger than dark dots. They were singing. On the ground, in a cornfield, a quail was singing too. The straw mat was spread nearby, and Ana realized that she ought to have stretched herself upon it. But she didn't dare to move, and lay still.

A frog with a wet back hopped towards her, up to her cheek. It halted and stared at her with open mouth. Its eyes bulged while its white spotted chin kept pulsating rhythmically like a watch.

Ana felt sick at heart and would have liked to drive the pains away. The pains, however, were too frequent now. She coiled up like a loose spring, groaning, hanging on tightly with her whole arm to the cart wheel. There was a sudden, bitter smarting in her knees. She felt as if her legs were being wrenched off her hips.

Then, suddenly, she turned cool, after which her heart and eyes were flooded with tears of joy. The arms round the wheel went limp; she shook the dust off her left hand.

She raised herself onto her knees; her eyes were still larger and more troubled. With uncertain hands which had gone bloodless, she bent to pick up from the stubble—her child.

Dust and straw clung to the baby's red flesh. She rose to her feet and turned it to the sunlight; she gave it a few jerks. A cry was heard. Ana drew him to her breast, wildly, kissing the top of the baby's head.

She brushed off the straws and the dust. She pulled away her apron, making it into a swaddling cloth. She quickly placed it in the back of the cart, stretching the rush mat above it for shelter.

Then, just as if nothing had happened, tying her skirt around her waist, she set out in search of her man, to work.

Petre Magaun was now soaking wet as if he had been bathing in a stream. Many sheaves lay behind him in disorder.

The scorching air grew still more sultry and the earth had turned almost purple, as if somewhere in the Baragan plains the fires of Hell were burning.

Ana had come near, yet Petre took no notice of her. Straight, sickle in hand, she waited for him to say something. Magaun, however, went on reaping furiously. The handful of wheat bending under the sickle's edge he cut with a single jerk.

"Petre," Ana said, "look. I've been delivered."

Magaun cast a look at her without raising himself.

Her voice was weak and there was an ashen taste on her lips.

"Yes, Petre, I've been delivered!"

He dropped his sickle, then stretched his back.

"What could I do? It happened once before, one drizzling autumn day."

Petre would have liked to say something, to curse abundantly; he picked up his sickle, however, and he continued reaping. He asked:

"Is it a boy, Ana?"

"A boy, Petre."

His neck, like that of an ostrich, stretched still further and he felt like laughing.

He asked: "Why have you come then?"

"But there's nothing the matter with me. I feel quite light."

Once more Ana lagged behind with her reaping, while Petre ran far ahead like a greedy wolf. He felt the wheat ears tickling him under his wet chin, some sticking to it.

A warm wind was blowing from Russia. It breathed dandelion-down and thistle-down, whirling them on.

As he placed the sheaves upon the earth, Petre glanced at his wife. Her apron was gone, and the skirt sat all awry upon her. She could hardly gather the wheatstalks in her hand, while her sickle trembled unsteadily upon the wheat before cutting it. It was a heart-rending sight.

She suddenly rose with troubled eyes. Sickle in hand, she said: "I am not well, Petre. I must go."

"Yes, you'd better go, Ana, and you mustn't come back. Stay and look after the child. See that ants don't bite him while he's asleep and cover him up warm."

Petre was left alone while Ana went down the field with bloodless lips to the cart where she had left the child.

She had hardly reached the spot when the same pains, sharper if anything, began again. She lay down by the wheel in terror. A child with a bottle in his hands came near her, looking for water, but suddenly took to his heels, stumbling as he ran.

Lisandru Lucea's ox had again come into the field, digging his horns into a haystack. Ana thought: "If Petre were to turn and see him."

The pains of childbirth again kneaded her body, curled up round the cart wheel. A groan and at last a feeling of endless, final relief. A cry was heard. Ana sprang up and, smiling, picked her second son from the stubble.

In the fields, under the scorching June sun, with no shade, the mewling of the two babies could be heard. Ana listened intently to the wailings of the one in the cart, musically mingling with the newborn's attempts to breathe.

A pair of butterflies fluttered nearby. Ana, however, anxiously shielded her child against them.

Soon the whole harvest field had heard that Ana, the wife of Petre Magaun, had given birth to two sons. Several midwives came, out of the blue, bathing the offspring in well water, binding their navels with red thread torn from the bottom of their skirts.

Petre came too, although he had not finished. He had seen a crowd at the end of the field and was afraid there might be something wrong with Ana. He leaned against the front part of the shaft, staring at nothing across the fields, a stranger to all that was going on around him.

The horses, with long tethers, grazed some distance away, pacing round rather than feeding. They had been trampling the whole stubble and had found no blade of grass anywhere. They were snorting, raising dust on all sides.

"Your horses are bare-boned too, Petre. One spatter of rain at least, or we all perish," said Antonie Lungu, leaning his elbows upon the polebolt.

Petre moved up and said:

"It's a hell of a life. I've got seven children—nine including these who've just come—and with the two of us, that's eleven mouths to feed. You might say that the little ones don't need much, but there are still nine of us. I've got only this one plot, an acre. Then I haven't paid the road tax; I haven't paid the pasture tax."

"You should hurry, Petre, or they'll come and seize your belongings. It's happened to some people: they've seized their blankets and covers."

"But how can I hurry up, man? A fine phrase, 'hurry up'!"

"You should sell something."

"What can I sell? As if I had anything to sell."

Clouds had unexpectedly begun darkening the face of the sky, dark clouds, rising from where one might think the Baragan plains came to an end, from the marshes. They were joined by others, bursting like vapor from the Danube. These were darker and closer. The sun was covered, its face joyless.

Dull heat lay upon the whole plain. It was sultry; yet, now and then, there were suggestions of coolness.

It thundered repeatedly and the clouds hung lower.

The ground was still burning hot underfoot.

"I'm going, Petre," Antonie said, "it's coming on, rain." Ana was alone on the top of the cart, holding the babies in her arms. Under her the peasant women had stuck piles of hay to avoid the jolting; she was raised almost completely above the cart. She was literally perched there and looked like the Holy Virgin.

It thundered in quick succession.

The thunder grew louder and louder. The first raindrops fell, large and heavy. Petre untethered the horses, harnessing them in haste. He threw his tools into the cart and walked round several times to see that he had not left anything behind.

"Are you all right, Ana?"

"All right, Petre, but drive slowly."

The horses started off of their own accord, and Petre felt glad. He was thinking: "Maybe they smelled the rain and that's why they're pushing on."

But from the village the rain was really coming. It came at full speed, spreading like a bead curtain, thick and filmy.

The horses snorted, pricking up their ears. Petre had spread the rush mat, tilting it tent-like over Ana and the babies.

First there was a kind of breeze, a fine spray of rain, then it turned into a furious downpour. The rain, however, ran ahead of them, unfurling over the Baragan plains, as far as it could. Petre too squeezed himself in, under the tilted mat, but his legs were still outside in the rain. Ana had doubled up over the babies, her body a second shelter to them. She held them in her arms, their backs upon her thighs. With every jolt she shouted: "Go slow, Petre, slow!" and raised them as high as she could, rocking them anxiously.

The horses trotted along, and from the road rose a pungent smell of soaking wet dust. The water ran down in torrents along the ruts in the road, rushing into the ditches.

All the weeds, the thistles, the burdock leaves, the tufts of hemlock, raised their heads from the ditches, washed clean and brimming with life.

The stubble field itself, wasted and dry, raised its bristly crop like a clean brush.

The water had come through the mat, wetting the back of the cart and the straw.

Ana huddled up as close as she could to protect her babies. Now and then she pressed her lips to their noses to see if they were still alive. A lukewarm breath of air stung her lips like pinpoints. They were breathing.

Petre came out from under the cover. He would rather stay in the rain. Inside there was the heavy, musty smell of lying-in. Only once did he glance at Ana, and he saw her eyes brimming with tears. The yellow kerchief, wet with rain, clung to her head. Her face was distorted, drained of blood.

Magaun felt something like a rush of hot water to his own eyes. Yet he didn't actually know whether he was crying or whether it was the rain trickling down from his head.

Right and left the fields now hurried past, under the spattering rain, freshened up and black. It was rain in June. The horses looked stunted with their harness, too large for them, rubbing against their wet shining flanks. They were now quicker, and Magaun struck them with the whip's handle right between their shoulder blades. After each stroke, which meant a fresh jolt to the cart, he turned his ear fearfully towards the mat to hear if Ana were calling. But Ana had long been quiet.

A thunderbolt had fallen somewhere, clearing the vault of the eastern sky.

Under the pelting rain the village looked dead. The cart creaked, wet about the axles, and turned in at the gate into the yard.

Magaun jumped down quickly. On the porch the whole swarm of children: they were sure that their mother was under the rush mat. They could not understand why it took her so long to get up. Petre ran to the back of the cart, shouting:

"Vasile, old man, and sister Maria, come quick and help get Ana down; she gave birth to twins."

The neighbors arrived in a twinkling, barefoot, with sackcloth upon their heads. Ana's two eldest daughters came running from the veranda crying that they didn't understand what had happened. Petre looked into the cart again, bringing out the two babies, one by one, from under the mat. He handed them to Mariana, who took them into her arms, covered them with a corner of her black head-cloth, and carried them in, running. Ana was still stiff and doubled up from bending over the babies. They stretched her upon the bed near the window, beside the babies.

The seven youngsters were left behind, some on the porch and some in the doorway, all scared and crying, not daring to enter the room.

They were ragged and dirty. Petre had no eyes for them and did not mind their howling. From time to time, like an obsession, the daily meals rose before his eyes, with nine mouths around the table, always hungry. And very shortly there would be eleven.

Out in the fields, the rain had fertilized only a narrow stretch of land for him. Other people held a hundred times as much and worked with hired hands.

He cursed and went out into the rain again to unharness his horses. He let them loose, to wander at will.

A duck quacked desperately, having lost her mate. The leg with the muscle cut off by the shell was smarting. The pains struck to the bone.

The two neighbors, Vasile and Maria, with sackcloth upon their heads, had come out upon their doorsteps.

"Don't be angry, neighbor Magaun; they're boys. God bless them."

Petre would have liked to reply, to thank them, but they were out in the street already. The rain had slackened. Only some small drops fell now, at intervals. The acacia trees shook their branches, waking up the sparrows in their nests.

The children were lined up again on the porch, seven of them. Inside, Ana raised her face to the window; it was waxy-yellow.

Petre stood alone in the middle of the yard, his feet sunk in the mire of the June rain. He preferred not to go inside. A horse neighed. His hungry whinny seemed to hang on to the acacia branches, before the very eyes of the children.

Magaun left the yard. He went to Antonie Lungu to find out how many people had had their belongings seized today for overdue taxes.

Ana and the crowd of children had no idea where Petre was going.

From the yard, beyond the fences, other horses neighed. Petre walked on, stunned, down the middle of the road; he actually saw before his eyes, constantly hanging on the acacia branches, the voices of his bay horses. He said to himself, trying to understand: "How in the devil's name can this be—voices hanging themselves?"

Dusk was stealing with ashy steps and no sound. The clouds broke, firing the peasant's windows with a crimson glare.

Geo Bogza

(b. 1908)

Member of the Rumanian People's Republic Academy, Geo Bogza is a past-master of literary reportage. His feature articles, truly poems in prose, pay tribute to the working people and their magnificent achievements.

Geo Bogza made his debut with surrealistic verses. After years of searching he finally worked out an original formula suited to his personality: literary reportage. His talent raised this genre to artistic heights unattained by any previous writer.

He published several volumes of literary reportage: *Lands of Stone, Fire and Clay* (1939), *The Book of the River Olt* (1944), *Men and Coal in the Jiu Valley* (1947), *The Gates of Glory* (1951), *Years of Resistance* (1953), *Geographical Survey* (1953), *Contemporary Pages* (1957), and others.

Geo Bogza is a remarkable and highly original stylist. The characteristic feature of his style is his "technique of intensification." Every aspect of the world assumes monumentality under his pen and the feelings depicted are rendered with vigor and pathos.

Geo Bogza is also the author of a short story, "The End of Iacob Onisia" (1946), reproduced in this anthology.

The End of Iacob Onisia

Christmas had come throughout Jiu Valley.

This great, dismal holiday had set in from Lonea as far as Lupeni, though many did not know what to do with it. The mining villages were wrapped in a deep, almost oppressive stillness. Not a single wheel was seen turning anywhere; everything stood stock-still, buried in silence. The last train had left the station at midnight, and no whistle had been heard since then. The siren had not sounded at ten o'clock at night nor at four in the morning.

At dawn the light fog soon lifted; by nine in the morning, a cold, clear sunshine flooded the whole valley, and everything looked like a mass of ice that no one dared break. Through its transparency everything looked as if it had fallen deep into water which had then frozen around, bringing all things to an absolute standstill. Christmas, with the perfect stillness it had brought, had pushed the valley farther north overnight, turning it into a polar region.

All around, things seemed to be congealed everlastingly. Who would have dared shatter the giant mass of ice covering the world? It was Christmas day in Jiu Valley.

Then, in this immutable vastness a human body tumbled down into the void from a height of over six hundred feet, and all around and a long way off, the air was rent by a fearful scream. Doors were opened, heads peered out of windows; that was how Jiu Valley finally began stirring. A little later the telephones began to buzz like mad at the managing office of the pits and at the mining inspector's offices in Petrosani.

"A man has fallen off the funicular railway at Dilja, sir! He's dead, sir!"

That was how the first telephone call began on that Christmas morning. It must have been quite unusual and unbelievable, for the chief of the inspectors' offices was staring with eyes wide open and kept speaking into the receiver: "It can't be! It is impossible!"

Impossible in this valley where so many misfortunes and so many disasters had occurred? The engineer said the man could not have fallen off the funicular railway that morning, because it had stopped running the evening before.

"He's just fallen, sir, this very minute!" the hoarse voice that announced the misfortune insisted at the other end of the wire. Then they rang up the funicular station of Aninoasa, then that of Petrila, the Cermini, and the police station. In Jiu Valley the telephone bells started ringing everywhere, and for a long time. The people, who had expected a day of rest and quiet, heard the long buzzing of the telephone bells and they all felt that they were ringing in an unusual way that boded no good. They reached out their hands, picked up the receivers, listened in astonishment, and spoke several times into them: "It can't be! It's impossible!"

The chief engineer of Aninoasa, who controlled the funicular, was away at Vulcan; they made the electric echo of the telephone bell ring after him, wherever it could be heard, and finally it found him. When he had listened to what was being said to him, he answered as the others had before him, but with even greater assurance: "It's impossible! The funicular stopped running last night!"

"The man is lying dead in the valley at Dilja. He fell and died this morning. . . . All the snow is splashed with blood."

Then, all of them visualized this picture and accepted it as something real and not subject to doubt. However, a question occurred to all of them, and some spoke it out, pushing it along the telephone wires, between the mountains, towards the station of Dilja: "How? How did it happen?"

At first no one could answer. The telephone bell rang everywhere. In the offices, in the engineers' homes, at the termini, at the gates—everywhere—those who had been called, called others in turn and questioned each other. It was Christmas day and a vast silence had pervaded the valley, but now the telephones were breaking it, in the air as in people's hearts.

Everyone was called two or three times from two or three different places and in his turn called others just as many times, as in a wood where a hundred people hail each other, awakening all possible echoes at once. They were sitting in well-heated rooms which they could not bring themselves to leave, while away among the snowcapped mountains a mangled man was lying, about whom they were trying to learn, from afar, why he had died and how, on that clear, motionless Christmas morning.

"Get some men to carry him away on a stretcher. He can't be left here overnight; the wolves would eat him up . . ." the same hoarse voice at the other end of the wire was saying once again, the same voice that had roused them all and that now could hardly utter the words. The telephone started buzzing again, calling the life-saving team from Petrila.

It was a quarter to ten when the schoolmaster of Aninoasa reached the market place in Petrosani, where several people had already gathered. As he came up to the first group, he said suddenly, gesticulating with both arms:

"Listen, friends, a great misfortune has happened at Dilja. A terrible thing! I saw it with my own eyes."

He need not have added the last word. His eyes were still wide with fright and white, and his face, although frozen, was as pale as a dead man's. "I've never before seen a man so pale on such a frosty day," those who met him that day said later. "He had death in his eyes, frozen and white like a ghost."

The schoolmaster of Aninoasa had witnessed the terrible misfortune that had occurred that morning.

And that was how it all became known—what the people had vainly tried to find out by asking one another on the telephone: how the misfortune had happened.

Then, on all sides, the telephone bell started ringing anew. At the mining inspectors' offices it was ringing for the twelfth time.

"Yes, I'm listening. He was in the car and came out of it? But, good God, what was he doing there?"

"Wanted to follow the wire cable with his hands? He fell into the precipice; yes, I see."

And that is how, on that Christmas morning, the chief of the mining inspectors at Petrosani started investigating the strangest and most distressing misfortune that had ever happened in Jiu Valley.

That morning two sledges started from the managing offices of the pits, loaded with men wearing black coats, among which the policeman's khaki overcoat was discernible. At the same time, the men of Petrila had left, carrying a stretcher, taking a short cut over the hills. The schoolmaster of Aninoasa was returning in one of the sledges to the place where he had experienced his great terror. The mining villages were smoking quietly through hundreds of chimneys.

At first the sun shone right in front of them, and they found it almost pleasant. Mount Paring rose along the skyline like one single dazzling mass. The sunlight came straight down on its snowcapped crests, while its three large peaks soared up into the sky like so many gorgeous pyramids of light. Only the mountains to the south, standing in the shade, had darker outlines, wrapped, as it were, in a thin, bluish mist. In contrast, everything in the west shone. They went on in this way for a good while. The bells of the sledge kept tinkling with a metallic sound almost sweet to the ear. They listened to them in silence, feeling the sound enter their brains, soothing them after the jarring buzzing of the telephones. Over and above the buzzing that still filled the people's heads, the melodious rhythm of the sledge bells fell like a layer of snow, quieting and covering everything.

Then they felt the cold. The sledges had taken another turn and started along a valley towards the north. The ridge of a hill had hidden the sun, and in the shade the cold became so bitter that they had to wrap themselves up well in their coats, shivering.

"It was twenty degrees last night," said a voice from one of the sledges. And the men felt even colder. Still, to the north, towards which they were going, the mountains, all bathed in light, shone more brilliantly than anywhere else. As they faced the south, the sunshine did not fall straight on the crests only, but on their entire height; they shone in one single mass, from one end to the other, on all sides, like a vast, white realm exposed to the sun. But the sledges were gliding along the foot of the hills in the shade and the cold, and the people in them seldom raised their heads from the upturned collars of their coats to gaze sadly and mistrustfully at the dazzling white light in front of them.

They had almost reached the heights above the place from which they had started, right against Petrosani, on the other side of the mountain, and they went on, still further uphill. Then, one of them happened to look up suddenly and see in the air, against the white background of the mountains, a black dot hanging above the chasm. It looked like an eagle, motionless in the air, watching for its prey. It was one of the carriages of the funicular railway. Soon another one became visible, hanging above the precipice. For a time this one too looked like an eagle; as the sledge advanced, the two birds of prey moved against the spotless background of the mountains, gliding along constantly until they stood out against the calm, blue vastness of the sky. There was not one single cloud.

Now the sledges were beneath them. On either side of the valley, on either crest of the mountain, stood, higher still, two iron supports, the tops of which were connected by four cables spanning the chasm at a height that shut them out beyond the boundaries of the world. There, as under a circus top where trapezes swing, was the realm of daring and madness. The men gazed at the two black dots, remembered why they were there, and shuddered.

They started climbing the western slope on foot, along a narrow path. They had to reach the other side where there was no road for the sledge. They walked briskly. There was no buzzing of telephones, no jingling of sledge bells—only the dry, harsh cracking of the snow. Sometimes it crunched under their boots like a piece of linen being torn. The iron support in front grew bigger and bigger, and gradually the numerous iron girders of which it was made became distinct. The ascent was becoming wearisome. The men were hot and panting. Then one of them said:

"On these slopes, no matter how bitter the cold, you are sure to sweat."

Then something quivered painfully like an indescribable foreboding in the heart of one of the six men climbing the mountain. It was as though two black birds which had long been looking for each other had met in the air, and the fluttering of their wings had come to his ears, troubling him.

If, at that moment, the chief engineer had slipped down in the snow and had been able to doze off and dream, he might have seen in his dream a man coming towards him with arms and legs broken, his face smeared with coal and blood and wet with snow, whispering again into his ear: "Yes, on these slopes, no matter how bitter the cold, you are sure to sweat." Then the two black birds would have been recognizable and known by name. Unaware, one of these men had uttered the sentence that cleared up the strange event they were witnessing; it was another who felt his heart flutter with premonition.

Twenty-four hours before, the same words had been spoken in this same place by the man who now lay crushed on the other side of the mountain.

On these slopes, no matter how bitter the cold, you are sure to sweat! And indeed the sweat was running in drops down Onisia's chest and back. And he had gone only half of the way over the hills. He had another mile and a half to go along the river Jiu, to reach Petrila.

From Aninoasa to Petrosani there were three deep valleys and the ridges of three tall hills to cross, at the edge of the mountains. The footpath led across them, dipping low into the valleys, then up the crests, and down again. There could not be a more severe ordeal. Each time he reached the summit of a hill with great difficulty and saw that he had to go down the other side at once and then to climb the opposite slope again, a dull rage seized him. "A real punishment!" he muttered. And he would remember he was really being punished.

He was not ashamed of being punished. The chief engineer had laid his hand on his shoulder and said: "Onisia, you've got to understand!" And, he had understood indeed. Two months would soon be over! He had not been sorry at the time. It was autumn, the plum brandy was being made, and he had come to the second shift walking rather unsteadily. As a matter of fact, he had walked quite unsteadily. They would not let him go down into the pit. So he had struggled and entered the cage by force. Those on the ground had tried in vain to shout at him. Did anything happen? No. They all admitted nothing wrong had happened. He had gone to the workings, had not quarreled with anyone, had worked quietly, and had loaded an extra truck of coal. But they punished him all the same.

Neither the overseer, nor the foreman, nor the engineer wanted to punish him. They knew Iacob Onisia too well to want to punish him. They knew Iacob Onisia well; indeed they did. But the chief engineer was easily alarmed: he said he'd have to report to the general board in Bucharest. "Why do we need to report to Bucharest?" the head of the sector had asked. "You're young," the engineer had answered. "You haven't seen much of life yet. Suppose some day others did the same and there'd be trouble and we'd want to punish them. Then they'd complain to Bucharest that we did not punish Onisia. And suppose the bigwigs asked why we had not punished Onisia. So we had better write and be on the safe side."

And they wrote to Bucharest all that had happened, that Onisia had been a decent collier for seventeen years at Aninoasa and that he did not deserve to be punished. A fortnight later the answer came from Bucharest: he had to be punished! He must be transferred to

Petrila for two months. They were all sorry; they laid their hands on his shoulder and said: "Onisia, you've got to understand!"

And he had begun his punishment on November 1. From Aninoasa to Petrila there were three kilometers in a beeline along the wire cable of the funicular railway. It took three quarters of an hour. But, on foot, over the hills, it took him nearly three hours. When he was in the first shift, he left home at three in the morning. His wife and children were asleep. At half past four, when the sirens whistled to wake up the men for the shift, he was climbing the second hill. By six he had hardly got to Petrila.

It had been going on like that for five weeks. Twice he had been in the third shift, from ten at night till morning, and twice in the first. Now he went down at two in the afternoon and came up at ten at night. A few days more and his trials would be over. And a good thing, too, for he was quite worn out. The way was hard. He had already worn out a pair of boots. It seemed as if all his life, as far back as he could remember, he had done nothing but go up and down hills. Above his head, the cars of the funicular railway kept coming and going like big, black birds. And he kept walking, sometimes on the ridge of the hill, sometimes low down in the valley.

At first it had still been autumn. Along the way there were straggling birches, their leaves turning yellow. Had it been only a walk, it would have been a lovely one indeed. Mount Paring was always before his eyes, dark about the middle of its height, but snowcapped. Nevertheless, here on the sun-scorched hills, the people of Dilja grazed their cattle among the peaceful birches.

About a week later, rain set in, and the footpath filled with mud. The way had become very hard. He struggled with the hills and thought wrathfully of the big men in Bucharest. "To be transferred to Petrila for two months! What did they know about the distance between Aninoasa and Petrila? They ought to come here and get into the mud if only once, at three in the morning, like ghosts, long before the cocks have crowed." Then things became worse. The rain became chillier and changed into sleet. If, at least, they'd allowed him to take the funicular! But no one was allowed to take it. Only the surveyor of the line passed once a day from one end to the other and then back, standing in the car like a huge bat, its wings spread.

A week before St. Nicholas' day—he was in the second shift then—the blizzard began, and for three days after there was nothing but snow everywhere. Sometimes it would snow for a whole night, but the following day the people of Dilja would make a footpath again. They needed money for Christmas and started for Aninoasa or Petrosani, carrying to market a sack of apples or a young pig.

When Onisia reached Petrila, a few old women dressed in black—they were widows—were standing in front of the entrance to the pit, selling *sorcovas** to the men of the first shift, just coming out. He entered the courtyard and then remembered his children at home; he went back and bought a *sorcova.* At night, when he'd leave work, there would be no one at the gate. The siren blew long to announce the two o'clock shift. He hurried toward the mine. A large iron stove filled with coals was blazing in the yard, and a young girl in trousers was warming her hands. He went by smiling and called to her without stopping: "Good luck!"

Seeing him come with the *sorcova* the men at the gate teased him: "Say, Onisia, if you take it down to the mine, it'll be a pretty sight when you come out!" and "Come along, Iacob, and wish the ponies a Happy New Year."

He left it at the surface, however, with one of the truckers. In the mine, he had found a good helper in a man from Cimpa, with whom he got on very well. Together they filled fourteen trucks.

That day all in the pit spoke only of wine, sausages, and roast pork.

Onisia had killed his pig three days before. And he would buy wine the next day, at Aninoasa. In front of them, all the while, they had a hard black wall of coal, but in their mind's eye they saw large joints of red meat, such as they had seen at home in their troughs, and then they swung their picks with increased mettle, almost with fury. Large lumps of coal fell to their feet. Only the ponies, well fed every day, fat and calm, pulled the trucks without sharing the eagerness that was exciting the miners and the joy that filled their thoughts. Not even the oldest of the ponies, who knew a lot of the secrets of the pit and had a sixth sense, suspected that the following day was Christmas and that they were to be blessed with two days' rest in the stables.

However, in order to see to it that nothing amiss could happen in the following two days, about five o'clock the miners lay down their picks and, taking hold of their hatchets, started the propping. By the end of the shift the workings were lined with new white boards, well supported on all sides. The seam of coal was hardly visible, and there was a smell of fresh pine wood. Now the pit could be left alone for two days to spend Christmas in quiet.

In the courtyard lighted by electric bulbs snow sifted down in

---

* *Sorcova* stick adorned with artificial flowers and ribbons which Rumanian children hold in their hands while wishing a Happy New Year to grown-ups.

small flashes. The colliers walked to the gate, their shoulders slightly bent, like living shadows. Each of them carried his round log of wood under his arm or on his back. They parted, wishing each other good luck; then Onisia was left alone, and he quickened his pace. He crossed the Jiu over the railway bridge and started climbing towards the mining village of Bucovina. In the dark he could hear the cars of the funicular railway pass. Tonight it was to be the fifth time. Only it was colder than ever and high up there he could freeze to death. But rather than cut across those hills, he'd . . .

Four times already Onisia had returned to Aninoasa by the rope-way, stealthily, in the dark, and he was going to do it again this time too.

No one suspected anything, and he passed over the three deep valleys, in a beeline, like a bird, without going up their slopes and then down into their depths. He crossed above and looked down at them with hatred and joy as on mortal enemies now become quite harmless. Down below, the valleys writhed like vile dragons, and they would still have liked to torture him, but could not get at him. He passed overhead in the funicular, and each time he felt as though he were thrusting a spear into their throats, like Saint George when he rode over the dragon.

Iacob Onisia walked through the village of Bucovina, between the two rows of lighted houses where people were making their Christmas preparations. In front of every house there was a black stain in the snow where the women had thrown out the basinfuls of lye with which they had scrubbed the floors of their homes. In his house, too, the floors had been scrubbed and there was a holiday smell about.

The cages kept clattering in the air, passing above the houses in the village. Somewhere on the hill, children were singing Christmas carols, going from house to house.

Onisia climbed the wooden scaffolding at the terminus as stealthily as a cat. He reached the platform, and then the cars passed by him slowly, one after the other, like the carriages of a train in a station when the train is starting; all you've got to do is to jump into one. He looked a couple of times towards the surveyor's lighted cabin, let two cars pass, and, when the third came up, threw his hatchet and the *sorcova* into it, and, taking firm hold of it with both hands, leaped into it over its iron railing. He felt the walls with his boots, found a log, and quickly sat down on it. Below, near the surveyor's cabin, a dog had begun to bark, so he buried his head between his shoulders, squatting on the floor of the car. Who could have seen him now? The car was gliding smoothly above the ground, towards Aninoasa. In an hour he would be home.

People who have pictured heaven to themselves and then related what it is like, have had little imagination. This thought dawned upon Iacob Onisia repeatedly in the first moments when he felt so happy to be carried through the air in the carriage. To be in heaven was to travel by the funicular over hills and deep valleys, without the slightest fatigue.

Far behind, Petrila was vanishing in the distance, looking like the Pleiades when they are setting. A short while after, however, when he was above Petrosani, the world burst into a fairy-like vision which no one could have credited. Holding the *sorcova* in his hand, Onisia sat on and gazed.

As far as eye could reach, the earth was like a sea of burning embers glittering all the time. Hundreds upon hundreds of lights, a myriad of will-o'-the-wisps, were shining in the night, far away, to the edge of the mountains. So many were crowded in the middle of the town that one could scarcely distinguish them from one another. It was like a jumble of lamps of all kinds—like people on a market day. One, a very tall one, rose high above the others, like a lonely man who does not mix with the crowd. On the outside came those in rows along the streets of the mining village, one behind the other, in straight lines. Then, they became sparser but kept stretching one by one farther and farther away into the depths of night.

In the middle of this sea of light, cleaving it in two, ran a river of darkness. Yet, against its pitch-black background there still could be seen here and there a few glimmers, red or green like so many sickly glowworms about to die. It was the railway station with its twenty lines, and between them the snow had been covered with coal dust and cinder so that everything was blacker than the very darkness of the night.

From the town there rose a sort of din, wave after wave, like the hum of an apiary in which the bees, coming across some sweet flower, want to carry all its nectar home. Above this sea of lights the car carried Onisia slowly towards Aninoasa. The lights gradually started sinking, but very, very slowly, like a world sinking into the depths. Lightly, almost imperceptibly, the cable was dragging the carriage towards the crest of the first hill.

To the north the snowcapped mountains loomed out of the dark and drew nearer, ever nearer, as though eager to be touched by him. When he was quite high up, at the side of the first mountain, Petrosani was still discernible far behind, as at the bottom of an ocean, with its lights merging and forming a huge diadem. One of the termini was drawing near, and Onisia lay low in the carriage lest he should be seen. Then he realized he was chilled with the cold, and he crouched close to the wooden partition to ward off the stinging cold a little. Above the frozen deserted plateau, the car was gliding between the iron supports like a ghost.

Then came the first of the three valleys. The cables of the funicular railway spanned the precipice from one end to the other, without any support, curving only slightly, and the car followed them, floating above the chasm in the dark. The cables then rose up the opposite slope, reached the strong support on which they rested for an instant as though to gather new strength, and immediately started across the second valley, which was also the lowest. At its bottom one could scarcely make out a few vague lights—the cottages in the hamlet of Dilja. The cage seemed to be on the same level with them as it passed in its aerial progress, moved forward slowly for a while, then stopped. The grinding of the wheels gliding along the cables stopped too. Suddenly there was a deep silence.

It could not be more than half past ten. Onisia huddled at the end of the carriage and waited. He thrust his fists into his pockets as far as he could, but between their edge and his coat sleeves, which were too short, there still remained a strip of bare flesh, and he felt the cold there as biting as though he had been wearing handcuffs. From there the pain ran up under his coat to his elbows, where it became very sharp. He tried to soothe it by pressing them against his ribs as hard as he could. Maybe it would have been better if he had gone on foot, seeing it was so bitterly cold. But he would have got home past midnight. A good thing there was no wind. The car would soon start. He rolled a cigarette and lit it with great difficulty.

The cigarette was almost smoked and still the car did not move. Then, at the moment when he was taking the last puff at it, the greatest misfortune in his life happened. As if kindled by a spark, everything was destroyed in an instant.

That is how things happen in the pit when gas takes fire. The rails of the trucks are wrenched from the ground and twisted in the air. Along the shafts men lie dead, their hair and clothes burnt. And some pony blocks the way—a mass of charred flesh.

Since evening, when he had left by the funicular, a gas had made its way into his head, accumulated within him, and now it exploded. And he was as completely destroyed as if he had been in a pit where gas had taken fire. Nothing might have happened. But a spark had kindled it at the very moment when the shafts were full. Now, within him, everything turned into smoking ruins. When had a man ever done so much harm to himself with one single thought? Suddenly it had occurred to him, "Tomorrow would be Christmas! The funicular would not start. It would be stopped for two days." And these last two thoughts, which were so closely linked with the first that he scarcely had had time to think them, flashed through him, sparking the catastrophe.

In one single instant everything was ruined: a real explosion had taken place within his heart and mind when he realized in a flash that he was the prisoner of the chasm, of night and frost. He suffered terribly. With eyes frozen by dread he viewed the world differently. It seemed to him a terrible, treacherous enemy; everything that had happened, beginning with the day in autumn when he had got drunk, seemed now a fearful trap into which he had stumbled.

All the men were at home now, enjoying the warmth of the hearth, and would stay there for two days. The pits and the installations above ground were deserted. For two days and two nights nothing would stir while he, suspended in the car above the precipice, would perish with hunger and cold. He felt like howling. Instead, it was a wolf that howled, away in the valley, at Dilja, on the skirts of the forest.

How would the hours pass for him from now on? And what would become of him? Like colliers who, having been saved from the bottom of the shafts, come out staggering, their lamps out, their clothes torn, his thoughts shaped out, torturing him, and prolonging the catastrophe. But this violent anguish of mind began to wane when, instead, two precise sensations arose and took possession of his whole being, like two implacable demons thrusting long, sharp spears into his flesh. He felt hungry. He felt cold. More and more, without any way of escape, he became a prey to this excruciating suffering. He was unable to endure it any longer.

And then, above Mount Paring, the moon rose.

Has any man ever had so fairy-like a sight before his eyes while suffering the pangs of death? A few tears gushed out of Iacob Onisia's eyes, trickled down his rugged cheeks and froze there. "O Lord, do not desert me!" his lips muttered while, mortified, he was gazing at the grand sight unfolding before his eyes.

The long shadows of the mountains had begun to move, gliding above the earth with a stately slowness that seemed to send a shiver over the world. Bulky masses of darkness hovered over the snow, turning round and round and trying to catch up with each other, like beasts of bygone times, roused to life in the dead of the night. Meanwhile, high upon the crests, the mountains shone as though ablaze. Glittering flames, some white, some blue, just as cold and unreal, danced above the peaks, as if all the treasures of the earth lay within them. Cold, silent and white, the moon flitted about the frozen glass surface of the sky.

To the north, the mountains nearly rose into the air like gigantic temples of white marble.

"O Lord, do not desert me!" the thoughts and lips of the man hanging above the precipice kept murmuring in a sort of mechanical prayer. Then this cold, polar landscape in which the big shadows of the mountains were the only moving things, suddenly became alive, and hope kindled in Iacob Onisia's heart. Yet this hope, like the lights that danced above the mountaintops, was unreal, unrelated to the heavy fate which from the beginning had pressed down upon the breast, on the life, on the heart of the poor collier from Aninoasa.

As in almost every year, as though it were a tradition, wolves entered the hamlet of Dilja on this Christmas Eve too. There were a few sheepfolds there. At first some muffled noises came up from the peasants' yards; then the dogs broke into a medley of frightful, desperate barking. The next minute all the doors were flung open, and inside, while the women turned up the light of the oil lamps, the men dashed out roaring at the top of their voices, like wild beasts. Seizing pitchforks or clubs, they rushed towards the sheep pens, running barefooted in the snow.

The fight seemed to be taking place at one end of the hamlet. There, men were roaring louder than anywhere else, urging one another while the dogs rushed forward, concentrating their barking on this place. Black patches were gliding over the snow. Most likely the wolves had stolen a sheep and were falling back with it towards the forest. Small, reddish flames blazed up several times, and the reports of a gun rang out from valley to valley.

Hanging above the chasm, Iacob Onisia looked down at what was going on, at first hopefully, then as though at a performance from another world. How could all this be of any help to him? The men's feet down below were stamping the ground, and they could fight the wolves. Lucky for them! His mind was sending them desperate messages: "Please don't leave me to die here; don't, please!" But his throat, stiff and dry, could not utter a single word. Who could have heard him?

Down below, the uproar of the dogs died down, and frightened bleating was heard. Towards him, too, big wolves were coming from the void, about to tear him to pieces; and he would not be able even to feel the warmth of his own blood flowing out his veins. He was frozen to the marrow of his bones. His fur cap, the worse for wear but still good enough, which had always kept his head warm, now seemed as thin as cigarette paper. Still, when he took it off, to stick his closed fists into it and warm them a little, he felt his forehead bound all around in a narrow circle of ice which burned like vitriol;

so he put on his cap again at once. His feet were as stiff and cold as stumps. And he was hungry, a deep, black hunger that drained all his strength. In the depth of his belly was a torturing, painful emptiness, more distressing than the chasm gaping below him. There, in the thick of the forest, the wolves were eating the sheep and having their fill. They too were lucky. And so were all those whose feet touched the ground. He alone hung between sky and earth, surrounded by the cold air, by the waves of cold that tore at him mercilessly.

His agony was to last long and to be accompanied by delusion. Several times he strained his ears; his heart was flooded by a sudden warmth when it seemed to him that the cage was starting. . . . Maybe the ropeway had only been out of order; maybe it would still run all night, until dawn. Those thoughts cast a warm, friendly light upon the world. He would soon be home, in the cozy, warm room, on the floor well scrubbed with lye. But, alas, the funicular was still motionless, still as a stone, in the black mass of the frosty night.

Had they known he was here, they might have started it and hauled him to the village. But what would the chief engineer have said? Another punishment—no doubt about it. Thousands of thoughts and familiar faces crossed his mind; his mate at Petrila, his own wife, his children, the chief engineer, the publican at Aninoasa, the shepherds of Dilja—all in turn came to him in the cage, spoke to him, scolding or advising him what to do, then faded away in the dark.

He felt the handle of his hatchet, the log at the bottom of the carriage, and an idea, a grand one, occurred to him, making its way with difficulty through his frozen mind. He sat the log upright and started chipping it. The hatchet rang against the frozen wood. Then he dealt a sure blow at it and split it in two. Plying his hatchet in the moonlight, he looked like a man busy at his work—weirdly at that late hour of the night and so high up, cut off from the rest of the world.

His hands numb with cold, he struck a first match under the heap of chips, but it went out before it could kindle them. He struck another, impatiently, held it underneath until the whole match burned and the flame licked his fingers, but still the chips would not kindle. Then he took the *sorcova* and set fire to it with a third match. The paper flowers caught fire at once, one after the other; their petals writhed, and he stuck them under the heap of chips which finally started crackling.

It may have been one o'clock in the morning, or later. The moon had sailed past the white crests of Mount Paring and was now above the dark forests of the Surduc pass. The huge shadows of the mountains kept moving, flitting over the whiteness of the snow. Now there were other shadows too, small, quivering, fleeting shadows that attended the unfolding of the drama being played in the silent realm of the night and the snows.

The shadow of Onisia's figure stood out up to the waist against the partition of the carriage, while his shoulders and head emerged from it; they were lost in the dark, their outline dim and much enlarged, like that of a giant. Maybe his shadow reached the white columns of the mountains to the north, beyond which lay, not a long way off, the site of the ancient Sarmizegethusa. Iacob Onisa was the last Dacian in those ancestral parts to spend the night in the open air, by the light of a pine-wood fire. But of the millions of men who in the course of two thousand grim years had spent the night in loneliness with nothing but a fire to keep them company, had there ever been a more tortured, unfortunate soul than his?

There was an old shepherd at Dilja, made rather simple because of a beating at the hands of the police back in the time of the Empire. The next morning, after hearing what had happened, he related the following: after the incident with the wolves, when the cocks crowed for the third time, he went out again and found himself standing stock-still with fright. In the black sky, very high up, his eyes saw quite distinctly a part of hell. There, in the murky night, was a cauldron with pitch like those in which sinners burn in Hell, such as are seen painted in church. Red flames and sparks rose from within it, and in the middle a man was writhing his body about. Alarmed at this apparition of Hell, especially because of its appearance during the holy night of Christmas, he went in, crossing himself. A little later, looking through the window, he saw the flames going out, and shortly after the cauldron of pitch vanished in the dark.

The schoolmaster from Aninoasa, whose wife had died in childbirth that autumn, had been asked to spend Christmas day with the priest of the Orthodox Church at Petrosani. Since he wished to attend Mass, he had left home early in the morning. There was a hard, dull bitterness of frost. He had climbed the first hill, then the second, and when coming down the valley to Dilja, the footpath he had taken suddenly showed the traces left by the fight waged that night. The snow had been swept away, and in the place where the dogs had fought the wolves, were strewn big tufts of hair. Soon, bloodstains could be seen, which made him sick. The memory of the hospital, as white as the snow, with stains of blood here and there, was still vivid in his mind and painful.

To avoid this sight, he looked up and in the very first moment saw the unusual thing that was about to happen.

High up, on the wire cable of the funicular, a man sat astride the side of the cage, looking down as though to sound the depth of the precipice. Whatever was he doing up there? The schoolmaster had been walking for one hour, and all the while he had seen the cars lined out along the route, motionless, at their great height. How had that man got into the cage above the precipice? It was not one of the red cages in which people down below were used to seeing the line surveyors pass. But he had not too long to wonder.

Dumfounded, he saw the man in the carriage, after a brief hesitation, take hold of the cable with both hands, letting his feet hang in the void. Then, after wavering one more moment, he advanced along the cable holding on with his hands.

Catching his breath, his blood frozen with fear, the schoolmaster realized what was going on. That man moving hand over hand along the cable above the precipice was trying to reach the iron support at the top of the hill. He might have some forty-five yards to go. And the cold up there. . . .

Against the blue background of the sky, the car and the man were two distinct blotches. The car stood still, while the long, thin shadow of the man moved slowly to the left. Hanging above the void, he was advancing. When he released one hand to place it farther on, his body lost its balance and threatened to break away from the wire that supported it. Then the man quickly brought his other hand up, resting like that for a few moments, while he hung on with both hands and his body got back its balance as he seemed to gather new strength. Then he rapidly jerked one hand farther along, as though to catch a bird, and brought his other hand ever more rapidly into line with the first, avoiding the danger of hanging on by only one hand. And his legs kept beating the air as though they were trying to help him along.

However, like a tired swimmer who sees the shore is still far away, his arms found it harder and harder to move. He had managed to move perhaps ten yards from the car. The time he spent clinging with both hands to recover strength was getting longer and longer. Once he lifted his hand to move on, but brought it back in no time. Shaking all over, his teeth chattering, the schoolmaster stood and gazed.

The man on high no longer had the strength to move on. Once more he tried to lift his hand and set it a bit farther on, but he pulled it back even more quickly.

Clinging to the cable with both his hands, he hung quite still while his legs beat the air slower and slower, as in the throes of death.

The schoolmaster felt his heart throbbing violently in his chest, sending hot waves of blood to his temples and his throat. And the ghastly climactic moment was not long in coming.

A bird flew past the line of the ropeway; perhaps the man up there had time to see it with his eyes wide with fear, thinking his last thought: "Oh, if only I had wings!" Then one hand detached itself from the cable, without moving as it had hitherto. The body hung for one moment by one hand; then his other hand detached itself too, and he began falling. He came down in the air, wheeling 'round and 'round, his arms and legs moving frantically as in an epileptic fit; at the same time the schoolmaster felt him falling through his own body, cleaving it like a knife from top to toe. When he had almost reached the ground, the schoolmaster thought he saw the doomed man's face under his disheveled hair, his eyes looking at him with awe and hatred; and at the very same moment the valley was roused by a heart-rending scream.

It was Christmas day.

Down in the village, at Dilja, there was a wide expanse of snow. When the men who had started from Petrosani reached the top of the second hill, they perceived far down on the white expanse of snow a somber group of men moving slowly hither and thither, changing places in turn. Those who had left from Petrila with the stretcher were waiting there.

The place where the man had fallen from the car bore traces of the night fight where the wolves had crossed on their way to the forest: tufts of hair and stains of blood. The impact of the man's fall had scattered the snow about as a big stone would have, and bespattered it with his blood. He was completely crushed—a hodgepodge of flesh, bones, clothes and snow mixed with blood and coal dust, all frozen into a single mass of different colors, painful to behold. His big hands, which had held his whole life in them and had not been able to keep it, were swollen and blue. His face, intact, was turned upward to the sky. His eyes, wide open and frozen, gazed at the heights from which he had tumbled. His struggle was over now. The valleys that had tortured him all through the autumn and which he had then crossed over in the funicular railway, like dragons transfixed by his spear, had taken a most terrible revenge on him. He had fallen into the lowest of them all as into the mouth of the most wicked and ruthless of all those dragons. High up, the car out of which he had fallen stood black and immobile, like an airbound coffin.

On either side the iron supports rose on the mountain ridges, rising to dazzling heights.

With shovels in their hands, the men from Petrila were drawing nearer, to clear away the snow.

The funeral passed through Aninoasa about noon, watched from all windows by sad, gloomy faces. Everyone knew Iacob Onisia, and this sudden violent death on Christmas day had filled them with deep sorrow.

In the dead man's kitchen, which they had to cross in order to carry the body into the room, the pig killed a few days before was still in the trough—large pieces of red bleeding meat. On the stretcher the four men were carrying other large pieces of crushed bleeding meat. While the dead man's wife sobbed and beat her head with her fists, all those present crossed themselves when the procession entered; and it was a dismal, somewhat threatening feeling of mournful silent protest rather than pious awe that could be read on their faces.

Yet another one of them had met a sudden, unfair death.

Two days later, when the funicular railway started running again and all the cages were searched, at the bottom of the one in which Iacob Onisia had traveled was found the hatchet, the heap of ashes from the fir-wood fire he had made, and in a corner the *sorcova* only half-burnt, its remaining flowers crumpled and covered by coal dust.

Marin Preda

(b. 1922)

Marin Preda is one of the most representative novelists of the younger generation of Rumanian prose writers. His first book, a collection of short stories and sketches, *Encounter in the Fields* (1948) revealed the writer's genuine talent. He is the author of two excellent novels, *The Morometes* (1955) and *The Squanderers* (1962), which are recognized as two of the most valuable productions of contemporary Rumanian prose. The former, drawn from village life, portrays the dissolution of the little peasant households on the eve of the second World War, while the latter novel, drawn from city life, debates a number of problems of ethical significance.

Marin Preda's works reflect his predilection for psychological characterization and analytical observation which reveal new aspects of peasant psychology. Rural literature in the past tended to lay special stress upon the elemental impulses of the country people. The new prose writers—and Marin Preda in particular—strive to bring out the humanity and generosity innate in the soul of the simple man.

In his novels *The Unfolding* (1952), *Windows in Darkness* (1956), and *Daring* (1959), characterized by their deep-searching insight and drama, Marin Preda illustrates conflicting concepts in the life of the contemporary Rumanian villages, which—in the new socialist system—are undergoing a vital transformation.

The novel *Fever* (1963) reveals a new facet of Marin Preda's literary activity—exoticism. The author carries us to countries in the distant East, depicting the struggle of the peoples for their national and social liberation.

Excerpt from *Daring*

At about 9 P.M. the First Battalion set off on one of those night marches which at first seem a blessing to soldiers but which later turn into something quite unbearable. With its brief and silent halts, and its strict orders regarding noise and smoking, such a march dulls the spirit to the extent that thoughts of the past and future mingle in your mind, and nothing is felt but the throbbing of the heart. The heart beats fast, the ear is on the alert, the eyes open wide in the darkness, and through the body run strange, cold shivers. Your teeth chatter. Your lungs seem full to bursting. You would like to cough.

You yearn to hear the commander's voice, to know what is in store for you—a danger greater than the one you have just escaped from, or rest and good food and sleep and warmth to your heart's content. But you cannot hear the commander's voice, and you mustn't cough. Time passes and the quickened pace of the march makes you realize that so far everything has been easy, and that from now on the going will be harder, and there can be no thought of the march coming to an end soon.

The pace has accelerated. More time passes; the quick breathing makes you choke, and hot shivers are now running through your body. Your legs begin to tremble, and gradually something new worms its way into your heart: a feeling of fear—fear that you can't carry on, that your legs will refuse to obey you. . . . You would like to groan, to tell Vasile or Gheorghe that you're on the point of collapsing, but you don't groan and you don't tell them anything. You realize that Vasile and Gheorghe would like to tell you the same thing, and for a time the thought puts new strength into you. But soon you are again overcome with fatigue. This time you feel as if you were going to faint; your eyes grow dim, and, without knowing what you're doing, you lose control of yourself and begin to groan. . . . Suddenly you start. A sound has reached your ears; you see something before you, there, a man at the top of a little mound. You are right in front of him now. . . .

"Come on, boys, come on, we'll soon be there!"

Ah! It's the captain! As if by miracle your legs stop trembling, your heart beats less fast. . . .

"A rest? Shall we have the chance of a rest? All right, sir, we'll keep it up, sir!" There is a new feeling among the men. The captain has ordered that the pace be slackened. Now they have slowed down and . . . can it be true? Have they really got there?

"Halt!"

The men drop to the ground in exhaustion. Quiet. . . . Somewhere quite close a cock crows. Had they really marched so long? Dawn is breaking, it seems. There is unimaginable delight in the rest—it's like a song of joy, and one's soul seems to spread like vapor over the earth.

"Line up, boys!"

Yes, we are lining up! Never before has the earth seemed so sweet to lie on. Never before has its rich clay been so soft to their hot bodies.

"Line up, boys! Only a hill to climb and then we can sleep. Forward, boys, it isn't far to go. . . ."

"Let's sleep now, sir. . . . Let's sleep, and then we'll attack as we've never attacked in this war. . . . We'll fight to the death. . . . But first a little nap . . . only an hour!"

"No, boys, it can't be done. Forward! A little sleep is poison. It sucks up your fatigue, but it also sucks up your strength. Forward, march! And silence! Check your arms! Don't lag behind!"

The hill! Nothing on earth seems as dreadful as that hill that must be climbed. If you have to pass through fire, you cover your eyes with your hands and run; and if it's water, you can swim across; but a hill leaves you helpless. Every step is a torture. Every time you raise your leg the hill is still there before you, its face close to your hands and cheeks, tempting you to lie down, never to rise again.

Anton went on trudging up the hill, his nostrils filled with the smell of the sweat of the horses drawing the guns by his side. How they panted! A sharp whistling sound like a death rattle issued from their throats. . . . Anton drew close to one of them, and laid his hand on its spine. But he couldn't feel the spine, only something moist, rounded and strained, which twitched under his hand and climbed and climbed . . . .

"Easy, easy, my pretties! We've got a long way to climb!" Anton whispered to the horses. "Easy! There's still a long way to go. . . ."

An hour or two before daybreak the battalion had reached the top of the hill and began to descend into a wood. The exhausted men were slithering between the trees and after another hour's march the order to halt was given. The men threw themselves to the ground and immediately fell asleep.

After three hours of sleep, they were up again, feeling cold, their teeth chattering, and their faces as gray as the soil. It was still dark, but a purple sky could be seen over the ridge of the hill toward the east. Captain Ioan went among the companies at his usual brisk pace, rubbing his hands, and his cheerful and contented voice aroused memories in the men's minds which saddened them and made them long for home. Way back, when they had been kids, their fathers had walked about like that in the courtyard in the morning, spurring them on to their work. . . .

Why must you always wrest yourself from sleep and always pursue your way towards some goal? In the evening you had gone to see her, and you had held her close in your arms as both of you were lying in the hay. And she had clung to your heart and you had been staying there. . . . It was as if your heart was afraid of so much happiness! And it had been late when you got home and you had hardly had any time to get a bit of sleep. And then no one had pitied you—neither your father, nor your brother, not even your mother. They had all called out to you to get up, get up, get up. "Come on, Ionica, come on, lad! You'll go on sleeping till noon; people'll make fun of us; the girls are going to laugh at you. . . ." And it's cold, with the hoarfrost a spar thick. The cart runs over the field, the horses snort, and here are the maize stalks, wet and stiff with the hoarfrost. Take hold of the sickle and cut them down, cut them down while they are still moist, while the sun is not yet up. . . . It is cold, the sky is leaden, and the thought of her makes you breathe deeply and your heart goes out to her. . . . She alone could make you forget your weariness, she alone. . . .

"Come on, lads, come on. It'll soon be over and then we'll sleep. . . . The women are waiting for us in the village. They have spread the table for us, lads."

"Oh, sir, stop it, sir, for right now I'll throw down my gun, and drop, and die. . . ."

"What's the matter, my boy, are you sick?"

Captain Ioan stopped by a soldier who had moved a few steps aside and propped his gun against a tree. He stood there, his head lowered, and his clenched teeth sunk into his arm. His shoulders quivered.

"We'll soon be out of this, my lad, and then we'll go back home," the captain said, shaking the trembling soldier. He looked at his watch, and an instant later came the order: "Ready! Lieutenant Petrescu, the signal!"

A rocket flared up! "We've reached the target!" It was followed by another, a red one: "We're attacking now." And that very moment the artillery began to roar somewhere in the rear.

"Well done, gunners!" the captain exclaimed with satisfaction.

The companies rushed forward towards the village. Soon they were in the streets. There were mighty cheers, the rattle of automatic rifles, the report of guns, and in less than an hour the place had been taken.

Actually it looked more like a sprawling hamlet than a village. The enemy units, few in number, were annihilated; they had no time either to fight or to withdraw.

Captain Ioan carried out his plan step by step. He had fallen upon the enemy's rear and was sure that the Germans would not abandon their front and run to occupy the hills and build up a front at the other end of the village. To prevent the enemy's withdrawal towards the bottom of the hill, which would have cut him off, Captain Ioan ordered First Company to advance in a forced march towards the end of the village, the place he had called the bend of the horseshoe. At the same time, to forestall the enemy pouring into the village and encircling the battalion, he ordered Second and Third Companies to advance along the flanks. Success was assured: First Company would occupy the bend of the horseshoe before the enemy could do so, and the other two companies would defend the flanks; this would make it impossible for the enemy forces to establish a junction. The regiment advancing in the rear would widen the breach made by First Company, completing the thrust. That's how things had been planned. Should the Germans continue to show a broad front to the Rumanian regiment facing them and not bother about the battalion in the rear, so much the better; the battalion would occupy the hills and the enemy would be caught between two fires. Captain Ioan soon heard firing on both flanks; the shots came from the enemy on the hill. Exactly what he had foreseen was happening.

The anti-tank battery had stopped for a while in the market square of the village, before being ordered to advance in the rear of First Company. Hardly were they out of the market square, however, than they had to halt anew. The horses were completely spent, almost unable to raise their legs, and kept turning their heads towards the closed gates of the courtyards.

"Corporal," the junior lieutenant called out to Anton in that awkward voice of his.

"Yes, sir."

"Take two men with you and then at the double into that courtyard over there!" The officer paused for a few moments—a habit of his which always caused the soldiers to feel uneasy. Why should the corporal take two men? And why should he run into the courtyard?

"And fetch two horses!" the officer added dryly. "March!"

Yes, two horses were needed. He was right, but couldn't he have said so at once?

"Ailoaiei, Radu Florea!" Anton shouted, imitating the officer's dry tone.

"Corporal!" the two men shouted.

"After me, march!" Anton cried with bulging eyes.

In mimicking the lieutenant, the men released some of their tension, though they made sure the officer was out of earshot. When they came to the gate, Anton knocked at it with the butt of his gun, while Radu Florea gave a long, shrill whistle and began to shout: "Hey, uncle! Come to the gate! Can't you hear? Are you deaf?" And he whistled and shouted again. Then, after a few moments he turned to Anton: "That gate, corporal. . . ."

"Let's take it off its hinges," Ailoaiei urged.

"That man in there'll get me off my hinges. Another minute and I'll put a few bullets through his window!" Radu Florea said.

"Heave, heave!" the men uttered with a groan and soon they toppled the gate over.

"There's the stable," Radu Florea said.

But they were met by a ferocious dog which, howling like a wolf, was ready to jump at their throats.

"Hey, shut up, will you, or I'll give you a few bullets to eat."

"A rich man's courtyard," Ailoaiei observed, his eyes sweeping round. Look! The fellow has a motorbike, too. And what would that thing over there be? A threshing machine, a reaper?"

The courtyard was paved and a concrete ditch ran along the stable. They rushed into the stable and Radu Florea had soon untied two big horses.

"How is it the German left such horses behind?" he wondered.

"Well, what would we have done?" Ailoaiei queried.

Hardly had they taken the horses out than they found themselves facing a fat, mustachioed man, dressed in a yellow leather coat with a black collar and jackboots. The man was in a fury. Wrenching the halter from Radu Florea's hands, he jerked the horses towards himself. His mustaches were all abristle, and he was mumbling something.

"Get hold of the horses!" Anton ordered. Radu Florea took the man gently by his coat collar and explained: "Chee, chee, chee, prr, prr, prr, prr, you must give us the horses. And don't give me such an ugly look!"

The man began shouting and threatening them with a boldness which first puzzled and then enraged Anton. They took the horses out and made quickly for the battery. The owner of the horses followed them, muttering all the time in his language. When he caught sight of the officer, he went straight up to him, took out a piece of paper and held it under his eyes, shouting something unintelligible. The officer took the paper, scanned it, and then said something to the man. The latter suddenly brightened up and exclaimed, nodding his head: "Ah, Rumanians, Rumanians!"

"What's the matter with him, sir?" Anton asked.

"He thought we were Hungarians and that's why he refused to change horses for us," the officer explained. "Change the horses and let's get going," he ordered dryly.

They had been left far behind the column of troops.

"Hungarians? What the hell should Hungarians be looking for round here?" Radu Florea wondered.

"Change the horses!" the officer shouted.

They felt uneasy. Something was up. On the right flank shots rang out continuously, but on the left flank there was a strange quiet that had already lasted too long.

"Many Hungarians withdrew from Budapest together with the Germans and are now fighting alongside them," Anton explained to Radu Florea. "That man in the village thought we were Hungarians. Their uniforms resemble ours."

The officer had climbed onto a gun carriage and was looking through his field glasses towards the left flank. He seemed very uneasy, almost alarmed, as he climed down and called out to the gunners to get a move on with the battery. Anton had bent down to wrap his puttees more closely round his leg. Suddenly he stopped, remained motionless for a few moments, then, quickly finishing with his puttees, made a dash for a gate and climbed on to it. He raised his field glasses:

"Tanks!" he shouted, and jumped down. "Look, sir, over there!"

The gunners were confounded. The officer ran towards the gate, but had barely swung himself on it when he fell back riddled with bullets. A rattle of machine-gun fire suddenly burst from the left flank, and then came the repeated, terrifying roar of heavy guns. Some fifty paces ahead of the battery a house went up in flames and the acrid smell of smoke filled the air. Before the gunners could realize what was happening, they found themselves amidst a mass of terror-stricken soldiers running in all directions. The men crossed the market place in disorder, but were soon back swearing and cursing. And this first stream of humanity had hardly scattered when a second poured over the place. Anton couldn't make any sense of their shouting. Several times he heard the words "Second Company . . . Second Company. . . ." Several men fell over the guns, seriously wounded.

"What's going on, brothers?" Anton shouted, rushing over to them.

One of the wounded groaned and, suddenly looking up, uttered a frightened scream: "I'm dying, I'm dying!" White as chalk, he slipped from the gun, face downwards, his arms spread out. Other wounded gathered round the battery. The roar of the guns now extended towards the right flank.

"What's happening?" a gunner shouted. "We've been left behind. Let's get away from here!" another shouted, terrified by the sudden quiet around the battery.

The gunners drew close together, puzzled, looking in all directions, then rushed towards the market place. Anton jumped up from among the wounded men, took hold of his automatic rifle and fired into the air. The gunners stopped, rooted to the ground.

"Tenshun!" he shouted at the top of his voice. "Where are you running to?"

He calmly slung his rifle over his shoulder and went up to them. Where they were running to? That question didn't mean that they mustn't run, but that they'd better know which way to take. The gunners rallied round the corporal, their eyes urging him to decide quickly, there being no time to lose.

"Battery!" Anton shouted, his eyes sweeping round in calm self-assurance. "I've taken over command. To your guns! Quick, march!"

And without waiting for his order to be carried out, he climbed the gate fearlessly, although it was there he had seen the officer fall, and raised the field glasses to his eyes while the gunners waited to hear what he would say.

Thus waiting, they calmed down a little. The corporal was taking his time. Of course, had he seen anything suspicious, he would have been quick to climb down. The gunners returned to their guns and prepared to move on with them. Their new commander gave no sign that things were in such a bad way that the battery had to be abandoned.

"Well, corporal?" some of the gunners shouted impatiently. "Stay where you are, boys, there's nothing wrong," Anton said, slowly getting down from his perch on the gate.

Nothing? Then why had the village been deserted? Where were the companies? Where had they fled to and why?

"Our men are turning around to attack the left flank occupied by the Germans," Anton said. "Boys, we must defend the market square, or else the Germans may fall upon the right flank of the battalion and wipe us out whichever way we run. Battery," he shouted, "into the courtyard, and face the market square! Quick, march!"

And without further ado, he himself rushed towards the gate of the courtyard they had entered before, thrust it open, ran back to the battery and pulled a gun inside.

"Radu Florea," he shouted, "take over command of the battery! Pull down the fence towards the market square, camouflage the guns and occupy a firing position! I'm going up on the roof."

He made quickly for the tall, two-storied house in the courtyard and knocked loudly at the front door. After waiting a few moments, he smashed a windowpane with his rifle, jumped into a room, found a staircase and sped up towards the roof.

Nothing of what he had told the soldiers had been true. He was now climbing to the roof to get a better grasp of the fearful situation of which he had become aware earlier. The Germans had the Rumanians completely under their fire and were now pouring from the left flank, cutting the village in two. And his fellow soldiers were fleeing towards the forest to avoid encirclement. Many of them could be seen reeling, dropping down, and remaining where they had fallen. From the left flank the enemy's machine guns were barking. . . . The left flank, the left flank! What had happened on that left flank? Where had Second Company, which made up the left flank, gone?

Anton was looking on horrified, choking with wrath. How had the Germans got to the left flank? What had happened to the company there? Why had no shot been heard from there for such a long time, and how had it come about that the enemy had suddenly invaded the village? "Now our men have vanished in the forest," Anton said to himself, "and the enemy columns have reached the end of the flanks; the village has been cut in two." The firing had stopped and everything was quiet.

Anton prepared to leave the roof, but then he stopped. What was he going to do once he got down? What was to happen to the battery now?

He must try to find out the enemy's moves. Did the enemy intend to attack the forest and wipe out his countrymen? He must find out; and then make his own plan carefully. . . . In order to attack the forest, it was necessary for the enemy to get through to the village square.

"Boys," Anton shouted from the roof. "It's all right, but get ready for a bit of firing! Radu Florea, that's not the place for the ammunition! Put it at the back of the stable! Ailoaiei, get your gun a little farther to the left, between those trees over there!"

Anton raised his field glasses again. Time was passing and no Germans were within sight. He remembered that before the companies had made a dash for the forest, he had seen the enemy's tanks descending the hill towards the left flank. What had become of those tanks? Where had they got to?

Gradually Anton became aware of the reason for the delay in the enemy's moves. The Germans had dealt a double blow: executing one single maneuver, they had cut the village in two and had brought the Rumanians' left flank under fire, at the same time forming a front against the regiment coming up from the rear. Anton could see the enemy consolidating their positions and realized that the Germans would soon try to make their way towards the forest in order to secure their rear. "That's where you're wrong, Fritz; you shan't get through to the forest, no fear!" Anton thought, his anger choking him. He counted his men. There were some thirty, including the wounded.

"Radu Florea," he shouted from his place on the roof, "There's a machine gun and some cases of ammunition at the edge of the square. Take the stuff to the loft above the stable! Hey, is there anyone among you wounded men able to fire?"

He got off the roof, installed the machine gun in the loft above the stable, and picked out three of the wounded who, although hardly able to move about, were not altogether disabled.

"Come on, brothers; when you start firing you'll clean forget your pains," he told them, while carrying them on his back to the stable loft. "A little later our people'll be coming and take you along, and then you'll be going home. But, if we let the Germans get beyond the square, our men will no longer be able to get here and then you'll never see your homes again."

They collected more cases of ammunition as well as some hand grenades and they also came across a small-caliber mortar. Another few of the wounded, realizing that the battery had been encircled and that the only way out was to organize a strong resistance, asked to be carried to the stable loft where the machine gun had been placed. They were given rifles and hand grenades.

After the enemy had withdrawn towards the hill, Colonel Atanasiu realized that Captain Ioan's maneuver had been successful and had given orders to advance. He hadn't decided to launch the battle for possession of the hill immediately; he first wanted to get into touch with the battalion. However, when the regiment came up against the new enemy front, Colonel Atanasiu got into a flap. There —the unexpected had occurred. What had happened in the village over there? What was Captain Ioan doing?

There was one thing the Colonel had been afraid of: maybe the enemy, not bothering about Captain Ioan's battalion and realizing that the units attacking from ahead had been weakened through the displacement of a battalion, would go over to the offensive and first annihilate him, Colonel Atanasiu, and then turn and wipe out the units which had fallen upon the rear of the Germans. And now he saw his fear had been justified, although the enemy had proceeded the other way round, first crushing the battalion—at least, so it seemed. And that was much worse, much more dangerous, as the Germans would now attack without any hindrance. Alarmed, Colonel Atanasiu arrested the advance of his troops, withdrew to his old positions and prepared for defense. Not for a single moment did it occur to him that the enemy were trembling at the thought that the units facing them would give them no time to consolidate their new position, that these units would attack them, force them to withdraw towards the hill and back up the battalion in its advance towards the bottom of the hill.

For the first time, Captain Ioan had lost his composure and had let the command of the units slip from his hands. There was only one order he had been able to give and the men had executed it. That had happened when First Company had rushed in disorder towards the village square. "To the forest!" the captain had ordered, though he himself did not know whether "to the forest" was a more sensible order than "to the market square." Scores of men had been mown down by the unexpected fire that had burst from the left flank. There was no trace of Second Company which was to have defended the left flank; it had disappeared without having fired a single shot.

It was only when they had reached the forest that the men stopped running. Utter consternation mixed with terror and anger could be read on their countenances. And it was this consternation, this terror and anger that helped Captain Ioan to regain firm hold of himself. He heard murmurs and felt angry eyes turning towards him. He realized the soldiers understood something he himself was not aware of. It was something that boded no good, something that worked against him; and all that Captain Ioan meant to the rank and file would this very moment come to naught unless he understood fully what they were so angry about.

"If you think I'm the one to blame for this, shoot me, men!" the captain shouted suddenly.

On hearing this, the men standing nearby threw their arms to the ground and began to swear angrily. "Sir, how is it you didn't see what kind of man Lieutenant Brasoveanu is?" a soldier's voice broke through clenched teeth. "Why did you entrust a company to him, sir? Curse him . . ."

And the soldier who had spoken dropped to the ground, gripped his bleeding shinbone, and burst into tears.

"I should have shot him in the head, right there, when I was talking to that German and he called me a liar," the soldier sobbed, his hands digging into the earth, tears streaming down his face distorted with pain.

After a while there was no longer any anger or terror in the men's eyes, but despair took possession of them all. The captain was silent. Even had he wanted to speak, he wouldn't have been able to, so tightly did he clench his jaws. Junior Lieutenant Petrescu was the only one who didn't lose his nerve. He was walking about, on the lookout for some rise in the ground. Then he called two soldiers to help him climb a tree. Being wounded in the arm, he couldn't have managed on his own. For a long time he looked through his field glasses, and then reported to the captain from up his tree that the enemy had built up a front facing the regiment. A little later he reported again with some anxiety that it seemed the Germans were preparing to send troops to occupy the rest of the village. What kind of troops? He could not say; all he saw was the movement of lorries, tanks and men, but he couldn't say for certain what was going on.

Anton, on the other hand, could see quite clearly from his roof a column headed by tanks making for the village square. There were five heavy tanks, the first one an enormous Tiger; it seemed to Anton he could already hear its rumble. He couldn't make out clearly what it was that followed the tanks—lorries or self-propelled artillery or infantry.

Anton hurried off the roof and rushed to the guns. "They're coming," he said turning to the gunners. "Now listen, everybody! Five heavy tanks are coming in single file along the road. No one is going to fire without orders. Don't get alarmed, lads! We'll let all the five enter the square, so as to destroy them all. If we don't, they'll rush on through the streets, and if their infantry comes over us, that'll be the end of it." Then he turned to the machine-gun crew: "You fire at the infantry together with us. Everything clear?"

Anton had hardly finished giving his orders when the heavy rumble of the enemy tanks reached their ears. Some of the gunners rushed to their shells, others knelt beside the guns. Anton was passing from gun to gun, checking the range and repeating in a tense voice: "No firing without orders! Aim carefully! The battery's camouflaged. The enemy doesn't know we are here."

He stopped between the guns in the middle, breathed deeply, took off his cap and mopped his brow with its rough cloth. Although it was winter, sweat glistened on his temples and on the back of his neck.

The battery was close to the market square, camouflaged in the courtyard of the local man who had mistaken the Rumanians for Hungarians. Its barrels were levelled against the market square and the main streets branching off the square.

"There they are, corporal!" one of the men shouted.

Anton raised the field glasses to his eyes.

"Radu Florea," he shouted.

"Corporal!"

"Fire at the first tank! Range 25 meters."

"Yes, corporal, I'll fire at the first tank," the gunner repeated, terrified at the distance from which he had been ordered to fire.

"Ailoaiei!"

"Corporal!"

"Fire at the first tank! Range 35 meters."

Ailoaiei gave no answer. He, too, was overwhelmed by this order.

Anton called out to them.

"Radu, Ailoaiei, lads! The first tank is a Tiger, as big as this stable here, and it's advancing alone, ahead of the others. Aim at its turret, both of you, and it'll go to the devil. Don't be afraid, boys; we'll crack its skull all right!"

He passed on to the other gunners, telling them, too, to take aim at the Tiger but not to fire at it without orders. Sweat was again pouring down his face, but he felt strangely calm, calmer, it seemed to him, than he'd be if he hadn't been here, in this foreign village, surrounded by the enemy and threatened to be crushed by tanks. It was only his heart that was throbbing too strongly, now in its proper place, now in his throat, now in his ears.

He knelt down between the guns of Radu Florea and Ailoaiei and raised his field glasses. The huge Tiger covered the whole field of the lenses and struck him in the eyes, as it were. Unnerved for a split second, Anton raised his arm and bawled out:

"Battery. . . ."

His voice broke; he had very nearly given the command for the whole battery to fire.

"Battery, wait for my order!" he shouted, his nails digging deep into the palm of his hand.

The Tiger was still a long way off. "I'll give you what for," Anton muttered.

"Radu Florea, Ailoaiei! The turret, brothers! Be calm, aim at the turret—sharp!"

The earth began to shake and the Tiger entered the market square like a huge, black buffalo made of steel. When it had reached the square it suddenly stopped and its metal trunk spat twice straight at the battery. The missiles flew overhead and struck the roof of the house, which collapsed with a deafening noise of falling bricks, broken windowpanes, and rattling tiles. Anton felt his blood freeze in his veins. The tank had come to a standstill some fifty yards away. Could it have discovered the battery?

"Corporal . . . Corporal . . . shall we fire?"

The tank moved on again, however, and Anton took a deep breath. The rumble grew louder, as the swaying monster approached, its caterpillars churning earth and snow.

"Corporal . . . " Ailoaiei cried.

As the monster grew to fearful proportions Anton could see in the gunners' eyes signs of fear and doubt as to whether their efforts would be of any avail. Anton rose to his feet. His right arm shot upwards, and he opened his mouth wide, his teeth gleaming like a wolf's. At the top of his voice he shouted: "Battery, fire!"

He let himself drop to the ground as the guns roared. His eyes staring, Anton saw the turret fly off the Tiger and cleave the body of the German tank commander in two. Controlling himself, he shouted: "Radu Florea and Ailoaiei, at the second tank, fire!"

Then he jumped up from his place and called out to the other gunners to fire at the third tank, following close behind. "Fire, boys!" he yelled, and again his right arm swung upwards before he flung himself to the ground.

The second tank was hit in its left-hand caterpillar, which flew off and spread over the pavement with a loud clanking noise. The third tank fared still worse. Black smoke and flames spurted forth from its turret. Meanwhile the last two tanks had entered the square and, noticing the plight of the others, began maneuvering at the utmost speed in order to turn back.

"Fire, lads! Fire!" Anton shouted, and seeing the gunners were not hitting their targets, he dashed over to Ailoaiei's gun, took careful aim and fired. With a grinding noise the fourth tank came to a standstill, belching smoke. "Here you are!" Anton seethed with excitement. "Fire lads, there's one more! Look, it's trying to get away! Fire!"

The machine gun in the stable had been firing away for quite a while, but it was only now after the four tanks had been stopped in the market square that the gunners noticed the enemy infantry who were hiding in courtyards and firing their automatic rifles. Anton ran to the stable, climbed into the loft, and surveyed the surroundings through his field glasses. Suddenly he flung himself down, got hold of a machine gun, and kept firing at a fixed point. His face was twitching with the strain; his lips, stretched taut, revealed his clenched teeth. After a minute, without stopping to fire, he motioned one of the wounded men to take his place. "Keep the road under fire until I come back!"

He hurried over to where the guns stood. "Radu Florea, Ailoaiei, fire at the tile-roofed house at the bend in the road. Fire for all you're worth!"

The guns roared, the house was hit and collapsed, and, all round it, enemy soldiers scattered like so many rats. The machine gun in the loft was rattling without a break. "At the house to the right, the one with the rusty iron roofing, fire!" Anton shouted again.

When Captain Ioan heard the first roar of the anti-tank battery and discovered the strong point through his fieldglasses, he started violently. True, the unexpected of which Colonel Atanasiu had been afraid had happened, and the threat of annihilation hovered in the air; but here another unexpected factor had turned up, demanding peremptorily for the resumption of action. Captain Ioan's hand, holding the field glasses, was trembling.

The soldiers jumped to their feet and climbed up the trees. "It's the battery! The battery is still in the village. The battery is firing, brothers!" There were shouts of joy and surprise.

In a flash all despondency had vanished; the platoons fell in, the commanders issued brisk orders, and while the battery continued its roar, the two companies took the village for the second time by assault.

When they reached the market square, the battery had almost

run out of ammunition. "Well done!" the captain shouted on reaching the gun crews. He looked round for their commander.

"Where's the officer?"

"He's dead, sir."

"Who's taken over command?"

"I, sir, Corporal Modan," Anton answered.

"Good lad!" the captain exclaimed in his high voice and, rushing up to the corporal, took him by the shoulders and gave him a hearty shake. "Well done, good lad!"

"What's happened to the left flank, sir?" Anton asked, quietly mopping the sweat off his forehead.

"Lieutenant Brasoveanu is a traitor! He's betrayed his men, and the Germans struck at our flank. But your battery has done a thoroughly good job!" the captain shouted again.

Then he took the two companies and stubbornly continued his attack in the center. Realizing that the battalion he had thought annihilated was attacking, Colonel Atanasiu, too, launched a frontal attack. The Germans abandoned their positions on the left flank and hastily withdrew from the village. The maneuver had been crowned with success; the road towards Height X was now open.

Eugen Barbu

(b. 1924)

Novelist and short-story writer, poet, playwright, and publicist, Eugen Barbu is one of the prized writers of contemporary Rumanian literature. He made his debut with verses and fiction inspired by sporting life (*Eleven* [1956], *The Ball Is Round* [1956], *The Golden Triplet* [1956]), and in 1957, with his novel *The Pit*—in which he depicts aspects of the life of the Bucharest environs—he created one of the best and most interesting Rumanian novels of today.

In his planned cycle of novels drawn from the life of factory workers, two have so far appeared: *The Northern Road* (1959) and *Genesis* (1964).

His short story collections, *Oaie and His People* (1958), *Tereza* (1961), and *The Sunday Luncheon* (1962), from which "In the Rain" was taken, are characterized by their modern touch and tense, compact style.

Barbu does not indulge in analyses, poetizations, and digressions, cultivating instead an "objective" form of prose fraught with drama and action.

He is also the author of a play, *Build No Steps to Your Shop* (1963), and two volumes of feature reportage, *O'er Hill and Dale* (1957) and *In Seven Long Days* (1960).

In the Rain

The mountain was quite near, like a naked, chalky brow. Lower down, in a valley, the forest spread out its tracery of fresh verdure. The wind was blowing, beating down the grass, and the whole scene looked like a rough sea petrified ages before. It was a Saturday, during the first mowing time, about midday. The sky kept darkening and clearing. Now the sun was burning hot; now it wasn't, and a sickly chillness set in, freezing the men's backs.

There were six of them and they had grown tired. The last were Lisandru and Ilie and Tutungiu—the tobacconist—who had got his name during the war. Having been wounded, he had got a license to sell cigarettes. They were brothers. The youngest was Marin—Ilie in his papers; he, like the others, worked by the day on the land of a man who owned more. He was not yet eighteen and was getting married the next day. The third, Lisandru, had been at the front, like

Rebegea, as they also called the eldest. They were talking about their own affairs in half friendly, half spiteful tones:

"How are you getting on, Tutungiu?" Lisandru asked, still thinking of something said before. "You're tired, aren't you?"

"The devil I am!"

The lame man looked at the sky.

"What rotten weather! The sun comes out and then hides again."

He was tall and wiry, and his face was swarthy. When he walked, he dragged his left foot a bit. It is common knowledge that a limping man is very fond of a bit of fluff. . . . He looked uphill for the women. It was time for their midday meal, and the women were sure to come soon with the food. Lisandru was wiping his scythe with a handful of hay, gazing at his youngest brother.

"You greenhorn, have you learned the Lord's prayer? You'll soon be looking for it in your pants and won't find it there. . . . "

"Ha, ha, ha!" laughed Rebegea, the eldest brother.

Marin did not look at him. He was cutting the grass in silence. He felt the cold on his back and this made him work on.

Until a week before there hadn't been a drop of rain. Now it went on and on. The rain would come in the morning, then stop a while, and by eleven a dark cloud would float down filling the footpaths with puddles. The men would run and take shelter under the trees and call to them to do the same.

"Hey, come into the woods, or St. Elijah, the master of thunder, will see you!"

They would not—just out of devilment and to show they weren't frightened of the rain. Besides, they had to finish their mowing, for the next day was Sunday. Their shirts, wet on their backs, were sometimes dry and at other times soaked.

Now the rain was coming. An hour before, the field had shone like a fur rippled by the wind. The ground was dry. But clouds were gathering above, roll after roll, and the light seemed to trickle away under the woods, hiding under its gloomy vaults. High up in the sky the thunder was grumbling.

"Listen, your uncle, old Nick, is thrashing his wife," the lame man added, his eyes glued to the mountainside in order to be the first to spy the women who were to come with the food.

Marin had stopped and was staring at his scythe.

"I say, what's the matter?"

A green and red capricorn beetle sprang from the grass.

"I was on the point of cutting it in two," the younger brother said, more to himself.

Tutungiu had started mowing again.

"See, that's the kind of weather we once had at the front. It kept raining for ages; are you listening, Lisandru?"

"Yes, I am."

"You'd have thought really the houses would sink into the ground. Wherever you turned your eyes there was nothing but mud, thick mud."

"I was there two winters. . . . "

Lisandru showed his gold teeth in a grin, looking again at the sky. He was the ugliest of the brothers, as though he were fed on shadows, so thin and hobbling was he.

"Have you heard?" Rebegea asked.

"What?"

"That we're getting land from those. . . . "

The second-born went on mowing, looking doubtfully at his brother.

"Why are you staring like that? Down at Piatra, at Osica last Sunday, they began ploughing the land of the monks at the monastery. All the monks, old and young, sallied forth and cursed them."

"And whoever let them do it? The gendarmes here glower at us whenever we barely mention it."

"Why, the Communists let them. Those who have been at the front, like you and me, must not be forgotten. There are orders. . . . "

"Well. . . . "

Marin was pricking up his ears as if annoyed at something. Another clap of thunder came from afar as if the whole mountain had crashed down over them. The three of them looked up.

"I'm afraid the women won't come in such weather," Rebegea said, a bit anxious.

"They will, for they're longing to see you, ha, ha, ha!"

Then they were silent and could hear the noise of their scythes. They were looking down in order to avoid snakes. The lame brother felt a sharp pain in his legs. "It's these damned rains," he thought. He was hungry, and there was still plenty of work to be done. The sky was growing darker and darker. Even the steel in the grass no longer glittered. All of a sudden everything was still and the wind abated.

"There is going to be a heavy rain. What are we going to do?" Lisandru asked.

"We won't melt. Come on! I'm not afraid of him."

The second-born spat wearily and asked somewhat casually:

"Tutungiu, what'll happen if the Communists come here?"

"Why, they'll come, that's all!"

"Well, but it seems that those like that fellow there are forced to work and they don't like it, so we'll have to egg them on a little. Those who haven't any can take some!"

"We'll have to force them, if we can't help it, poor devils."

Rebegea gave a soft, almost affectionate laugh.

Marin (Ilie in his papers) stopped to breathe. Then he went on with his mowing, more leisurely.

"You've been eavesdropping, youngster, haven't you?" said the lame brother, satisfied.

"Of course he has, for Zamfira's giving an acre tomorrow just to throw dust in his eyes, and he's becoming a boyar. It's what I'd call a fine dowry."

The rain didn't come on suddenly. First they heard it above the woods, falling on the leaves with a fine patter. Then it spread over the field, pounding the grass which glittered, silent and green, with a deep, fresh color.

"Come into the woods!" the men in front, three neighbors of theirs, shouted, scanning the edges of the sky and the mountain as if trying to guess how long the downpour was going to last.

"Oh, we'll come!" said Lisandru half-heartedly, swearing at the day with its sunshine and rain, with the field to do and money to get ready in the evening. They were all to contribute money for the wedding of the younger brother, who hadn't a copper to pay for the priest and the feast, who had nothing, just like any other pauper.

"What are we going to do?" Tutungiu asked.

"We're staying here, or else we won't get anything if we don't gather in the fellow's hay by evening."

Each spoke in almost the same way, with a disrespectful fear—sarcastic and contemptuous.

Behind them there was a deafening clap, and a thunderbolt fell somewhere in the woods nearby. Marin started.

"Hey, what's the matter? What is it?" said the lame brother, with a thick laugh.

The younger brother said nothing.

"He's scared; that's the trouble," giggled Lisandru, rather anxiously. "What if he leaves his wife with the job unfinished, right now, at the wedding. . . ."

Marin would have liked to fling back some kind of retort, but he went about his work. His shirt stuck more heavily to his back. There was a smell of wet fresh hay. From the woods the men were waving to them:

"Come here!"

Tutungiu looked at them and, hearing again the peals of thunder in the sky, rejoiced aloud:

"The devil'll strike them there, under the trees!"

The echo of the surrounding valleys increased the din. The air was vibrating, and they no longer felt the rain. They attended fiercely to their work. There was not actually very much to do; still there was a fair amount. The rain would stop, for it was summer. The clouds floated down, hiding the chalky mountain. Marin had begun to feel cold.

"I'm going into the woods," he said.

"Stay here; don't be a fool! It's not wise to stand under a tree in this weather."

"I'm cold."

"Well, just bear it."

"I'm past bearing. . . . "

But he did not leave. The handle of the scythe was slippery, and the water was pouring down his forehead. He was sweating and shivering with cold. "I'll be ill tomorrow, of all days!" he thought. Lisandru had a sheepskin coat he had left lying by the roadside. Sorry for his brother, he put down his scythe and ran to get it. The coat was as heavy as lead, for the rain had beaten through the roof of leaves under which it had been sheltered. "It's a big coat and will warm the three of us," flashed through his mind, on his way back.

"Hey, come here!" he called to them. "It's not dry even under the trees. The rain has passed through them as through a sieve. Pick up your scythes and let's all wait until it stops. . . . "

The lame brother looked at the field once more, measuring how much they still had to do, and came to them. Marin left everything as it was and drew nearer. Tutungiu approached closer slowly, reluctantly. He carried the steel blade on his shoulder, to show them he did not care what was around him. His bare feet shuffled in the grass. "Blasted cripple!" cursed Lisandru. He looked out again. Tutungiu was quite near them, his small eyes screwed up to avoid the rain that trickled on his forehead. Then, almost at the same moment, a thunder bolt struck, dropping them to the ground in an instant.

The men in the woods saw only a rapid light that streamed down into the ground and heard the astonished cry of one of the brothers and the noise of the coat rent by the current as by a red-hot wire. Then there was a fearful peal so near them that they thought the entire forest and the field had taken fire at the same time. Afterwards, however, they heard only the rain dripping on the grass as though someone were running barefoot, in front, behind or alongside them.

The rain no longer came down in buckets and the only noise to be heard was the soft weeping of the women, who had come running. The men had dug three pits, side by side, deep enough to hold the three men struck by the lightning; they had them buried up to their armpits. The men had pushed them in with laths, lest the current in them should discharge. Then they had thrown shovelfuls of loose earth around them. Rebegea's swarthy face had become deathly pale. Lisandru had grown stiff; his eyes were open and his mouth rigid. The youngest, Marin, was looking in bewilderment at the black crowd of women around, all drenched by the rain, their blouses sticking to their skin.

"Tutungiu's dead," said one of the women. "Look at him."

The whispers were drowned by the noise of the drizzling rain. It had grown cold. The pots with food had been left in the grass. The smell of the vinegar and onion sauce was strong, and the corn porridge had gotten cold. The water fell mercilessly in the earthenware pots; it was useless to cover them with pieces of linen as the women had done.

The people were no longer hungry. They stared at one another dumfounded.

"And how did it happen?" somebody asked, breaking the uncanny silence of the moment.

"We were standing there under the trees. We called them, but they would not come."

"They were in a hurry. Tomorrow the youngest one was going to church with Zamfira."

"But where is she?"

"She works in another village. She won't be back until night."

"Does their mother know?"

"No, she doesn't. She'll soon be here, poor soul!"

The women looked at the three brothers, with fear in their eyes.

"Tutungiu seems to be moving."

They watched silent a few moments, but Rebegea had not moved. He was stiff, and his eyelids were stone-still.

"Let's open his eyes and see if he's dead."

"Don't touch him, or you'll be struck too, you fools! Come away," an old man shouted at them and went up to them.

"Shut up, you old dodderer. Don't put your back up. We've seen this sort of thing before. Three years ago some men were struck, away at Balcesti. People kept them buried in the ground, and one is still working," said a woman who was standing in front.

Then there was silence again. The crowd stood around and looked with unsympathetic curiosity at the three thunderstruck brothers.

"Fancy their not taking care!"

"They stayed on in the fields. The lightning was attracted by iron, and they were struck. . . ."

From the foot of the mountain there came a long wail that made them shudder.

"Lisandru, Gheorghe, Marin, my sons, where are you? Where are you?"

Along the narrow road, flooded with water, a woman was running, her hair all undone.

"Their mother's coming. Stand aside!"

The women separated to make room for her.

The cries stopped. The woman no longer ran; she walked slowly, as though on unsafe ground, as though not seeing, her hands stretched out, feeling the wet air and working her fingers slowly.

"Lisandru . . . Lisandru," she called her son softly, as if he had been very near and she did not want to annoy him. "Lisandru, where are you, Lisandru?"

She saw him. She saw the three of them, buried in the ground up to their armpits, but she wanted to put off the moment for weeping.

"Gheorghe, Gheorghe lad, where are you?"

The women burst into tears all at once, turning round as if to avoid some strong light. The patter of the rain on the grass was the only sound.

"Marin, are you dumb? Where are you, Marin?"

She had come near them but was looking for them higher up, above the ground, where they should have been standing; and they were not there, and she did not want to see them where they really were.

"Why are you dumb, Marin, why?"

The smell of vinegar from the food brought by the women filled the air; but no longer the smell of wet hay, or the fragrance of the forest breathing softly under the steady rain.

Suddenly the woman's scream broke out. They were all expecting it, but when they heard it they stopped their ears and walked away a bit, in the grass, as though wanting to scatter.

"Lisandru! Gheorghe! Marin! Is that where you are?"

She went down on her knees, and the puddle under her splashed the trousers of the men standing nearby, looking at her, fear and concentration in their eyes, ready to stop her if she tried to do anything.

She was still a few paces from them, but did not rise to her feet; she dragged herself through the hay, on all fours and looked at them, one after the other, turning to the people with a dumb, fierce surprise, as though mutely scolding them, as though asking something or calling them to account, or pleading for pity. The oldest among them took one step towards her, but the woman raised one hand and shrieked:

"No-o-o!"

The man staggered as though the shout had struck him. He only watched her tensely, covered with sweat under his wet clothes.

The woman paused before Tutungiu's bluish face, looked at his motionless eyelids carefully, then crawled on towards Lisandru's livid face, and when her eyes fell on her youngest son's open eyes, she tried to kiss his parched lips. The old man's hand pulled her away forcibly, hostilely, and threw her on her back. For a moment all thought the man would not catch hold of her shoulders, and when they heard her cry, "Leave me! Leave me!" they threw themselves upon her and beat her with their fists as if she were a sack.

The woman was strong; she rose a few times and rushed anew towards the fresh pits, but each time she was pushed back. And when she was no longer able to fight the excited crowd that was swearing at her and shouting unintelligible words, she fell to one side weeping softly, her head bent low.

The gendarmes arrived half an hour later. The sergeant, wearing a khaki greatcoat, his rifle resting on his hip, swinging his fat buttocks, was swearing from a distance. The men made room for him in silence.

"You're always up to some mischief, you bloody fools! You've made my hair turn gray. As if I didn't have enough trouble!"

When he saw the three buried men the sergeant stopped, his legs astride, and turned to the gendarmes who were following him:

"Push the people back, d'you hear? Don't stand there staring like stuck pigs! Beat it, all of you! D'you think this is the wonder of Maglavit, you damned yokels?"

"Don't swear at us, sir!" the old man said. "It's no fault of ours."

"It is! Why do you work in the fields in the rain?"

"If you've got a field, you've got to mow it!" someone behind said.

"Shut up! You've turned mighty uppish! How did it happen?" he asked without addressing anybody, looking at the men in turn. "When did it happen?"

One of the three peasants who had taken shelter in the forest related briefly part of what had happened. In the meantime the gendarmes were looking at the buried men. When the gendarme learned everything, he said aloud:

"Keep off! There's danger of electrocution. Or don't you know what electrocution is?" He looked at them scornfully and then turned directly to the men: "You come along with me to the police station. We'll have to draw up a report, for I am held responsible for each of you as if you were livestock. I'll send a soldier for the doctor; he lives a long way from here!"

The sergeant was annoyed for some unknown reason; still he could not leave at once. He saw the old woman fallen in the mud, wanted to swear at her, but changed his mind and went near the three brothers and examined them closely.

"Tutungiu's dead," he said positively, with some regret not unmixed with a little sympathy. "Light a candle for him. Don't you hear? Run for the priest and get him to come here. . . . Lisandru'll last till the evening," he declared now, a little quieter.

"He may survive, sir," said the old man suddenly frightened lest the others should hear him.

"He won't," snapped the gendarme. "The younger one, Ilie . . ."

"His name's Marin, sir."

"Maybe, but in his papers he's called Ilie. He's still moving. If he's lucky he may last till tomorrow at midday. . . ."

He had squatted on his haunches and now he was panting. He pulled out his handkerchief and mopped his brow. His rubber greatcoat made him feel hot, and he unbuttoned it at the neck. The fine rain was dripping from the peak of his cap.

"Why don't you cover them with a rug or something?" he asked them all sharply.

"What do they care about the rain?" one of the men asked with a stupid laugh. The gendarme did not answer. There was silence. The sergeant looked at them in turn, then struck the butt of his rifle with his hand.

"There Tutungiu, there Lisandru, there Ilie—you wanted land, and you have it now up to your necks. Pooh!" He spat and turned his back on them, walked away as fast as he could, calling over his shoulder: "Go home and don't start any trouble here, or you'll catch it. Leave them alone; they won't mind being lonely. And you who have to write the report, follow me."

Yet the crowd did not budge. The men did not follow him. Not hearing their footsteps behind him, the officer turned angrily.

"What? don't you hear?"

No one answered.

"Hey, you men, come to the station, and we'll write the report on the electrocution!"

One of the men said wearily: "Go ahead, sir, and we'll be coming along."

The rain had not stopped. It was getting colder and colder. Darkness was coming on. A chilly wind was bending the unknown grass. The mountain seemed to be far away, wrapped in mist and sheets of water. Around Gheorghe's head five candles were burning down sheltered by the women's hands. The wax sputtered in the wet grass, and the little flames flickered, on the point of going out. Near them, the old mother, her hair suddenly white as if she had emerged from a salt lake, was wailing softly on her knees, covered with a rug somebody had brought and put on her back.

"Oh, Mihalache, where are you to see your sons buried in the earth up to their mouths! Where are you? You died and went away and left me all alone to bring them up and now look at them! They were big and strong, and now there's nothing left of them. . . . !"

"Stop!" a woman begged her, but the old woman didn't hear and stuck her fingers into the moist earth and plucked a handful of grass.

"They were taken to the front, Mihalache, and tortured, and the eldest was maimed, Mihalache, but he came home. My God, my God. . . . And Lisandru too got off and came home safe and sound and was our breadwinner. . . ."

"Please stop it," the woman kept begging her while shielding the candles.

The molten wax sizzled in the burnt grass, and there was a smell of smoke.

"And you, Marin, what have you done to me, you who were to go to your own house tomorrow, you my baby, to your own house; and now you're here in the grave, and the earth will eat you up. Oh, Lord, take me! Oh, Lord, I wish I were dead."

It was getting darker. Tutungiu's ghostly face seemed bluer in the candlelight. His beard had grown, and someone said with weary hope:

"Maybe he isn't dead. The sergeant may have made a mistake. Look, his beard is bristly like a brush! Look, folks, call to him!"

No one came near, and the men went down on their knees and took turns in calling to the elder brother:

"Gheorghe, open your eyes, man. They've sent your license to sell cigarettes. . . ."

"Tutungiu, give me a drag. I'm dying to fill my lungs. D'you hear?"

"Rebegea, get the people in Bucharest to make you one of those tin pipes in which you can sell us cigarettes and make the tax collector die of spite, for you'll get his commission."

The men soon wearied of their sad jokes.

"Here's the priest," someone said.

"He is slow in coming, for he knows he won't be given any alms."

They made room for him. His Reverence was wearing a long, black coat, and his boots were soiled with mud.

"Good evening, folks," he said gently, smoothing his hair which was silvery around his ears. "But what's happened?" he asked in surprise, as if he did not know what he would find there in the middle of the field.

It was getting still darker. The women moved aside, and the priest saw the faces of the three men buried in the ground. The candles shed a wavering light on Gheorghe's purple-bluish face. The newcomer was not startled; he raised his eyes to the mountain now hidden in the dark and pulled out a black book from which he read without looking:

"He is the master of everything. He sendeth fear, for he keeps good order in the highest places. Canst thou count His hosts? Be there anyone who doth not rise in His light? Then how can man consider himself righteous before God and how can he of woman born be pure? Even the moon doth not shine bright enough and the stars are none too pure in His eyes. So much the less man, a small insect, and man's son, a worm! . . ."

* * *

Zamfira arrived after the priest's departure. Now she was sitting by Marin, looking at him. The rain had stopped, and the women had brought some lamps and placed them around the three men. Lisandru was turning blue too and no longer opened his eyes. As the sergeant had predicted, he died about eleven. In silence they lit candles and placed them near his face. The night was passing very slowly and no one made to leave, though it was cold and there was a high wind. The wet grass had been crushed all around, and there was a smell of burning. The people lit candle after candle. The mother's sobs were still heard now and again, but towards dawn they too stopped.

Daylight came, and the sun rose on the wall of motionless women all around, with their wet, tattered clothes drying in the wind. They were all looking towards the hill now. When the mist rose, they could see their houses under the mountain. Zamfira's house stood on a high spot, jutting out, and when Marin opened his eyes, he saw the newly whitewashed fence and the wedding fir tree, so green and fresh, stuck in the gate. Suddenly his voice returned, and the men stepped nearer as though confronted with a miracle.

"Zamfira, Zamfira. . . ."

The girl was on her knees, not far from him. She did not go too near, as the others held her back.

"What is it?"

"That's our wedding fir tree, isn't it?"

"Yes."

There was silence. The only sound was the breath of the first wind on the bright day that had hardly begun.

"He's recovering."

"He'll get better."

"Hey, Marin, are you alive, lad?"

His mother seemed to have turned deaf. She stared at him askance and said nothing. Then she crumpled, and beating her forehead against the ground she shouted, "Marin, Marin!"

"The doctor! Get the doctor!" some of them shouted, but they knew quite well that he could not arrive before midday and only in the gig, if they could find him.

"What do you feel?" the old man asked the youngest brother, driving away the curious women standing there.

"Leave him alone!" someone said.

Marin seemed to have tired, for he closed his eyes again. Maybe he was thinking, for he finally said:

"I feel neither cold, nor hot; I'm stiff."

"Stay on there, in the ground, and let the sickness go out of you. . . ."

His mother had come nearer and tried to embrace him, in an impulse the others could hardly restrain.

"Stop, woman! Are you mad or have you had enough of life?" Marin seemed to come out of a dream. He glanced towards the other two, hardly turning his head. He saw the candles burning and their faces the color of ink.

"What's the matter with you people?" he asked softly, with a voice full of fear and hope. "Gheorghe! Lisandru! Say something, men. Mother, what's the matter with Lisandru and Tutungiu?"

His eyes sought the others, and the men stepped back, keeping their eyes riveted on the ground. Then his face filled with fear:

"Zamfira, tell me, are they dead?"

The girl, her hair falling over her eyes, sat near him and said nothing. She seemed all of a sudden out of her senses.

Marin fell into a heavy sleep, and the people thought he had died, but he still breathed very gently. He slept like that for about two hours without waking. The sun had risen above the chalky mountain and lit up the green valleys. The grass was of a painful freshness. In the village no one took the cattle grazing. The children too had come; driven home once, they had returned even more inquisitive. A neighbor had gone uphill to ask the carpenter to make two coffins. He had not said a word to anyone. Now he was back and was staring blankly at the three buried men, looking very tired after so long a vigil but somewhat satisfied. Presently they heard the pounding of a hammer on boards. They looked at one another meaningfully but nobody asked anything. It was Sunday; the joiner was a God-fearing man and would not have answered the door to anyone, but on such a day. . . .

The forest cast a short shadow, darker at the foot of the mountain. The women's clothes were steaming. There was a smell of wet shawls and clothes. The vinegar and the chopped onion had run over from the food pots. The man for whom the three had been working was away in another village, or he would have come too, and the people would have cursed him. Now they gazed only at his wife, who was present and kept her face hidden in a black kerchief. "You're to blame for their deaths!" the women's eyes seemed to say.

It was quite warm now. The air was stifling and wet. High up, above the fields, new clouds were already gathering, big white clouds, like ships on high. The bell rang for mass. The women crossed themselves and said, avoiding the mother's eyes: "May God rest their souls!"

Marin awoke and looked around him in dismay. He took some time to get used to the sight of the people around. Even the children, usually so garrulous, said nothing; they stood quite still, staring at the man buried in the ground.

"Zamfira! Zamfira!" cried Marin. "Don't you hear the bell? It's ringing for us! You've got to go to church."

The girl burst into tears. The buried man moved his stiff arms as though he meant to pump out of the pit; they would not obey him and hung limply by his sides, helpless. Marin peered at his rigid, yellow fingers with their purple-blue nails.

"I'll get out of here," he said with desperate conviction. "I'll get out, d'you hear, folks?" He spoke sharply in a thin low voice. "I'll get out of here. I will, for we've got to have the wedding."

And exhausted, he fell back into his heavy sleep, while the men stood motionless and looked at him.

By noon the people had scattered a little. The sergeant had come for the men, though he knew he could not draw up the report unless the doctor was present. He ordered the women away, prodding them with his rifle and threatening to fine them.

Some people began to feel hungry. The priest had sent for some food for no one had gone to church that Sunday. Who cared about the service? The gendarmes chased the children up the hill, and the place was clearer. It was hot, the sultry heat before a storm. The clouds kept wheeling above the forest; they were quite dark but had not covered the sun, which cast yellow flames over the wet fields. The smell of hay was intoxicating. It was a soft, quiet, gorgeous day, with the kindly air of a quiet holiday.

Marin had wakened and driven his mother back spitefully.

"Zamfira, stay here with me!"

"Yes," she said with helpless obedience.

"And these people ought to go home, and leave me alone. . . ."

The men and women moved off a step or two. They still did not sit down, though the grass had dried a little. They were dog tired, but seemed afraid of something unexpected which had to be prevented at all costs.

The two were left alone. The bell rang again, tolling slowly.

"Zamfira, what time is it?" he asked looking up.

"It's midday," the girl said softly, as if frightened that the others might overhear her, but they were too far to hear anything.

"We're late."

Zamfira did not understand. For a moment she thought Marin had gone mad, and she did not say anything.

"Zamfira, will you still marry me?"

The girl looked at him, astonished, then cast down her eyes.

"Zamfira, you won't marry me any more!"

"Why not?" she asked in surprise, after a short, oppressive, painful silence.

"Your mother won't let you."

"As if I cared . . ."

"But where is she?"

"She's weeping at home and wouldn't come to see you."

"She may be listening to the fiddlers."

"She can't feel like it."

A few tears ran down the man's livid face. His numb arms seemed to double up for a moment, trying once again to push out of the pit.

"Send for the priest," he suddenly said resolutely, and his voice seemed to have grown louder.

"What for?"

"To wed us!"

Zamfira looked at him again, as if he were mad.

"Or maybe you won't have me now that I'm a cripple."

"You aren't a cripple. You'll get over it. If you can speak, it means you're well."

The buried man's eyes shone with a shameless hope, for there was something male and lewd in it.

"I'll stay as I am another day, and when I get out I'll be strong. D'you get me! I'll tup you till you call your mother to rescue you!"

The girl's face flushed crimson, and she looked around.

"Hush! People'll hear."

"What if they do? I'll see if you've been a whore or if you give me your maidenhead."

Marin was amused with some strange thought as if about to climb out of the pit and show the girl that he had not spoken idly, but meant all he had promised.

"I'll get back my strength and I'll crush you all right."

Zamfira was no longer embarrassed before the others. Perhaps she believed those words helped the man near her.

"How can you speak like that, you stupid one!" she scolded him fondly in a voice he alone knew.

Suddenly, in the silence all round, while he was silent and tired, trying to find his words, he heard the carpenter's hammer. At first he pretended not to understand, then looked quickly at his brothers, at their bristly blue faces; and something in the depth of his eyes betrayed a joy that could not be owned.

"Who's working today?" he asked with fear, however.

The people too heard the question, for the buried man had spoken sharply.

"It's some child, knocking on a fence."

Marin listened tensely. Here everything echoed like the notes of a violin. The tappings grew, beating against the lonely chalky mountain, and the valley around helped to intensify them.

But his trained ear isolated the sturdy blows of the hammer against the wooden boards.

"They're making my casket, aren't they?" he asked peevishly, his eyes bulging with hatred. "I won't go. No, I won't. Go, call the priest! Do it quickly! And your mother too, Zamfira. Mine's here already. Call the priest; we'll have our wedding now, as it was agreed. Come on, is nobody going?"

No one budged.

"Marin," his mother tried to say gently, crawling almost up to him. The people could hardly keep her back.

"Hey, mother, don't you hear? Bring the priest. And you, Zamfira, fetch your mother and the wedding rings, and we'll get them on our fingers. And get the fiddlers to come, don't you hear, you women?"

The women rose to their feet startled and set out uphill, followed by the puzzled looks of the others.

* * *

His Reverence refused to come. Midday had passed. It was sultry and the sky was dark. The sun was invisible. It looked like rain. The wind was blowing from the forest. Marin, in his grave, kept swearing by all the sacred things he knew. His mother was listening to him, resigned, begging him to stop, in a low voice:

"Marin, son, don't! It's a sin."

Zamfira returned with her mother and the fiddlers—three scraggy gipsies, looking up at the threatening clouds.

"Is that you?" the buried one asked the old woman who looked like his own mother.

"Yes, it's me."

"Is the feast ready?"

"Yes, it is."

"What about the guests?"

"They are here. I haven't asked them all. . . ."

She looked at them over his shoulders as if taking them to witness this misfortune which she had not been able to prevent.

Marin turned his eyes away from her.

"Zamfira," he called to the girl, "Why haven't you brought a bottle of plum brandy to give the people? Give them something to drink. Bring some food, and then get the fiddlers to play. I don't care if the priest won't marry us; I want our wedding today; and when I get out of here I'll set his church on fire. Hey, you fiddlers, bring your fiddles nearer and play me something! Don't stand there staring at me."

The fiddlers shuffled nearer, pretending to be cheerful and hiding one behind the other. The girl had gone with his mother to fetch the food and drinks to serve to the people; they had no other use for all they had prepared. Zamfira's house was not very far. Half an hour passed before the women returned with a big basket, filled to the top. In the meantime the doctor had come along the lane still full of puddles. He had driven in the sergeant's cabriolet. In the driver's seat sat the soldier who was driving the horse and the sergeant whom they had picked up on the road.

The three men alighted. The sergeant dispersed the people again, looked in bewilderment at the fiddlers but said nothing, and followed the pale young doctor, who asked how long the three had been standing in the pits, though he had learned everything from the officer before coming.

Marin's eyes asked the doctor's, trying to guess if he would recover or not. A painful silence set in. A greedy hawk, with keen, steely eyes, hovered overhead. The women came nearer as if someone from behind had been pushing them and no one could compel them to go back.

The doctor said nothing. He had hardly looked at Gheorghe and Lisandru.

"What do you feel?" he asked Marin.

"The earth is squeezing me very tight."

"Are you hungry?"

"No."

"Do you feel any pain?"

"No."

"Is your body quite stiff? Can't you move?"

"My hands seem to be deserting me."

Marin looked at his benumbed fingers with a little hope, but he was unable to move them.

"Do you feel you are suffocating?"

"A little."

"Is your heart sore, or is it the earth hurting you?"

"I think it's the earth," lied the buried man, not knowing why, though several times he had felt his heart beating more feebly.

The doctor rose to his feet, looked again at his face which had begun to turn blue. Then he walked away with the sergeant, avoiding the curious crowd.

"Will he recover?" the noncommissioned officer asked in a whisper.

"Only if his heart is good."

"Can anything else be done?"

"If he doesn't die by nightfall, we'll take him to a hospital somewhere."

The two men were about to get into the cabriolet, but the wall of people stopped them. They did not ask anything, yet the doctor guessed and said:

"Leave him alone till evening; he'll come back to life."

Only the men felt a vague suspicion, but then they rejoiced.

"Wasn't I right, folks?" asked Marin from his pit, with a tired cheerfulness. "Hey, fiddlers, you gipsies, start playing. Mother, why are the women late with the drinks? Give them drinks, mother, for by nightfall I'll be all right. I'll recover . . . I'll recover, boys. I didn't have my scythe with me, and the lightning went round me."

* * *

There was no more to drink. A mournful giddiness filled the men's heads. The women still sat on the grass. It was going to rain again, and the air was stifling.

"Didn't I tell you, Zamfira?" the buried man kept scolding the girl with a nasty sweetness mixed with a little flattery.

"Stand there quietly; be quiet . . ." was all Zamfira could say.

Now that they had drunk heavily, the fiddlers started playing. The violin and the dulcimer produced meaningless sounds. The men around would have liked to say something aloud, but this merry-making without rhyme or reason had something forbidding about it. They gazed at the two dead men, standing stiff in the ground up to their armpits, and at the face of the third growing bluer. Some of them thought that the dull weather was partly to blame, for the sky had become quite dark. The women only spoke aloud, looking up towards the hill with fear in their eyes. Someone said the joiner had finished the job and did not know what to do with the coffins.

The two old women had gone after the doctor to learn if Marin would recover or not. So much waiting had made them stupid, and now they had awakened. The buried man urged the fiddlers to keep playing and talked to Zamfira.

"When I've set fire to the church, who'll dare judge me? I'll go to the Communists and come back with them and take those people's land and divide it up. And if we have land, we won't need anything else. We'll work for ourselves."

He felt suffocated and grew tired very quickly, but was frightened to show it. The girl saw how his face, too, was beginning to turn purple-blue, and, gradually, seeing the fear in her eyes, Marin guessed it all. He was seized with a boundless hatred of everybody and he again tried to move his hands. Now he looked to something within him; he thought he could move his legs, and at the thought he perspired with joy. Then he fell into black despair and struggled with himself for a while. He again called to the fiddlers and swore at them. He thought the people around were drunk and making a fool of him. His jaws began to stiffen again, as they had at first, when he had felt as though his face were in a plaster mask. He spoke incoherently, only to keep from himself how his bones were freezing as in bitterly cold weather. He looked at his brothers' faces and asked Zamfira quickly:

"Am I turning blue?"

"You aren't," lied the girl, filled with a growing fear.

"You're lying, Zamfira."

"I'm not."

Again he was cheerful, called the fiddlers and asked them to play. Then he snapped at the girl:

"Come, Zamfira, dance here by me!" The gipsies seemed to have turned to stone, but the buried man flew at them, "Hey, don't you hear me?"

The women started weeping again, and the giddiness caused by the plum brandy vanished in a trice. The two old women had not returned either and, suddenly, the rain fell again, a thin cold drizzle.

"Dance, Zamfira," ordered Marin. "Don't you hear?" And he turned to look at his dead brothers and said to them: "Lisandru, Gheorghe, can't you hear the fiddlers playing at my wedding?"

The girl stood motionless. She was sobbing aloud, out of her senses; when she could no longer stand it, she jumped up and ran away. The drops fell faster and faster. The buried man's face turned bluer and bluer and was washed by the water. The rain put out the candles, which sputtered and melted near him. It was only then that Marin was seized with unfathomable fear. The fiddlers played on dispiritedly, pleading, as it were, with those around to pity them. When the dulcimer and the violins filled with water they could no longer go on, and they ran towards the stark, merciless mountain.

Simion Pop

(b. 1930)

After a tireless and fertile career as a newspaper reporter, results of which are the volumes *The 45th Parallel* (1958) and *The Year 15* (1959), Simion Pop dedicates himself to epic creation. The volume of short stories entitled *Posters for a Ball* (1960) heralds a prose writer of sober realism, concerned with throwing light on man's inner life. "A Way to Heaven," a short story from this volume, is the creation of a writer who rejects any sentimental effusion, faithfully preserving the forcefulness of facts. Their dramatic intensity associated with accuracy of psychological analysis lends the characters independence, making them the bearers of a peculiar, distinctive message. The prose writer's interest in how the present realities of socialist construction affect people's mentalities and conduct is to be seen in the volume *Warm Hours* (1962), a blend of feature reportage and portrait drawing. His ability to capture the essence of a developing social phenomenon and to immediately arrange his impressions around it, highlight his interesting travelogue, *A Pedestrian Cuba* (1963).

The Triangle, a recently issued novel of modern form, places Simion Pop among the more gifted prose writers of the new generation.

A Way to Heaven

Moise Augustin was to be shot. He had known about it for the past two days and had resigned himself to it. He had even gained some peace of mind in a way. He was waiting for the German to drop in and shout at him: *"Komm! Komm heraus!"*

But so far the Jerry hadn't come and the man had nothing to do. He walked about in the empty stables unable to concentrate on anything. When his left leg, which had been shortened in the first World War, began to hurt, he sat down on the edge of the manger. He wished he had a cigarette to smoke. It would have given him something to do.

He ran his hands over his face and thought that he might as well shave. There was no need for a razor. The Nazis had some special kind of soap that simply melted away your beard. After you lathered your face with it you could shave even with a stick. Augustin ran his hand over his face in a gesture of surprise: "They've got everything, those Jerries!" and then put a straw between his teeth and started chewing on it.

The wind caused the gate of the stables to rattle. The prisoner inside thought a man's hand had caused the noise and jumped up. He stood for a moment, tensed, then sat down again. No, it hadn't been a man's hand.

Moise Augustin was tired of waiting. When they first locked him up he thought everything would be over in no time. The Jerries had only one way of dealing with everything and that without too much expense: a wall and a cartridge were all they needed. And they had plenty of cartridges.

A shiver ran down his spine. But Moise Augustin was not afraid of death. True, he felt a kind of tightening in his throat which made him feel sick. His overwrought imagination was ready to conjure up a thousand evils. He could visualize the set face of the lieutenant who had struck him with the butt of his pistol. The lieutenant's forehead, framed in silky blond, almost white, hair, had been covered with perspiration. He knew the way to strike people without getting tired. But he often took off his thin glasses. Perhaps they became dim. . . .

Moise Augustin had expected rough handling from the Jerries. And yet he hadn't tried to evade them. He had his home and wasn't young. "If they press me, I'll tell them I know nothing, haven't an idea of anything," the peasant had told himself in his simplicity. And so he had waited for them.

His son, Chirila, employed as a miner at Baia Borsii, had taken to the forest some two months before. The front was near and the partisan detachments being formed in the woods did much to harass the Nazis.

"My place is among them!" Chirila said one night. It was mealtime, with the three of them seated around the serving of corn mush. The white willow spoon shook in Moise Augustin's hand. But he immediately steadied himself. He asked for another helping of corn mush and cheese so as to have something to do until he could think of what view to take. He cut a piece of corn mush with his spoon, thinking that it would be best to speak sharply, decisively, so that the other two would understand that he was giving an order.

"Put something to eat into your knapsack, Carolina, for I must send you to your people," he said to his wife.

When he saw the surprised look on his wife's face, his words lost something of their sharpness. But it was no use giving reasons for his decision.

"In the river Iza meadowland that belongs to your parents there's a place where red birches grow. Stay with your parents for a while and make a few bundles of the birch twigs."

"But that's only a day's work," Carolina objected. "We can go there by cart, cut them, and be back home by nightfall."

"Take that knife we made out of the old scythe and cut nothing but long, thin twigs," Moise continued, ignoring the remark. And then he managed to appear annoyed and, without any reason, said as if amazed: "You seem to have dropped from the blue, Carolina! Don't you know I've got to weave a top for the cart and repair the barn? But now bring a pitcher of cold water, for with this salt cheese and everything I am thirsty."

He then considered the matter as settled and turned to his son: "Bring those shoemakers' tools," he said.

He sat on the little three-legged stool, thrust the last into a boot, and put it between his knees, making it fast with his leather belt. He examined the sole of the boot and pressed it with his thumb. He filed the awl and then filled his mouth with wooden nails as shoemakers do. After making a hole he took a nail from his mouth, fitted it into the hole, and with trembling hand brought the hammer crashing down on the nail.

"Don't be in such a hurry, Father," Chirila remarked.

"A woman has no business among men who are handling gunpowder," Moise Augustin explained irrelevantly. "Let her go and cut birches. Am I right or not?"

"You're right, Father."

To emphasize his approval of his son's answer he struck the boot hard another couple of times.

"Of course it's right," Moise Augustin said; after which he loosened the belt that held the boot and examined it in the lamplight.

It was not quite clear whether the man referred to his son's answer or to the job he had done.

He took up the other boot to sew it with homespun hempen thread. He handed one end of the thread to Chirila so that he might rub it with wax in order to strengthen it against the marsh water.

Carolina came in with a full pitcher. She filled a cup and put it down on the ground beside her husband, who was busy with the needle. Then she undressed, let down her hair, and got into bed on the wall side.

"Don't forget to blow out the lamp," she warned, and was soon asleep.

Moise Augustin again ran his needle two or three times through the leather of the bootleg, then, putting the boot under his arm, went up to the bed and covered Carolina by drawing the quilt up over her white shoulders.

When his father returned to the shoemaker's stool, Chirila sat watching his fingers, all worn and knotted with hard work, and was surprised to see how deft they still could be. He could not remember anyone in the house ever taking footwear to the shoemaker's. "Have you nothing else to spend your money on?" Moise Augustin would remark in a huff and would do the job himself as far as his skill and the tools he had at hand would permit. The neighbors also brought their shoes to him.

When Moise Augustin completed the work he said to his son, "Put these things away, Chirila," and then he hurriedly thrust his bare feet into the boots to try them out. He walked from the table to the door and back, put his two feet together as if to make sure that they were the same size, and then took the boots off quickly and put them into his son's arms, saying: "Here, you take them. You'll find them useful for your work wherever you are going. I'm old, my son, and will no longer be walking the hills and fields and forests."

He put out the light and lay down fully dressed. But he couldn't sleep. And neither could Chirila. Father and son spent the night in thought, their hands pillowing their heads. Each of them knew the other was awake by the little glow of their cigarettes.

At dawn Chirila kissed his mother's hand, made his farewells, and went quickly down the steps of the veranda. Silent, leaning against a pillar of the veranda, Carolina watched her son walk away.

The boy took leave of his father at the back of the yard by an old cornel tree where a narrow path led into the woods. Moise Augustin took from his shirt a small piece of lambskin in which his razor was wrapped—the razor he had brought from Italy where he had fought in the first World War. It had worn thin, as thin as a rush leaf, but use could still be made of it.

Chirila dropped it into the woolen, red-striped knapsack which Carolina had got ready for him, putting all kinds of things in it, and then the two men embraced each other.

As the boy was about to leave, he said to his father, in an attempt to make their parting more cheerful: "Buckle your belt, Father, and keep the line unbroken; you haven't been through a war for nothing."

The old man gave no answer. He merely leaned against the fruit-laden cornel tree and stayed there until Chirila disappeared into the forest.

By noon Carolina also departed—on her errand of cutting those red birches in the meadow along the river Iza.

And Moise Augustin remained alone in his house to keep the line unbroken.

Quite soon Carolina sent him word saying that she had cut enough red birches and was waiting for him to come with the cart to take her home. Moise Augustin sent back word that she should keep on cutting birches.

He also heard from Chirila: his son was all right and was leading a group of men who were busy in the neighborhood of the village blowing up bridges, tearing up the roads, harassing the lines of army trucks, and disarming the patrols. The Germans had put a price on the head of the miner Chirila.

Unable to get hold of the son, they kept close watch on the father until they saw him going into the forest with a little bundle when they brought him in for interrogation. The old man lied to them, saying he was going to the sheepfold though he didn't have a single sheep of his own. Finally he told them that he had nothing further to say.

They tortured him for a week until at last the fair-haired lieutenant had become so incensed with the man's silence that he had struck him in the face with the butt of his pistol, knocking out some of the old man's teeth. After this the lieutenant had his orderly wash the blood from the weapon so that he could put it back in his holster and then announced that Moise Augustin was to be shot. From that moment on, the old man had been kept locked up in his stable, waiting for the German's order to be carried out.

Thinking about death, Moise Augustin felt a kind of listlessness numbing his senses and providing a kind of peace of mind.

Through the thin stable wall Moise Augustin heard the heavy breathing of the mule locked up in the barn. When they moved their front to the West, the Nazis had dragged after them an old mule caught somewhere in the Carpathian foothills of Moldavia. On reaching Moise Augustin's village, they had put the mule in Moise's grain barn, tying the animal to a bin full of wheat flour. The hungry animal would thrust his head deep into the powdery flour and sneeze in such a funny way that the Jerries would hold their sides in laughter. This was the fifth day that the mule had been snorting and sneezing. But since early morning he had been breathing with increasing difficulty. A strange rattle came from his lungs. By evening, or during the night at the latest, the dough that had formed inside him would swell and the mule would surely choke to death.

The man's eyes fell on a cobweb in a corner of the stable. In the dimness he could just make out the gray arachnid with a cross on its back. He remembered how sometimes a spider would drop into the animals' feed and how, if it were eaten with the hay, the animal would swell and die of a disease called the "spider illness."

Remembering this, he rose to his feet and climbed up on the manger in order to crush the spider with the palm of his hand. But then it occurred to him that he was putting himself to useless trouble.

He no longer had any cattle. The German regiment had eaten them, sparing only the bullock.

"Where are you, beastie? Come over here," he called in the lisping voice of a toothless man, seeking the animal with his eyes.

Aware of the man's presence, the piebald bullock jumped to its feet and came up to its master, unsteadily, on its thin legs. It was not yet two months old, a gentle, silly beast. Coming close to the man, it licked his hand. The peasant scratched it on its head, between the little horns no bigger than two buds. He scratched it with the nail of his thumb and then suddenly struck it on the forehead with his open palm so that the animal was half stunned. The peasant explained to it: "A bullock must be able to use its horns. Come on, use them. That's it. That's better."

Moise Augustin was glad to have found something to do. He decided to teach the little animal to use its horns. He liked the idea so much that he went down on his knees and, pulling his cap over his forehead, prepared to play at butting with the little piebald bullock.

But he had no time for it. The stable door was flung wide open. Within the doorway was the German sentinel—a stripling. His eyes must have been unaccustomed to the gloom for at first he didn't seem to see the prisoner. When at last he saw him on the ground, he shouted as if in fear: *"Hi, komm! Komm heraus!"*

Moise Augustin, surprised to find the German had really come, thought of asking him what he wanted. However, he merely put his cap in place and went out. The bullock remained alone in the middle of the stable, deprived of its butting partner.

The daylight outside was too strong for Moise Augustin; it hurt his eyes. He covered them with his hand for protection. The air was cold and fresh. He breathed it into his lungs grown weak with the stench of the stable. It revived him. His mind, as if suddenly awake after a bout of drunkenness, cleared.

There were four green-uniformed men in the yard. He knew three of them: the sentinel, the red-haired sergeant who had arrested him on his way to the forest, and the young lieutenant. The fourth must be a driver. They were intent on a motorcar. They were young, the three of them: they looked no more than eighteen or twenty. And they seemed in high spirits too.

The red-haired sergeant and the lieutenant got into the car. They made Moise Augustin sit next to the driver. The latter looked him over and then started the car.

They were making for the mountains. "Where can they be taking me?" Moise wondered as he looked about anxiously.

Half an hour later the car was on a hillside somewhere near the peak of Inau. At a sign from the lieutenant the driver stopped. They got out—the Germans first, then the Rumanian.

There was a deep chasm near by. On its edge stood a fine, tall fir tree. It leaned forward slightly as if looking into the abyss. The Germans examined the tree closely. The sergeant even gave it a kick to make sure it was well rooted in the rock wall.

Moise Augustin looked at them calmly. "Examining it as if they were going to buy it," he thought to himself. The driver found some blackberry bushes and busied himself with them. The red-haired sergeant started exercising, grunting with the effort. The lieutenant, bored, sat down on a boulder and began munching on chocolate. He beckoned to Moise Augustin and motioned him to sit on the grass. He gave him a piece of chocolate. Moise broke off a little bit of it. It was good. He put small pieces into his mouth and let them melt slowly, pushing them about his mouth with his tongue. His gums hurt when his tongue touched them. Blood oozed from the soft flesh. But Moise didn't let a small thing like that spoil his pleasure. He was eating chocolate with the lieutenant, sucking carefully and closely watching the German's mouth. It was the first time that Augustin had tasted chocolate.

After a time, the lieutenant slapped the peasant on the shoulder and smiled.

He said something in German which the sergeant translated, mauling Moise Augustin's language.

"A nasty thing, war, and a great bore," Herr Lieutenant says.

"Why do you go on with it, Mr. Herr, God damn you, if it's so nasty and such a bore," Moise Augustin thought to himself as he looked quietly at this talkative German.

Then the lieutenant again said something in German. The sergeant interpreted again.

"Today it is also Sunday in the Tyrol, where Herr Lieutenant's homeland is. It's the traditional holiday of friendship. A holiday of fun and merriment. Herr Offizier wishes us to forget the war today. He wants to have some fun."

"Let him have it," the peasant said.

The lieutenant liked Moise Augustin's answer. He explained what his fun would be. He was going to make a tempting proposal to Moise Augustin on this day of joy and friendship. A kind of sporting gesture. If Moise had the guts to climb up the fir tree with an axe and cut off the branches to the top, the German would make him a gift of his life. The rule of the game was that he should start cutting off the branches from the lower part, with a soldier's knapsack on his back. When he saw the peasant had understood, the officer rubbed his hands, well pleased with his ingenuity. The peasant gave the matter a moment's thought—just long enough for the thirst of life to rise within him. Then he accepted. He had been a woodcutter in his youth. Could he have forgotten how to handle an axe?

He took off his boots and placed them carefully under the tree he was to climb. It was only then that he noticed that one of the heels needed mending. He was given a short-handled axe of the kind used at the front and a knapsack containing something heavy. He ran his thumb over the edge of the axe. Quite sharp. He spat on his hands and with a spring was up the tree.

The green-clad men moved some distance away and watched him.

Moise Augustin climbed up steadily, keeping his eyes away from the chasm below. It was as if he were climbing a high ladder propped against the sky. He had to cut away at those branches. If only he could manage to keep from becoming giddy there was nothing to fear. The load on his back interfered with his work. At every movement the heavy things inside moved up and down, pushing him this way and that. Maybe there were rocks inside? To find out, he shook the bag. He heard the rattle of metal. Tins. The world is full of German tins Moise Augustin decided.

He went on cutting. The branches he chopped dropped off the tree and rolled from boulder to boulder down to the bottom of the valley. Moise Augustin did not watch them fall. His eyes were glued to the axe. He neither saw nor listened. He simply cut away at the branches.

Standing some hundred and fifty feet away, the Germans watched the man's efforts, their eyes showing interest in what was happening. But the sergeant soon got tired. He took a mouth organ out of his pocket and began to play a slow waltz on it. But as he played he kept looking up.

The lieutenant seemed to grow impatient. He lighted one cigarette after another, throwing them away unsmoked. His glasses often clouded over. He would take a green handkerchief out of his pocket and wipe them, though he never took his eyes off the man in the tree. He went on lighting cigarettes.

The driver kept fairly cool. He lay on his back on the cushions in the car, his hands crossed under his head. He did not stir. He merely looked. And waited.

Moise Augustin found it increasingly hard as he advanced towards the top. The thin branches gave way under his feet. His tired hands were burning. The tins in the pack moved up and down. He felt their cold touch down his clammy back. He tried to make as few movements as possible—to slide up the trunk like a cat. His feet bled. He propped his pack on a branch to breathe more freely. He looked around and filled his feverish lungs with the air of the mountains. Snowflakes fell slowly from on high. The first snowflakes of the year. "Winter has set in. Rather early, blast it. Yes, rather early." Moise Augustin might have been communing with God and reproaching Him for such unwise doings. And the snowflakes came fluttering down, like white rags. Moise Augustin craned his neck to right and left in order to catch the light flakes in his open mouth. The game seemed to cheer him up.

Then he remembered he had work to do. He took hold of the axe he had stuck into the tree trunk and hitched up his pack to a better position on his back. The tins started rattling again, knocking against each other and against his back. He stretched his hand to get the leather straps into a less painful position. Then he ran it over the pack so as to feel its contents better. Suddenly he froze. There were hand grenades in that knapsack. He felt them through the rough cloth and also felt the rings with their silk cords. The blood in his veins seemed to ebb away, his mind to run wild. The world spun about him. There was enough life left in him, though, to clutch the trunk tightly. He remained as if petrified in that position, close to the bark of the tree. Within his breast he felt his heart beating against the tree. He did not even breathe for fear of letting loose the death that he carried on his back.

Over all hung a purple-red twilight. The scent of the resin filled his nostrils—a sweet smell. "I've lived to see another Christmas evening," Moise Augustin thought to himself in wonder. It was August and there were another three or four months until the day of Christ's birth. And yet the man kept hearing Christmas carols in the villages down in the valley and thought he saw tiny tots walking about through the snow seeking a gift of nuts and rye-cakes.

Moise Augustin suddenly found that he had wet his pants. He felt the wetness run hot down the leg which was shorter because of the first World War. The cold of the day seeped into his bones. But not for long. It was as if a leg of ice had grown in place of his left leg. A long, strange leg on which he could support himself on the ground. A new thing, which pleased him. The senseless man rejoiced at being able to hold so high on his ladder and to be able to see the Christmas of the earth. He desired only one more thing: to keep still so as not to spoil his numbed leg of ice.

The lieutenant's metallic voice awoke him from his reverie. He shouted something and signalled to him to climb higher. Moise Augustin strove hard. He struck his axe on a branch, but the branch would not come off. It remained attached by its bark. Moise kicked it with his heel until it came off. Then he crawled on to the next branch and began hacking at that. He was cutting the branch from under his feet. "Branches are like the years. A branch cut off means one year less in your life," Moise was thinking, rejoicing at having so sharp a mind. And then he looked up for some assurance: "Can this tree have fifty-nine branches?" But there was no time to count. He went on hacking at the branches. He was climbing up to the skies, carrying death itself in his pack.

Then, through carelessness, Moise Augustin dropped his axe into the chasm. The sergeant ceased his song, though the mouth organ was still at his lips. Lying on his back on the cushions, the driver held his hand up. He had a blackberry between his fingers. The lieutenant munched away at his chocolate, playing at the same time with his pistol.

Moise Augustin understood. He began tearing away at the branches with arms and breast.

Suddenly something occurred that the peasant least expected at that moment. From a long distance away white rockets sped upwards, lighting the sky. "The front's broken!" Moise Augustin realized in a flash. "The Germans have ordered a retreat."

The Germans down below gave a start. Yet they were not surprised. They merely looked at their watches to see whether they would be in time. They went up to the car, and the driver took the wheel. The sergeant put his mouth organ inside his shirt and climbed in at the back of the car. The lieutenant looked up at the sky where the evening star shone. He carefully buttoned his black cloak.

"Saved," Moise Augustin panted. "Saved!" he shouted under the showering rockets.

Then he remembered the grenades. His hand went to his pack; he loosened the straps, undid it.

He took out of the pack the first grenade he could get hold of, ran his thumb through the copper ring, and pitched it vigorously, almost wrenching away the silk cord. The grenade made a short swishing sound as it darted downwards. He had no time to look and see how things were below. He knew that those playthings in his knapsack were killing the Nazis and that was enough for him. Dizzy with that overwhelming joy, he pitched those iron eggs one after the other and, his senses in a whirl, shouted: "There's death for you, you worms! Have you had enough of it? It's a day of joy, is it? Ha, ha, ha!" Thus did Moise Augustin laugh amidst the roaring of the cannons. Then he addressed his son whom he imagined wrapped up in cartridge bands: "See Chirila, your dad is keeping the line unbroken!" Then, recalling something, he added: "If you're home before me, get my shoemaking tools ready, for with all the trouble I've had I've spoiled my boots."

He longed to see the little two-month-old bullock and would have been overjoyed to walk barefoot with it in the lush, wet grass of the meadows along the river Mara, and also to teach the young animal how to use its horns. But he wouldn't have a minute to spare until spring. Carolina would have cut all the red birches he needed down at the Iza, and all winter he would do nothing but weave cart hoods. "So that all the peasants in Ieud shall have hoods woven by Moise Augustin," he added just to give himself courage. "Yes. All the peasants'll have nothing but hoods woven out of red birches. Ha, ha!" Moise Augustin laughed but he was weary. He laughed and cried at the same time. The fir tree swayed to and fro with his laughter. It swayed and leaned low over the chasm. He seemed to find things rather difficult now. With an effort he tried to raise the knapsack on high and to hurl it at the Nazis at his feet.

But his imagination had run away with him.

The evening star has come out over Magura Hill.

The fair-haired lieutenant stands beside the car, a leg on the running board. He lights a cigarette, then begins to put on his leather gloves, working on one finger after another. He takes a pull on his cigarette and then looks up at the treetop; another pull and he looks up again. The peasant's big hands, which are trying in vain to get that pack of death off his back, get mixed up in the straps. The lieutenant is studying his jerky, untidy gestures carefully through his glasses. The glasses have become misty again. He wipes them with his green handkerchief. Then he coolly takes the automatic pistol from the sergeant's hand and, a protracted report sounding through the evening air, he concludes the fun of the day.

The knapsack on the man's back explodes with a short sound, and violet flashes like firecrackers shoot up.

It is two minutes past seven in the evening. At Rodna, the German lines have been broken.

Titus Popovici

(b. 1930)

One of the most talented prose writers of the new generation of novelists in Rumania, Titus Popovici made his debut in 1950 with stories and tales, and established his reputation as a novelist in 1956 with *The Stranger,* representing a broad view of Rumanian society at the end of World War II and during the first months after Rumania's liberation from fascism. The novel *Thirst,* published in 1958, reveals Titus Popovici as a worthy follower of the classical Transylvanian prose writers Slavici and Rebreanu. Considered among the most significant achievements of contemporary Rumanian literature, these novels have been translated into several languages.

Titus Popovici is also author of the play *Passacaglia* (1960). Following a trip to Cuba, he published a volume of feature articles on that country. He was also a script writer for the films made of *The Forest of the Hanged* and *The Stranger.*

Excerpt from *Thirst*

Ana Mot remembers everything with a strange clearness these days. Slowly she lays her small, yellow, wrinkled hands on the big kitchen table and sits staring in front of her. For years—she no longer remembers how many—her recollections have always centered in the same way around the same fact.

First she remembers how she went to Czernowitz in 1890, in the month of March, to see her husband, who was serving in a Hussar regiment. He wore red trousers and a dark-blue coat, with a lot of black tassels, spurs, and a sword. Mihai was orderly to a bluff lieutenant, a heavy drinker and card player always on the lookout for a duel on the pretext of a mere word or a sidelong glance. To "keep in trim," as he said, he would go out into the yard with Mihai every morning, and they would have mock duels with blunted swords. The officer would dance around Mihai, round and round like a fish, repeating again, and again, the devil knows why, the words: "En garde! En garde!"

Then there floats up before Ana's eyes a picture of their little home on the bank of the Teuz, their patch of land with its poppies, cornfield, cucumbers, and potatoes, and the strong, thickly-woven wattle fence. . . .

What a handsome fellow Mihai Mot had been when she first danced with him in the village *hora;* tall, green-eyed, raven-haired, with a silky, slightly turned-up moustache. The young men of the village knew him as a first-class farm worker; the girls were crazy about him. Wicked old Labosoaia kept a close watch on him, thinking she could do with a son-in-law like that, but he took a liking to Ana, and they were married. After that people began to make fun of them, and talked of birds of a feather; but they didn't laugh for long. Mihai, despite his dandy-like appearance, one day pitched into young Flondor, knocking him flat on his back in the middle of the road with a battered head. And no one could object; they were all witnesses that Flondor had had rather too much to drink, and had been offensive towards Mihai and Ana and got no more than he deserved.

A year after the marriage Mihai was called up for military service. In retrospect it seemed to Ana that that time passed quickly, but at the time she thought she would go mad: night after night she tossed around on the bed that seemed full of nettles; she moved around as in a stupor and trembled like a leaf whenever unmarried young men of her own age accosted her. She had no means of knowing that at the inn a bet had been laid as to who would be the first she would take into her bed on a winter night. Warmed with *palinka,** the young men had fairly outdone each other in bragging. Only Miklos, the crown-land overseer, sat on the edge of his bench, twirled his long, thin moustache and sneered. He knew what he knew: like nearly everyone else in the village, Ana worked on the crown-land about half the summer and went on working parties in autumn and winter. She had no parents; her sisters were married and had their own affairs to look after, and Ana was alone.

When she returned from Czernowitz she found the waiting harder to bear than ever. She had grown thin and hollow-eyed; her walk was no longer as lively as before. For some time now she had been aware of the meaningful glances that Miklos darted at her, and a blind fear came over her. Miklos had been a non-commissioned officer in a Hussar regiment, and it was said that he had behaved there like a brute. He wore a black jacket with silver buttons, a thick nail-studded leather belt, and high top-boots with heavy spurs, for he

---

* A sort of plum brandy made in Transylvania.

rode on horseback more than he walked. When on horseback he enjoyed scaring the women he met by making his black stallion with the white forelegs rear as he approached them.

The crown administration thought highly of him because he was a willing worker and not a thief. He merely liked to drink in the Hungarian way at night, getting drunk towards morning; then he would fling the bottles and glasses to the floor, bury his forehead in his hands and weep, singing in a low voice about a sweetheart whose love would drive him to the grave. On Sundays he would come to village dances and pinch the girls as they passed. The young men ground their teeth, fingering the knives in their belts. Some well-intentioned flatterers of the regime warned him to look out, but Miklos laughed uproariously at them.

"Get along with you—you're a fool. I wouldn't be scared of you chaps, even if there were five times as many of you. Don't worry about me."

The thought of Ana gave him no rest. Until her husband came back—and it wouldn't be so very long now—he could go to her every night, lie with her in bed, and thus a joyless wanderer like himself would have a sort of home. His wife had left him when he was a private in the Austro-Hungarian army; she had eloped with a young Austrian officer. He had forgotten her, but he remembered very well how good it was not to wake up alone in bed, especially in autumn when the long rains set in.

He began to seek Ana out. The time of the corn harvest had arrived, and the plantations were full of women. They plunged deeper and deeper into the cornstalks as into a forest. The coppery hues and wistful winds of autumn hung over the field workers. Miklos spied Ana among the yellow stalks, dismounted, tethered his horse to a small tree, and walked over to her, whistling.

"How's work going on, little wife?"

"Well." Ana cast frightened, sidelong glances at him.

"It's going well, is it? Really?" he gulped. He couldn't think what else to say, came closer, and his breath quickened.

"D'you know, Ana, little wife. . . ."

She turned with a frown. "Go away now, or I'll call Uncle Irimie. What d'you want?"

"You know all right what I want," laughed Miklos, peering at her out of narrowed eyes.

"Go your own way," cried Ana, raising her voice to attract the attention of those working nearby.

"We'll see again another time. But I tell you you're a fool. . . ."

"That's the sort I am. Please go away, and good luck to you."

"I'm thinking you'll be sorry, wife . . ."

"Don't worry about me. And go!"

When the day's work was done and the overseer's assistant had credited each with the amount of work done, the farm workers set off homeward. Ana never went with the others along the country road. She took a short cut through the plantation and then along a winding path that brought her directly to the bank of the Teuz. She preferred to be alone; with the others she would have to talk and laugh, and she didn't feel up to it. She knew the path so well she could have gone blindfolded, listening to the rustle of the corn-stalks and the singing of the wind. As she walked, she thought of Mihai's homecoming. Then they would get down to work, have more money. Within a year they would buy a few acres of land from the crown-land; a year later a few more; then they would build themselves a stone house with a blue porch and have a big yard with fruit trees and stables for cattle, and a watering hole or well for them.

Suddenly she heard the hoofbeats of a horse approaching from behind at a fast trot. She quickened her steps without turning around, in order to get out of the maize.

Now she could hear the snorting of the horse and the tinkling of the little bell at its bit, and Miklos, one hand gripping the bridle, brought his mount up close beside her, so that she felt its hard, glossy rump against her shoulder.

"Now, you'll see," murmured Miklos, and began to dismount. When he still had one foot in the stirrup Ana hit the horse in the stomach with her fist, putting all her strength into the blow. The stallion reared on its hind legs and Miklos rolled in the dust, striking his head hard.

A stream of oaths burst from the man's lips as he tried to staunch the blood flowing from his temple with his sleeve. "I'll get you, you hellcat, I'll. . . ."

Without stopping to think, Ana ran and ran, until she reached home.

That evening she wrote to Mihai: "Come home; I can't bear it alone any longer."

From then on she was given no rest. Miklos would come to her at night drunk, and she could hear him trying to break the door down. She had a hatchet ready beside her bed, determined to brain Miklos with it if he succeeded in forcing entrance. But the door was strong. As the day of Mihai's discharge drew nearer, Miklos progressively lost control of himself and accosted her openly, regardless of who was present. Let someone just dare to say anything! When he thought of Ana, he felt like setting the whole village ablaze; he'd have given half his life to rape her in the village street with a crowd of onlookers gathered around.

The day after Mihai's return—it was on a Sunday—Miklos came to church purposely to see them together. Throughout the service he was on tenterhooks. Ana clung shyly to Mihai's shoulder and whispered to him continuously. Mihai stood erect in military fashion and crossed himself over and over again.

After lunch, according to custom, he went to the inn with his boyhood friends to tell them of his experiences and the places he had visited. The priest joined them, toasted six glasses of brandy with them, then went about his business. One thing led to another, and the men told Mihai how the overseer had chased Ana. From then on he didn't say another word, but drank off glass after glass, as if there was nothing in them but water.

"God damn him! the Lord forgive me," exclaimed old Patru, a distant relation of Mihai's. "Why, the fellow's so bloated with conceit, you would think he was His Highness the Archduke."

"There's not a man among the lot of you," Mihai burst out, biting his lips.

"What can we do? He's the boss here. Do you want him to run you out of the village?"

"We'll see about that!"

"Easy Mihai. You are behaving like a fighting cock. He took a liking to your wife; that's all. She didn't want him; once she even knocked him off his horse. . . ."

"We must have fallen pretty low with women showing more fight than us," said Mihai morosely.

At that moment Miklos entered the tavern. He looked around, frowned, rolled a cigarette, and took his seat on the edge of a bench. Old Labosoi brought him a bottle and asked him what else he wanted.

"I want you to go to the devil."

"Now be careful, Mr. Miklos," said the old man in warning tones. "Be careful! You're in my tavern and you can't treat me like dirt."

Seething inwardly, Miklos drank awhile, then went over to the table where Mihai was seated.

"So you've come back! I hear you were a Hussar. So now they draft all the fools and blockheads into the Hussars?"

"Keep a civil tongue in your head," growled Mihai, "and be careful I don't get up from here."

"Wha-a-a-t?" sneered Miklos. He waved his arms imperiously as if enjoining silence on those present, and deliberately cursed Mihai up and down.

Slowly Mihai rose to his feet, carefully moved the table to one side, stepped up to Miklos, and struck him between the eyes. Miklos went sprawling across the tavern, rolled over, soiling his white shirt, and then quickly scrambled to his feet, pulling at the pistol in his belt. In a twinkling Mihai's friends were upon him, beating him with their fists till the blood spurted.

Ana asked Mihai no questions when he came home drunk, downcast, and savage. She washed him, pulled off his boots, and helped him to bed.

"I've given him his beating," he mumbled, his voice filled with hate. "Perhaps you're sorry, Ana? I'm ready to break your head, too, any time."

"Shut up and go to sleep," she snapped. "What nonsense are you talking, blockhead!"

When he began to snore she went out into the narrow yard, leaned her forehead against a plum tree, and wept for a long time; her heart felt like lead, and she did not know why.

It was noon the next day when Mihai awoke; his head heavy, his tongue thick. For a time he pottered about in the yard, mending some gaps in the fence and removing withered branches from the fruit trees. He did not dare to look Ana in the face, but suspicion still lurked within him. They had all been talking about it in the army: "We chaps rotting away here, and back home who knows who's tickling our wives."

For a time there was a stupid feeling of awkwardness between them. Mihai still looked cross, so that Ana might not realize how ashamed he felt of his suspicions. She, too, was proud by nature and refused to show that she was hurt. She cooked meals for him, looked after him; at night, despite his fiery caresses, she set her teeth and refused to respond.

Swathed in bandages, Miklos lay prostrate for a week, then he recovered sufficiently to return to work. Before a number of people he swore that he would kill Mihai Mot like a dog. He had forgiven the others. He went around as if out of his mind, saying to the Hungarian notary public, who was his friend: "My heart's bursting."

When work on the farmlands was resumed in the spring, Mihai turned up with Ana. Miklos went green in the face at the sight of them together. "So you've come too?" was all he could say.

"As you see," returned Mihai quietly.

"Good. Then. . . ." He left the sentence unfinished.

A few days later Ana became aware that she was with child. She spent a sleepless night. Beside her Mihai breathed peacefully.

"He's asleep," she thought, and began to weep softly, soundlessly, without sobbing; only the tears ran down her cheeks onto the pillow.

"Ana, why are you crying?" came Mihai's anxious voice through the darkness. "Has anybody been annoying you?"

She nestled up close to him.

"I think I'm pregnant," she whispered.

A week later Mihai's manure cart suddenly broke in half in the middle of the road. He stood frozen to the spot, his whip swaying above the heads of the snorting, frightened horses. At that very moment Miklos passed on horseback. When he saw the damage, he came over.

"Why aren't you more careful?" he cried to Mihai, avoiding his gaze. "Now you'll have a pretty penny to pay, cousin. That's a good cart, bought last year at the Debreczen fair. What on earth have you been doing with it on this smooth road?" That was that; Mihai suspected foul play on Miklos' part, but he had no proof.

Then the gendarme caught Mihai fishing in the Teuz on a crown-land bank. All the Lunca people fished there as much as they cared to, but Mihai was the one to be made an example of. He was fined, and, having no money, went to jail.

Mihai couldn't understand it; ever since his return from the army things kept going wrong. Ana had stopped going to work; her baby would soon be born. Her looks had changed for the worse; her complexion was a blotchy yellow. She walked with a labored, rolling gait, and it hurt Mihai to look at her. He told himself that this was woman's lot, ordained by God; she had to bear their children in pain. He had plenty of other things to think of without worrying about her too.

One day he returned from the Arad market in a thoughtful mood. All evening he pottered restlessly about the yard, and that night he made an unusual suggestion.

"Wife," he suddenly said to Ana, "suppose we both went to America?"

"What?" exclaimed Ana in fright. "The Lord save us. What's come over you, Mihai?"

"I've been speaking to some people in Arad. They say our journey there will be paid for and once you're there you can have as much land as you want, provided you know how to till it."

"Leave our village?" Ana exclaimed sharply. "Go to the ends of the earth?"

"A lot of people have gone already."

"That's their concern."

Mihai spoke no more of emigrating, but he became more and more thoughtful. He kept accounts: half his earnings from that summer's work was forfeit because of the broken cart and the fine. After that, Miklos had also blamed him for laming a horse; he was accused of hitting the beast on the leg with a pitchfork handle. Mihai saw that the men who had once been his friends now spoke to him disdainfully; when he sat down at their table in the tavern they fell silent, as if to indicate that his presence was unwanted. He had fallen to the level of Cracea and Picut, the outcasts of the village.

Early in May, Ana gave birth to a son, whom they christened Todor. They had no one with whom to leave the baby, so she continued to stay home from work. With funds so desperately low, Mihai was at his wit's end. Finally he wrote to his brother Iosiv, who was in business in Hungary, telling him of his plight. Unless help were forthcoming he would hang himself. He hoped Iosiv could lend him some money so that he could buy a few acres of land. A few months later he got a reply. His brother told him to come to Hungary, where he and his wife could work as servants on an estate near the Tisza belonging to Count Aladar Bornemisza.

Mihai and Ana read the letter over and over again, until they knew its contents by heart. They were broken-hearted, but realized they had no choice but to accept. Ana was pregnant again, and Mihai wanted to wait until after the birth of the baby, but Ana was ready to go.

"We won't wait. If we're to be servants, then better among strangers. At least no one will laugh at us there."

"We won't stay there long, Mihai," she consoled him. "We'll come back with plenty of money. Hungary isn't America. It'll be all right for the children and we'll have them with us in our old age. You write Iosiv that we're coming. D'you hear me? Hurry!"

He stared at her in amazement; she had become so sharp-tempered that he hardly knew her. Her dark eyes seldom shone these days, and then only with the glitter of anger.

Mihai didn't know that a few days earlier, returning from the well, Ana had met Miklos. The latter was as arrogant as ever, although he looked older. His hair was thinning on top and his moustache hung like a tuft of uncombed tow. At the sight of Ana, Miklos had stopped with his hands on his hips and laughed, baring his decaying, tobacco-stained teeth.

"Heigh-ho, woman of God. You'd be as thin as a rake if you weren't pregnant again. One can see your man's always on top of you. If you hadn't been a fool you'd be a lady today."

Ana cursed him up and down and threatened to smash her pitcher on his head.

"You sound like a frog croaking," were Miklos' parting words.

Back home, after she had put Todor to bed, Ana picked up a

looking glass, went to the window, and scrutinized her wind-tanned face where wrinkles had appeared so early. Something seemed to snap within her. She had been merry and carefree as a girl; at village dances she fairly flew, and now, suddenly, without having had any pleasure, she had grown old, wrinkled, and ugly. In those moments she hated and cursed Mihai, Todor, and the one on the way.

Then fear came over her, and she fell on her knees and prayed for forgiveness. Mihai had gone into the forest for forbidden firewood. All the time he was away Ana was on tenterhooks. God, suppose someone caught him! Or what if the guard shot him? When she saw him entering through the gate she ran to meet him as of old. Mihai was so tired he could hardly stand.

"They didn't catch you?" she breathed.

"Like hell they did. I left the wood with Bitusita on the outskirts of the village. Tomorrow night I'll go fetch it."

Ana was at her wit's end to do something to raise his spirits. Finally, though she hated to, she caught and killed the rooster and prepared Mihai a savory soup. Then she went to the tavern with three eggs in a handkerchief and returned with a packet of tobacco and a bottle of *palinka* "on tick." She sat beside him and watched him as he ate, so famished that he was unable to utter a word. "An able-bodied man and yet we're all but dying of hunger," she thought. She cleared her throat and spoke in imperious tones. "Sit down and write to Iosiv. We're going."

"All right—there's time for that after you've had your baby," he mumbled.

"Don't worry about me. D'you know what? It'll be better if I write myself." Ana had been a bright pupil. She could read, write, and read music. Sometimes she would sit idly down with a sheet of paper before her, sharpen a goose feather, and repeatedly write her unmarried name—Ana Ardeleanu—and then her married name: Ana Mot.

A few weeks later, with Ana in her seventh month, they received news that Iosiv had indeed found them jobs as promised. To start with, Mihai could only be appointed an assistant swineherd, until they knew what sort of a man he was.

"His Grace the Count is all kindness," wrote Iosiv. "If he takes a liking to a man he is always very kind to him. Have you thought the matter over carefully? I'm thinking of returning to the village in a year or two. Write me when you are coming so that I know. Next month I'm going to Szolnok and I'll speak for you again. Your loving brother and brother-in-law, Ioszef Mocz."

They began to sell some of their few belongings, thinking that they could count on some help from Iosiv in the beginning. Mihai brought some boards from the attic and knocked together two big cases into which he piled all his things. Every evening the house was full of neighbors coming in to bid them goodbye and remarking at their pluck in making up their minds to leave behind them both their village and their poverty. One evening Miklos, too, dropped in. He was drunk and prone to sentimentality.

"So that's how it is; you're going to Hungary. As for me, who can tell? I think my bones'll rot in this accursed Lunca here. . . ."

Noticing Mihai's hostile glance, he went over to him, walking rather unsteadily.

"No hard feelings, man. What the devil—what's past is over and done with. God damn anyone who thinks of it. Look, now: I've brought you something. You can't go to Hungary in rags like that. Here are some clothes of mine. They may be a bit small for you, but never mind; you won't be in rags. Here you are." He tossed a parcel wrapped in paper onto the table.

Mihai saw red. His fists were clenched, but just as he was about to consign Miklos to the devil, Ana smiled and curtsied as low as her pregnancy permitted.

"Thank you, Mr. Miklos," she said, "thank you kindly."

"Heigh-ho!" resumed Miklos, and sighed. "Now you folks will find how easy it is to be a servant over other servants. I thought it was a good thing, too, when I came here. I thought I'd make money, go back home and buy land. This," he went on, raising the wrist from which his lash hung, "this is all that's left to me. This, and men's ill will. One day they'll do me in. Well, a pleasant journey and God help you."

After he had gone, Mihai remained standing for a long time in the middle of the room, his chin on his chest. Suddenly he flushed a deep red, went over to Ana and without a word struck her in the face. She retreated a step and stared at him wide-eyed. Mihai hit her again. Then Ana sprang at him, gripped him by his shirt, and with unexpected strength sent him staggering.

"Don't you dare to hit me, d'you understand? Or I'll break your head! Think yourself high and mighty, eh? You should count yourself lucky he was drunk and brought you clothes so you've got something to wear!"

"Woman!"

"No 'woman' about it. And . . . don't you ever hit me again, d'you hear? Never again, as long as you live!"

Todor, disturbed in his sleep, began to wail loudly.

"You be quiet, too, or I'll get that cane from behind the door. Go to bed and to sleep both of you."

Struck dumb, Mihai went to bed. Later, after Ana had joined him and he lay staring up at the roof, he spoke at last.

"Ana, don't be angry," he pleaded.

"Why should I be angry?" she answered in surprise, and sighed.

"Because I hit you."

"Go to sleep. It doesn't matter."

They left a week later and the whole village saw them off. When they passed in front of the church they stopped the cart, got down, and knelt in the dust in the middle of the road. Mihai felt a lump in his throat and swallowed hard. He peered sideways at Ana. But her face was like stone as her dry lips soundlessly uttered the words: "Our Father which art in Heaven . . ."

When the village had been left behind, Mihai could control himself no longer. He jumped off the cart, threw himself into a ditch, and began to weep. After a time the creaking of the cart was lost in the distance. Only then did Mihai get up and begin to drag himself after it with leaden steps.

Three years after their arrival they had forgotten the grinding poverty of the past. On the estate the overseers and others in positions of any authority stole all they could. Only the hired laborers had a hard time of it, but that was no concern of Ana's. She wanted to save as much money as she could, return to the village and buy land. They had a heavy oaken chest into which they had built a false bottom. There they kept bank notes and gold coins, together with a big pistol, and on top, clothing and various other belongings. In the evening, when Mihai came home from work, they would lock themselves in the room at the back and count.

"That will pay for nine and a half acres of first-class land at Grinduri," Ana would say with a frown.

"Yes, Ana."

Mihai was satisfied. Everybody thought well of him, because he struck the right note in his dealings with the men. He dressed well; he wore a black jacket, a broad leather belt studded with silver buttons, soft top-boots and a snow-white shirt. But he did not carry a lash.

When he went to inspect the herds, he would borrow a lash from one of the lesser swineherds. There were two frequent visitors to his home: the overseer, a fat man, almost clean-shaven except for a few stiff hairs on his upper lip like a tomcat's whiskers, and the Protestant clergyman. Every three months Mihai would go to the castle to render accounts. Count Bornemisza liked his hard-headedness and often directed a few pointed remarks at him to see how he would respond. "He has a certain elegance and distinction, my dear," the Count would say to his sister, an old maid, who lived for the memory of a fiancé who had died fifteen years before after falling from his horse during imperial maneuvers. "The Wallachians are a good race!"

"Why should you think of going home?" the Protestant pastor would ask in surprise. "Haven't you got a good home and a job here?"

"We're Rumanians," Mihai would answer curtly.

"Oh, yes, quite. Blood doesn't turn to water," admitted the pastor.

Sometimes in the evening Ana would suddenly begin to laugh, still not believing that they were no longer poor.

"You see, we did well to come?" she would say to her husband.

"We were lucky to have Iosiv," he would remind her, superstitiously annoyed at this ill-timed merriment, which might bring bad luck. "Do you think anyone else could have done as well as we? His Grace is heavily in debt to the merchant Iosiv works for. That was why he took us, to please the merchant."

"Nonsense," Ana would answer with a flick of her hand. "People who are real workers do well anywhere. It's only the lazy that go under."

"Hm," mumbled Mihai, and would say no more; he knew it was no use contradicting her. She had changed so much that often he hardly knew her. She no longer had the look of hunger, but she was growing old. Mihai, though, defied time. Tall, broad-shouldered, green-eyed, he wore his moustache town-fashion; his back was as straight as a young tree. On several occasions Miss Bornemisza, seeing him on horseback, found herself comparing him as he sat in the saddle to her fiancé, who had died a hero's death. Ana, too, saw how the women—the pastor's wife and the overseer's elder daughter—stared when Mihai passed, but she didn't care. The money was piling up in the chest.

"Listen, Mihai," said Ana one day, "I think we ought to put the money in a bank. Ask somebody about a good bank."

She didn't like the idea of keeping money anywhere but at home and the savings book from the Allami Bank seemed so worthless, but she had heard of so many holdups and killings that she began to fear she might lose the fruit of so many years' work. The girls were big now; Anuta was in the fourth form in school and Emilia in the first, so Ana had help in the household. Leaving most of the housework to the girls, Ana took up geese and turkey-breeding and kept four cows. She sent the milk to town with the produce of the estate. . . .

Year after year they planned to go home in the spring, but they couldn't make up their minds to give up their comfortable circumstances, although they could hardly wait to become real landowners. Mihai let Ana decide everything; it was only occasionally that he would get really homesick. At such times, when he came home drunk and looking for trouble, Ana was careful to say nothing. She let him grumble all he wanted; then Mihai would go to the bank of the Tisza, sit down on a mound overlooking the broad, slow-moving river and lachrymosely hum:

Green leaves, leaves of the plum
How I long for the time to come!

He would fling himself down on the floor to sleep. Next morning he would wake up with a headache and say gloomily to Ana: "For God's sake, woman! It's time we went home. Surely you don't want us to be buried here!"

The children were growing. Ana had caught Todor in the stable with a little servant girl and had given him a sound whipping. Anuta, the older girl, was rather plain, a hard worker and not much of a talker; Emilia, though, was a pert young lady who was in the habit of stamping her foot, especially before her father, who would do anything to placate her.

"Emilia, dear, don't shout so, or your mother will hear you. I'll bring you whatever you want from Pest next week."

"Not Pest, Budapest," she would correct him. "Won't you ever learn to talk nicely?"

In 1912 Ana was pregnant again. For the first time in her life she felt like a real mother. Mihai was rather embarrassed, feeling it wasn't proper to have children at that age, and he felt like sinking into the ground when Count Bornemisza congratulated him. He noticed that the children felt uncomfortable about it too. Todor came home one day with a black eye and a missing tooth.

"What's the matter with you?" asked his mother. At first he would say nothing, but when he saw she was getting furious he burst into tears and told her how a stableman of about forty, named Joska, had called after him: "You people are multiplying fast, hey? You must be having a good time of it here."

Todor and he had fought, but Todor got the worst of it.

"Oh, is that it?" growled Ana between set teeth, tying her kerchief and lashing a woolen girdle around her middle. "We'll see about that."

"Where are you going, Mother?" asked the girls in alarm.

"Be quiet and stay at home, and see nobody comes and steals anything."

She went straight to the stables and called Joska out. The man, his curiosity aroused at the summons, complied, but before he could say a word Ana gave him a resounding box on the ear, then another, and finally a heavy punch in the chest, knocking him clean off his feet. At that moment the gate opened and Count Bornemisza entered in his carriage. Joska ran to him complaining, leaning against the carriage step.

"Why, go to the devil, you stupid ass!" exclaimed the Count, laughing derisively and raising his whip. "What good are you to me if even a woman can beat you?" Thenceforward the farm hands began to fear Ana, and this even included Mihai for a long while.

The child was born with fair hair and light blue eyes, and they christened it Pavel, but she called it Pali in Hungarian. She lost all interest in the other children and took no notice even when she heard that Todor was carrying on with a schoolgirl. She bought the finest things from town for Pali and was fairly beside herself with joy and pride when the overseer's wife said: "He could be the son of a nobleman, God bless him!"

They sent the girls to Budapest; Anuta to a homecraft school and Emilia to a nuns' institute for the daughters of country merchants and well-to-do peasants. Mihai had become the Count's right-hand man, and his employer even planned to appoint him administrator as soon as he could find a pretext to get rid of the old one, a brother of his mistress, who already had borne him three children. Thus Mihai had occasion to travel more and more often to Budapest. One day some merchants, after a feast, took him to a big house full of carpets and mirrors, and women in short silk chemises. Mihai had entered the room of a girl named Juliska, and she had loved him in a way that Mihai had never imagined. . . .

* * *

When Pavel was two years old war broke out. At first people didn't realize what it was all about. It was said that the mad Serbs had killed the Emperor's only son and his wife. Mobilization orders began to arrive and grey-coated troops set off for the front, singing:

Serbia, Serbia, hold your hand;
Not for you is Herzegovina land!

But within a year there were few families who had not received a notification framed in black and bearing the Austrian coat of arms. One day an order came that all the church bells were to be rung in honor of the great victory at Belgrade, which had been occupied by the Austro-Hungarian troops. But a few days later the news came that the Serbs had put the Emperor's soldiers to flight and driven them into the Sava.

Some of the wounded home on leave told gruesome tales of the horrors of Serbia; how on entering a house they had found it empty except for an old woman on her deathbed, that they had ignored her presence, and she had pulled a pistol from beneath her pillow and shot four men before the others could bayonet her; about the *comitadjis* dressed in dogskins or sheepskins, who stabbed sentries and kidnapped officers from the very midst of their quarters, and many similar tales.

Todor, barely eighteen, was called up. Mihai took him to the station in the cart and they wept on parting. After three months' training at Cluj, Todor wrote that he would soon be sent to the front. Ana prepared a wooden box crammed with food and set off to see him. Cluj was teeming with conscripts of all ages—youths whose moustaches had scarcely begun to sprout and elderly fellows, all in worn grey uniforms. With great difficulty Ana succeeded in buying some thick woolen gloves and socks for Todor, since his regiment was said to be going to Russia. She stayed in Cluj six days, but she didn't spend much time with Todor. She was alarmed by the fear she read in his eyes; she saw that he could hardly keep from bursting into tears. That was perhaps why she maintained a rather distant manner towards him. When it was time to part, Todor smiled rather bitterly. "Mother," he said, "you would have made a good sergeant-major."

When Ana got home she found herself in full charge of the household. Mihai was away on business almost all the time. Count Bornemisza suffered from rheumatism; otherwise he would have gone to the front. But he invariably wore a uniform, his sword hanging from his belt, and wanted to introduce military discipline on the estate.

One night, with Mihai away, Ana was awakened by a great commotion in the yard and the sound of pigs squealing. The girls woke up and stared at her wide-eyed.

"The gipsies have come! They'll kill us!" shrieked Emilia.

"You shut your mouth," snapped Ana. She opened the chest in which she kept her money, took out the pistol, put on her husband's short coat and went out.

"Who's there?" she demanded, making her voice sound gruffer, though there was no need to, since she had a voice like a man's. Without waiting for a reply she opened fire. The pistol—it was a heavy revolver—never once kicked in her hand. Somebody screamed long and loud.

"Who are you there?" She shot again. There came a shuffling of feet and then the creak of a cart. Ana rushed over to the houses of the swineherds and woke them, cursing them heartily.

"Snoring! The gout strike you all, with thieves out among the pigs!"

"Aunt Ana," mumbled one, "you don't think we'd get up to be knifed by gipsies for the sake of the Count's swine?"

"You shut your mouth. Go round up the pigs, all of you. They've scattered."

She had become a harsh woman, seemingly without a scrap of tenderness, and when she wanted to fondle Pavel she did so when no one was looking, as if she were afraid they would cease to fear her once they had witnessed her act of tenderness. Pavel was allowed to do exactly as he liked: to roll in the mud in his new velvet suit, break windows, climb trees, hit anyone, and woe betide whoever raised a hand against him.

On the very day that Rumania's entry into the war was announced, Ana and Mihai received a notification framed in black. Todor was reported missing in a battle in Galicia. Mihai wept loudly, beating his head against the table; Ana wept too and spoke to no one for two days.

A man from the neighboring village who came home three months later told them how the battle had gone. The Cossacks had charged, yelling, whistling, waving their swords, thrusting with their lances, sweeping all before them. Then Todor Mot, who was lying prone on his stomach in the front line, rose to his feet, threw away his gun, and raised his arms in surrender. That was all the neighbor saw, for the wave of horsemen had blotted the scene from view. The man had felt the fiery breath of a horse rearing on its hind legs; had heard a loud whistling sound, had felt an awful spasm of pain, and saw his hand and forearm fly off, severed at the elbow. Unless the Cossacks had cut him down, Todor must have been taken prisoner.

Even harder times lay ahead. Anti-Rumanian feeling ran high, and even Count Bornemisza was no longer so friendly towards Mihai; still he couldn't do without him.

That winter Iosiv paid them a visit. He had grown old, but there was a look of prosperity about him. He told them that he knew of a hotel for sale near Debreczen railway station.

"It would be a fine opportunity. The station's close by; all the merchants patronize it. We could buy it in partnership."

"Why should we stay among Hungarians?" burst out Mihai, roused to such anger as few had seen in him before. "I'm fed up! My children can hardly speak Rumanian. I'm fed up!" He turned furiously on Ana. "For God's sake, are you so insatiable you want to buy up all Rumania? We've been eating the bitter bread of the foreigner long enough!"

"I would say it wasn't all that bitter," smiled Iosiv indulgently. "D'you prefer poverty at home?"

"I do!" shouted Mihai. "I wish we'd never come!"

"Never mind about him," said Ana, eyeing Mihai disdainfully. "He gets like that at times; doesn't even know what he's talking about. He's fed up with well-being; he wants to go boozing in the Lunca tavern with all the tramps there. As to the proposition, we'll think it over; we must see how matters go . . ."

"Mind somebody doesn't get there before us. It's a real good thing."

"We're thinking nothing over," growled Mihai, rising to his feet. "We're going home to Lunca." He looked angry enough to assault his wife and brother.

From that day on a single thought was uppermost in Mihai's mind: to go home. The war was nearing its end; there were rumors going around that the Germans had made an offer of peace to the French and English.

Then revolution broke out in Hungary.

Mihai set off for Szolnok to get his money from the bank. The town was almost deserted, the shops battered and broken, the streets dirty, the people ragged and fear-stricken. When Mihai saw the bank he was taken aback: its walls were pockmarked with bullet holes, the windows smashed and boarded up. In place of the stout manager with the silky white beard Mihai found a seedy-looking clerk who, after taking his savings book and glancing through it listlessly, told him that he would bring the money at once.

"If you don't mind," said Mihai, bowing, "we aren't natives of these parts and . . . we want to go home."

"And what about it?"

"Please give me gold coins, as I gave you."

The man burst into uproarious laughter. Tears streamed down his cheeks, reddening his watery eyes.

"I haven't heard such a good joke since the times of His Majesty Franz Joseph. Gold! Gold! Mr. Mot, I'll give you two bagfuls of paper; you'll have enough paper to light your pipe as long as you live. Come along."

Mihai followed him in bewilderment. It was only when he saw the pile of paper currency that he knew to be worthless that he realized what had happened. He rushed at the mirthful little man as if to seize him by the throat, then wept and all but fell to his knees.

"Are you living in another world? Great families have lost everything, Mr. Mot; Hungarian traditions have collapsed. It's the end, sir!"

"I live in the *puszta;** I'd no means of knowing," groaned Mihai. "In the *puszta!* The war came, and the revolution; I'd no means of knowing, my dear sir. I've toiled for seventeen years; I was a servant. . . ."

"I feel sincerely sorry for you. But that's how it is."

Mihai found himself in the street, carrying the bags of paper

---

* Hungarian steppes; wasteland.

money. It amounted to several hundred million—scarcely enough to buy a thin cow! He entered a tavern, began to drink, and as his mind clouded, a peaceful feeling akin to death stole over his body. He didn't know how he got home. He had been picked up in the square by a fellow villager and pitched into a cart. All the way home he lay on his back, staring up at the spring sky. When Ana saw him, she was frightened by his appearance; she quickly grabbed him under the arms and lugged him indoors. Mihai let her place him on the bed and it was a long while before he uttered a word.

"We can go home now exactly as we came," he said. "We haven't a penny left."

"What?" shrieked Ana, and rushed over to him. But Mihai was fast asleep.

From then on, they avoided each other. When Mihai arrived for meals, Ana stayed at the back of the yard; at night Mihai slept in the attic. The girls walked on tiptoe in the house as if there were a dead man in it. By night, though, they slept in the same bed and mourned their shattered dreams together.

Count Bornemisza, who was their last hope, returned from Budapast, and, instead of rewarding them for having more or less preserved his property, told Mihai he could pack his things and go. He was himself, he said, now a poor man; he was selling his estate to a factory owner.

"You'd have done better to stay at home, Mot. They've passed a land reform law in your country. Yesterday at the Café Pretzler I was talking with Count Széchenyi of Satu Mare. He arrived here with nothing but the shirt on his back. Your Rumanians were wise; they went while the going was good. Imagine, in Budapest I was arrested and held hostage!"

"God damn you here and now!" Mihai suddenly screamed, in a high-pitched voice like a child's. In his emotional state, he set off at a run along the Tisza bank, looking for a place to drown himself. The children had grown up, they could make a living for themselves now. . . .

Ana found him sitting at the water's edge. She sat down beside him, her knees drawn up to her chin, and began to speak without looking in his direction, as if to the river.

"What's gone has gone for good," she said. "We've still got three cows, six fat hogs, and furniture. We can sell them, buy as much land as they'll fetch, and that's all there is to it. Don't be downhearted now. We still have strength in us, praise the Lord."

In January, 1920, they set out on their homeward journey. The girls began to weep as they looked behind them at the Tisza, at the *puszta,* at the house where they had grown up, at the deserted yard with its fences glistening in a frosty sun; at the manor half demolished by shellfire, with some hired men removing Count Bornemisza's goods and furniture.

At Arad they sold the cattle and everything else they could do without, and scraped together some money.

Mihai felt no joy at the thought that he was returning to his native village; nor did his heart leap when he caught sight of the church tower rising above the massed foliage of the old chestnut trees. They continued their way down the village street, beneath the inquiring gazes of villagers who no longer knew them, and towards the bank of the Teuz. When she saw the poverty-stricken cottage, with its rotting window frames, its roof eaten away by rain, snow, and scorching heat, its backyard where the weeds had sprouted waist-high, Emilia hid her face in her hands and began to cry shrilly. Ana gave her a resounding box on the ear.

"You won't come to shame if you work like your father and I did. Now, stop snivelling!"

With most of the little money they had, they bought the four-acre holding of a gipsy named Creitar, who had received a grant from the archduke's estate.

With what was left of the money they repaired the cottage. The village carpenter, Tulea, was a distant relative, so he didn't charge them much. They felt like strangers in the village; the people they had known were long dead. Miklos, one frosty winter morning, had been found frozen in a runnel.

But Ana found nothing to grumble at. Unaided, she mowed down the weeds in the yard, gave the house a fresh coating of blue paint, dug up and weeded the garden, planted vegetables, and patiently got together some poultry. Mihai, on the other hand, had fallen into a state of utter slothfulness. He would do no work; even when he began something, it took him hours to finish, and he would constantly complain of pains in his chest. He had a younger brother, Dumitru, to whom Ana hinted that they hadn't returned from Hungary quite as poor as it seemed; it was rumored in the village that they couldn't sell the valuables they had brought because they had been looted from the houses of the nobles during the revolution.

Dumitru was a decent sort of chap who had had no luck in life. His wife had died of consumption six months before, leaving him with a child of two, Mitrut. He lived on the same street as his brother, in a mud-hut near the gipsy quarter. Ana invited him to come and live with them, which would also assure that the child would be better looked after. She really did all this to make sure that the daily work was done, since now she could expect no further help from Mihai. He would idle away whole hours on a seat in the garden under an apple tree, Bible in hand. But he did not read; he stared at the river, at wisps of cloud, at the bluish-green hill on the horizon, the last remnant of the old forest. He would stay like this for a long time, until he felt a sudden spasm of pain in the area of the heart, when the tears would well up in his eyes.

Ana endured this for a while, then she tackled him. Mihai merely stared at her with his green eyes, now pale and dim, and his reply was evasive.

"Don't disturb me," he answered. "I'm mourning in my heart for Todor, who is no longer among the living, but with the Lord."

Ana was alarmed and left him alone. She was very fortunate to have Dumitru around; he was an amiable soul who never complained, although he worked from morning till night without pay, in the hope of future reward. All the household worries devolved on Ana. Emilia had entered a teachers' college and would qualify as a teacher in three years; Anuta had got a job with the state railways and hoped to earn enough money to buy her own trousseau; Pavel was in the first form at the commercial lyceum. Emilia was a brilliant student and every fortnight she would write glowing reports of her progress; but Pavel wasn't doing so well. Ana went to visit him once a month and discussed him with the headmaster.

"My good lady, he's no fool," the latter would say. "He's intelligent, but I don't know what's the matter with him. The whole school doesn't give me as much concern as your son does. You'd do well to talk to him and explain how hard you work to give him a chance in life; perhaps he'll understand. If he doesn't, I shan't put up with him much longer."

Ana listened in silence, her jaw grimly set. "May the Lord smite you," she thought. "You dislike the idea of education for the children of poor people."

She was happy only when Pavel came home on holiday. She lavished every care on him, did all she could to please him, and wasn't angry even when she caught him smoking. "After all, everybody smokes," she said.

She remembered Todor at times and paid Father Pinteriu for memorial services so that her firstborn might sleep happily and peacefully in distant soil. When she tried to visualize him she remembered only a plump child and a reserved, taciturn youth who had not yet begun to taste of life. She wished at least that he lay buried in the graveyard on the outskirts of the village, like her parents.

Emilia was in her last year at college when one night during the Easter holidays Ana heard Mihai gasping for breath.

"Ana," groaned Mihai, "I don't know what's the matter with me."

"You're doing too much thinking," she whispered. "Take it easy. We lived well in our time. . . ."

"What was the good of it?" he murmured. Suddenly he was bathed in cold sweat. He tried to get up and couldn't. "Ana," he said ashamedly, "I want to go outside for a bit and I can't. . . ."

"Wait a minute." She quickly got up, dressed, and lit the lamp, lowering its wick so as not to wake Pavel and the girls, who were asleep in the next room. Anuta, too, had arrived home from holiday that very day.

"Come on, then. Lean on me."

"You're strong as a man, Ana."

They went out into the yard, their backs bowed. He looked around and then towards the sky; a full moon hung there amid ragged wisps of cloud. He shivered. "Let's get back inside. I'm cold."

"Yes, it's chilly."

"I feel like a cigarette."

With considerable effort—he felt heavy as lead—she took him indoors and laid him on the bed, then handed him tobacco and paper. His fingers trembled; he was unable to roll himself a cigarette.

"Give it to me; I'll roll you one. You're wasting expensive tobacco." She handed him a cigarette, but now he couldn't answer her questions. His breathing was labored; he kept trying to say something and finally managed to utter: "Ana . . . what the devil . . . was the use of working . . . so hard?"

His gaze clouded, he felt an icy grip compressing his heart, and died. Ana closed his eyes, lit a candle, and placed it between his fingers, which had begun to turn cold. She then put on her top-boots, fetched Dumitru, and the two of them together washed him, shaved him, dressed the corpse in clean garments, and lit two tall candles decorated with blue ribbon left over from Pavel's christening. When all was ready Ana went into the next room and woke the girls.

"Anuta, Emilia . . . wake up. Your father's dead."

Lumps of earth thudded down on the coffin. Ana covered her dry eyes with one horny palm; her other arm was around Pavel, who stood beside her sobbing. She sighed heavily. "If only I can bear up till my lad becomes a man," she thought. "Then I can lie down in this earth too." It seemed to her that the day of eternal rest was no longer so remote. If only Pavel would do well, so that she would have that to be happy about when she died. Around her she heard men's voices. "The Lord rest his soul. He was a hard-working and righteous man."

She bowed. "Dear friends, come and eat in his memory."

After the guests had drunk in honor of the deceased and talked about him for a while, they began to remember their own concerns and gradually withdrew.

That night Ana paced up and down in the garden, thinking. She was now a widow and there was the girls' and Pavel's future to be considered. It was true that ever since they had returned to the village she had had little help from Mihai, the Lord forgive him, and had done nearly everything unaided, but still the mere presence of her husband had meant something.

A little later she had a talk with Dumitru, with whom she had always got on well; he was shy and irresolute, didn't know what to do, so he was very eager to listen to her suggestions.

They decided to cultivate their holdings jointly, and later on Emilia was to look after Mitrut. If he showed an inclination for learning then she would send him to study to become a schoolmaster or a priest. He was a bright, lively boy, and from the age of six he had been helping in the household, minding the geese and the cows.

When Emilia finished training college they had the biggest quarrel they had ever had. She wanted to go on with her studies, qualify to teach in a secondary school, and settle in town. Ana was against it, and much surprised that Emilia should dare to differ with her.

"You won't feel comfortable as a schoolmistress in Lunca? Nonsense!"

"I haven't the least intention of burying myself alive in the mud here. And you, Mother, you'd do well to realize that you can't give me orders any longer. You sell my share of the land and give me the money!"

Ana clapped her hands together in sheer amazement. "What share?" she asked.

"What share? The share you should be giving me when I get married!"

Ana began to laugh. "You haven't any share at all as long as I live. Not a scrap."

When she saw Emilia was crying she sought to comfort her. "Don't be silly, Milia. A swineherd's daughter has done very well becoming a teacher!"

"Father was an administrator!" Emilia screamed furiously. "Why do you degrade yourself?"

"No, dear," answered Ana calmly; "your father, the Lord forgive him, and me, were servants. Now don't let's argue about it any more. You can be a teacher here; and you have Pavel to look after."

Emilia had no choice but to comply, but she never forgave her mother, not even later when she got married and began to do very well indeed. Then, at moments when she saw Emilia was happy, Ana would ask whether life in town could have had more to offer now that Emilia had all she wanted.

"Be quiet, Mother!" Emilia would reply angrily, and a frown would cloud her face at the thought of the many joys that might have been hers elsewhere—joys of which she had not even an inkling.

The eldest daughter Anuta married a railway clerk rather against her own inclination, having been more or less compelled by her mother, who was still intent on her plans.

"Listen, my daughter," she had told her after the betrothal. "You two don't need land; you're town dwellers, and you either have to work hard on the land yourself or it brings you loss and no gain. I'll sell your share and send you the money. Leave it to me."

She sold the allotment, two and a half acres, at a fairly high price, although she felt she would rather have cut off her own right hand. But she gave Anuta only three-quarters of the proceeds and the rest to Emilia, who had an obstinate nature and a long memory.

"Town dwellers waste money. We must buy land, to make good what we've lost through her."

With her salary as a schoolmistress, Emilia bought herself new dresses and shoes every month, and Ana was happy to see how pretty she was. In the village, a tall, well-built, earnest lad of only nineteen, George Teodorescu, had been appointed headmaster of the school. Every evening Emilia would tell her mother about him, how full of energy he was, what a worker and what a capable teacher, how the other masters respected him although they were older than he. Ana held her peace; she had planned to have Emilia marry Doctor Halmagianu of Zerind, a bald, portly, hard-drinking bachelor who made a good income from the patients he fleeced to the best of his ability in every village in the district. Once a month he would come to Lunca, and Ana did everything she could to persuade him to come to lunch though she knew that Halmagianu lived with his servant, by whom he had had two children.

When she mentioned him, however, Emilia flushed a deep red, screamed, smashed some plates, and threatened that if Ana ever once again mentioned "that satyr," she would pack her things and leave the village. They didn't speak to each other for nearly a fortnight. Then one day Emilia spoke to her mother in a tone that brooked no opposition.

"Mother," she said, "poor Mr. Teodorescu leads a wretched life alone. He's as thin as a lath. What about asking him to move over here and have his meals with us?"

Ana eyed her in alarm. "What will people say?" she queried.

"What do I care?"

"Have it your own way. Where'll he sleep?"

"In the big room. You and I can sleep together. I'll let him know today."

On the one hand, Ana liked to see Emilia so sure of herself, but she had not yet given up her own plans. George moved in soon after and Ana took a malicious pleasure in showing Emilia his patched shirts, torn socks, and worn suit with the threadbare elbows. She watched them both narrowly and never left them alone for an instant. Her manner towards George was cold, almost hostile. True, he was a handsome fellow, but that wasn't enough to make a proper husband. He had a face like a sensitive child's, flushed readily, and his thick black hair would cascade over his forehead whenever he moved at all briskly. His big, cool gray eyes made him seem older than he was and compelled respect.

At Easter Ana decided to make one last attempt. She invited Halmagianu to lunch. The doctor arrived in a carriage, bringing with him ten bottles of expensive wine and cakes from town. At the table he merrily confessed that he knew nothing of medicine and that if his patients recovered he wasn't to blame! George eyed him in disgust and several times tried to point out to him the error of his ways, referring to the responsibilities of the intelligentsia. The doctor laughed heartily and replied that he was very sorry that his own age would prevent him from speaking with George some ten or fifteen years later. He patronizingly patted him on the shoulder, addressing him all the time as "young man," and only once as "Mr. Headmaster." Ana noticed that Emilia was red with annoyance and realized that nothing more could be done. After lunch Halmagianu lay down for a nap in the big room, and within five minutes could be heard snoring loudly in contentment. Ana moved in the direction of the little garden where she could hear Emilia and George in conversation.

"You know," Emilia was saying, "I'm sick of the whole thing. Halmagianu goes from village to village visiting the homes where there are marriageable girls and crams himself with food. Mother is afraid I'll be left an old maid. She's gotten to be a regular old harpy. I'm going; you'll see, George, I mean to leave the village and go to Bucharest."

"Please stay," he whispered, looking at the ground.

Towards evening Ana unexpectedly asked the doctor to take a look at Emilia because it seemed to her that she was a bit weak in the lungs. The doctor said he would be glad to do so at once while it was still light.

Without a word, Emilia got up and left the house. She went to spend the night at the home of Notary Meliuta, with whose young wife she had struck up a friendship.

A month later, after the end of the term, George suddenly came into Ana's kitchen and began to speak rapidly, as if repeating a lesson learned by heart.

"Dear Mrs. Ana," he began, "I should be happy for the privilege . . . of being able to call you . . . Mother."

"What do you mean, Mr. Headmaster?" demanded Ana, staring hard at the pot on the stove.

"I mean . . . that I want your consent to marry Emilia. I love her very much."

"If that's so," replied Ana, turning deliberately to face him, "let's talk it over. Bring over a chair for yourself." She took a bottle of plum brandy from the little cupboard, filled two glasses, emptied her own at a single draught, and seated herself in a stiffly upright manner, her hands crossed on her lap.

She asked George how much he earned, on what he expected to support Emilia, since she had always been well-off, and it was only because of a misfortune that she was a schoolmistress. Otherwise she would have been a physician . . . or even better.

Flushing a deep red and beginning to stutter, George told her that apart from his salary he was entirely without means, but that he would work ten times as hard; his father had died in the year of his birth, and his mother lived in great poverty.

"Uh-huh . . . so you want to bring her here too?"

"No—you know what old people are like. They don't like leaving the place where they . . ."

"I know," Ana interrupted. "I pray God will let me die here, when I know my children have settled down." She felt she had hurt him, but she wasn't sorry. He should know whom he had to deal with.

"You're not much of a drinker," said Ana, changing the subject (It was her fourth glass). "Don't you like it?"

"I certainly don't," George almost shouted.

"That's not bad, but let me tell you, Mr. Headmaster, that a man who's afraid of alcohol is soft by nature. . . . What else can I say," and tears welled up into her eyes, for she felt it was time for tears, "except that I've worked hard all my life to provide for the children I brought into the world. I have had no luck, and . . ."

George jumped up and kissed her hand. Remembering that she had forgotten something, Ana blew her nose, wiped her tears and indicated to him that he would have to see to Pavel's future; the poor little lad was fatherless and exposed to temptation. George was happy to accept.

Emilia wanted a simple marriage, but Ana would have none of it.

"What? Do you want the Lunca trash to laugh at us? Don't you see they're laughing at us already because we were fools and came home from Hungary utterly ruined? The Lord rest your father's soul, but his mind was weak. If we'd bought that inn at Debreczen you'd have been a great lady today and could have married a well-to-do Hungarian, perhaps some lieutenant, the son of a count. You're pretty; you've got sense; you deserved something different." This was especially for George's benefit.

At the wedding the priest praised Ana for the fine future she had created for her children. There was heavy drinking and Anuta's husband, Octavian Sabin, who had a good voice, so deeply impressed the people of Lunca with his singing that in later years, whenever he visited the village, they used to beg him to sing the *apostol* and the *priceazna* in church.

Slightly the worse for drink, although there was nothing unsteady either in her voice or in her speech, Ana reminded herself that this was the end of her domination.

A few weeks later they moved into the stone building, formerly a government office, that now housed the school. The entire responsibility for the new household fell on Ana. She looked after the pigs, milked the cow, counted the chickens, looked for broody hens, did the cooking, baked bread, and during summer planned the work in the fields, to make sure that Dumitru, who worked the farm, made no mistake in distributing produce.

They began to prosper, and the village elite, who at the beginning had looked askance at George because of the single wooden suitcase, bound round with string, with which he had arrived, were now glad to welcome him. Very soon he began to set the pace in their society. The land allotted to the schoolhouse amounted to fifteen acres, six of which had been given to the headmaster and two to Emilia by way of a marriage gift. At the end of a year they bought three more acres of the best land. Every year they bred three or four pigs, dozens of fowls, geese, turkeys. Yet Ana wasn't happy; she no longer knew where the money was going or how much there was at home. One summer Emilia and George went away to visit other parts of the country. When they returned Emilia complained of the "wretched, dirty life in which they had buried themselves." Ana felt a stranger among them. At the table they discussed all manner of things she knew nothing about, and when she tried to get in a word or two, George would look at her politely and Emilia would silence her sharply: "Oh, drop that, Mother. We're not interested in who is living with whom or what old graybeard of yours has died."

Then a feeling of anger would surge through Ana. "Yes," she thought, "I'm a peasant woman; they're gentlefolk. I'm only good enough to do the household work; God forbid I should have no strength left to do it."

She often picked quarrels with Emilia, threatening to leave them and go to her own home. But for Pavel she would perhaps have done so several times. He had been expelled from secondary school and later from the training college, where he did no work; he merely drank and gambled.

"It's your fault, Mother!" Emilia had said innumerable times. "You brought him up as though he were the son of a count; you didn't teach him to work! You'll see, he'll turn into a highway robber . . . disgrace us in front of the whole countryside!"

At such references to Pavel, Ana would remain as silent as if she were deaf. They secured Pavel an apprenticeship with the Astra works at Arad, where he succeeded with great difficulty in qualifying as a skilled worker. Emilia often went to Arad, but she never found him at home. Pavel's landlady, who had also been Emilia's in the latter's last year at school, told her that Pavel came home drunk every night "with women of the lowest kind, my dear."

"If he weren't the brother of such a charming and distinguished lady I wouldn't tolerate him here a single day," she would add. "I keep telling him: 'Don't disgrace your sister.' But he's an obstinate fellow."

Emilia would report all this to Ana without omitting any of the harrowing details, revelling in the opportunity to show that she had more sense and foresight than her mother.

Now and again they would get a telegram: "Send money; I'm in hospital, Pavel." Surreptitiously, like a thief, Ana would send him some, although she knew he was lying, for she was powerless in dealing with this boy. When he was away she hated him, swore she would never send him another leu, even if he collapsed with hunger on the streets of Arad, but as soon as Pavel came home, thin, hollow-cheeked with hunger, and listened as humbly as a beaten dog to Emilia's scolding and abuse, Ana would forget everything and wholeheartedly take his part.

In her little room they would talk together all night. She would tell him all her troubles and the humiliations she had to endure.

"Yes, Pavel, now they put on airs like gentlefolk. It's my fault, for working like a slave for Emilia. I'm their servant and nothing else. 'Mother do this; Mother go here; Mother bring that.' O God, if only you had been the kind to find a good job, my little Pavel, and marry a decent well-off girl, then you could have taken me to live with you and I might have had a little happiness in the few years I have left."

Lying back on her bed, Pavel would begin to weep, swear by all that he held dear that he would change; he made plans for the future, saying he would buy a cottage on the outskirts of the town, get married, and his mother would live like a lady.

"You'll see what things will be like when you stay with me, Mother dear. I'll wait on you hand and foot. If you will only help me this once to get back to Arad in decent clothes! You know what people are. If you're not properly dressed, they don't even look at you."

When he left, Ana would secretly give him all the money she had saved on purpose for him, and no sooner was Pavel off the train than he would enter the "Blue Pipe," where he was known as a regular patron, and there he would spend all his time.

With time, Ana stopped asking herself what was the matter with her boy and why he behaved as he did. When she thought of him it was only in weariness and sorrow. More and more rarely she prayed God to make a better man of him, sensing that she was kneeling on the cement floor in vain. She began to send him less and less money, giving it all to Emilia. At least she knew what Emilia did with it: there was nothing lacking in the home—new furniture, paintings on the walls, clothing, linen, crockery.

Then her grandchildren came: Anuta's boy Andrei and Emilia's Dan. Every summer Anuta and her husband would come and stay with them, and the children grew up together like brothers. On one occasion, watching them playing together in the sun, the old woman felt an unexpected thrill of happiness coursing through her. "O God, how wonderful life is," she thought. "Men are born, grow up, and die when their turn comes. And after them others are born and then still others and so on until God puts an end to life on this earth . . ."

She gave no thought to her own death. She had arranged everything in the cupboard: napkins for the priest and those who assisted him, black clothes, the shoes that would never tread the earth, the candles and the lesser expenses, arranged in paper rolls marked: For the priest. For the death *hora*. For the poor.

* * *

Her brother-in-law Dumitru Mot died one winter. The ice had broken as he was crossing the Teuz and he had stood there, waist-deep in water, for nearly two hours getting the horse and cart safely out of the icy, swift-flowing water. George had borrowed them from Gavrila Ursului. All his relatives, even the most distant, came hurrying in to take charge of Mitru, who had just turned fourteen, intending to get hold of his one acre of land, but the one-acre inheritance was merged with the old woman's holding and the money due the boy put in safekeeping, so that he should have something with which to make a start in life at the age of eighteen.

Mitru was a rather delicate boy, good at his lessons and hard-working. For months he felt ill at ease in the headmaster's house, starting fearfully whenever someone spoke to him. Ana began to feel better now; she had someone she could order about and scold. She nagged Mitru all day long. When she saw him reading or doing his lessons, she immediately went for him.

"Leave those things alone awhile, my boy; they won't help you make a living. See that you do your work well, and we'll be satisfied with you and give you a helping hand when you go out into the world."

The boy would obediently get up, put down his book, and go where she sent him, but he was beginning to dart odd, sidelong, gimlet-like glances at the old woman, and there was a hostile gleam in his eyes—quickly concealed. He had never been a talker, but now he scarcely spoke more than four or five words a day. That greatly annoyed the old woman; she would have liked to hear him thank them every day, to see him ingratiating himself, and because Mitru did neither of these things she began to suspect that he was plotting against them. Now she had somebody to talk about whenever an elderly female neighbor came over. They would sit together in the sun, and Ana would begin by deploring the wickedness of the world, citing the example of this orphan who should be praying to God from morning till night to keep them in good health, and who, instead, of all things, cursed them and wished them every kind of ill. She spoke in a loud voice so that the ungrateful one might hear. One day Mitru had enough. He faced her squarely and began to shout at her in a voice that was comically off-key because it was changing at the time.

"Oh, leave me alone, Aunt Ana! Why d'you keep picking on me? Be quiet! You ought to be ashamed of yourself, that an old woman like you can't live because of me! You deceived father all his life with your tales and made him work for you like a beast of burden. You told him you would send me to school, so that I could become a gentleman. Don't you fear God, now that you haven't long to live?"

He threw the water-jug to the ground, turned on his heel, and ran out of the yard. He didn't come home for the evening meal, nor the morning after.

Ana didn't sleep all night. She was afraid. Not that she feared what George would say, or the village, but because she couldn't understand why the youth was angry. In the morning, when George asked her where Mitru was, she felt like sinking into the earth.

She went red in the face. "He got . . . cross with me and . . . he went away," she stammered feebly.

"For Heaven's sake," exclaimed Emilia. "George, go find him. Mother, Mother how could you . . ."

An hour later George was back, his hand on Mitru's shoulder. The lad was sobbing. When the old woman saw Emilia rush out to meet him and kiss him on both cheeks, she went into her little room and began to pack her things in a big wicker basket. Emilia, who had come to scold her, found her kneeling on the cement floor pushing her clothes into the basket.

"Whatever are you doing, Mother?" she demanded in astonishment.

"Nothing . . . I don't belong here. You're gentlefolk. But I want to tell you that I'll make you pay for all the years I've been your slave, and if you won't pay I'll sue you in court. . . . I won't give in, even if I have to sell my land and spend the money on lawyers. I'm going to Arad to my poor little Anuta, whom I treated so wickedly, all for your sake, for you and for your husband. And all so that you could live in plenty and laugh at me, and keep me in this cold room in winter where my rheumatism kills me!"

Emilia was shaken by those unexpected words and burst into tears. At that moment the old woman realized that she was the stronger after all; she went on pressing down her clothes, although she could have laughed for joy.

"George, George," called Emilia, "please come. Mother wants to go. . . ."

George was there in an instant. "Why, what's happened, Mother?" he asked.

"Nothing. When people don't like me, I don't like them either."

But at lunchtime she had forgotten all about going. She seated herself at the head of the table, cut the bread and, as if suddenly remembering something, called: "Hey, you over there; whatever your name is! Come here and I'll give you some fresh bread."

"I'm not coming," came Mitru's voice, hoarse with crying, from behind the oven. "I don't like fresh bread. It gives me a stomach-ache."

Then Danut, who was seven years old and a quiet, thoughtful child, took the bread from the table, ran over to Mitru with it, and said he wouldn't ever again eat at the family table unless Mitru came too, because Grandma had a way of eating that made him sick. George got up to punish his impertinence but Ana stopped him, laughing.

"Let him be, George. I must have fallen very low, with even the children laughing at me. Come to table, Danut, and you, too, you obstinate fellow."

* * *

She never realized how this change of heart had come over her —why she changed her behavior towards this orphan who refused to cringe. On winter nights she slept little, and to have someone to talk to she kept Mitru by her side, telling him stories from her youth, about Miklos: "He was a man, and no mistake. When he looked at a woman . . . oho! she felt herself going all hot and cold. . . ."

"God made man like a beast of burden," she went on. "He gave him a mind, and in exchange for that he compelled him to work. There is no deed without its reward, nor joy without sorrow, nephew. D'you pray?"

"M-m-yes, Aunt Ana. . . . Well, as I was taught: Our Father which art in Heaven . . ."

"Listen," she whispered, "I pray in my own way. I speak to the Lord as I think best. I'll tell you more about that. D'you know, you're like your uncle Mihai, the Lord rest his soul. He held up his head too; no one could tread on his toes. But it's no use being proud if you're poor. Take my sheepskin tomorrow morning when you go to the pigs; it's cold."

Mitru had begun to attend the village dance, the Sunday *hora*, and from him Ana could get the latest village gossip, and would tell him her own worries.

"When a peasant becomes a gentleman," she said, "then he's neither gentleman nor peasant. He hasn't lots of money to throw about as he likes, the way the nobles used to have, and he doesn't know how to husband the little he's got. However well-off you are, always remember that there may be hard times ahead and you may go hungry. There's never so much it can't run out, nor so little it isn't enough. Mark my words, Mitrut, for I'm an old woman; I know what I'm talking about. You find yourself a rich girl, and get her into trouble if you can, so that her father will give her away to you whether he likes it or not. When a man's poor he isn't human; he's a dog, and no one cares a scrap about him. You can be ugly and a fool; if you've got land, the village will think you are handsome and wise."

When Mitru was eighteen she bought him a suit of Sunday clothes out of her own money, and when Emilia began to laugh at her, reminding her how she had disliked him at the beginning, the old woman was offended.

"You don't like to see a peasant happy. You've become gentlefolk, my daughter; God grant that you don't some day regret you didn't stay at the plough-handles."

A year later Mitru thanked them for all they had done for him and said that from then on he would earn his own living. The old woman gave him her land to cultivate on the share-crop system and until he was called up for military duty she had no cause for complaint. He would consult her, asking her advice as to what he would do best to sow; when they sold their wheat he would take her with him to the Chisineu fair and let her do the haggling, then he would bring boiled brandy to the cart and they would drink together. It was only in the matter of marriage that he didn't follow her advice; he married Florita Busuioc, a pretty, well-behaved girl, but the daughter of a ne'er-do-well, a thief, who had died in prison. Ana bought him a table, two chairs, and a cupboard, although she felt like scolding him because he hadn't married a wealthy girl. But by now she felt she was growing old and did not wish to quarrel with her loved ones. Besides, hadn't the whole village laughed at Mihai when he chose her? If they had had luck in Hungary, today she would have been the wealthiest woman in the village.

• • •

The second war. . . .

Pavel left the very first day with a mountain infantry regiment; so did George, who had been doing periods of military service since 1938. Ana's grandsons were in high school at Arad. Emilia was left in charge of the school; all the masters had left for the front, so she had to accept the midwife's daughter and the wives of the priest and notary public as substitutes. She did remarkably well and won much praise from the inspectors. She tried not to show how deeply she felt George's absence, but it was an uphill struggle, and many nights she would weep on the old woman's breast. Ana did her best to carry on with her work the same as ever, but her strength and eyesight were failing, though she didn't tell Emilia so as not to give her an added cause for worry.

In September, 1943, they received the news that Sergeant Pavel Mot had died a hero's death in the fighting at Naltchik. They wept bitterly; only Ana sat bolt upright at the head of the table, staring at the courtyard bathed in the rays of a pale autumn sun. It was she who after a time broke the silence.

"The Lord have mercy on him," she said in a hollow voice. "Now let's have lunch, or the soup will be cold."

"For God's sake, Mother!" Emilia exclaimed through her tears. "You think of nothing but food!"

Ana smiled enigmatically.

"We won't bring him to life anyway," she said. "That was his predestined fate, the same as my first-born Todorut. The Lord rest their souls."

Then she began to talk about Pavel's childhood days, when she had loved him so deeply; and she talked as if he had been dead a very long while.

More and more death notices reached the village. At the village hall and in the school hung a blue poster showing a soldier with a bayonet fixed to his rifle, and the bayonet's point covered the ceded province of Transylvania. Above the poster appeared the words, "Fallen for recovery of territories temporarily seized," and below came a casualty list:

"Mihai Lung, fallen at Dalnik; Petre Ilies, fallen at Kiev; Gheorghe Neteda, fallen at Simferopol; Avram Lung, fallen at Yalta; Mihai Trifut, fallen at Krivoy Rog; Daniel Gurca, fallen at Kharkov; Dumitru Palincas, fallen at Rostov; Pavel Bogdan, Grigore Mot, Petre Albu, Alexa Ardeleanu, Vasile Purcaru, Florea Mihaies, all fallen at Stalingrad; Pavel Mot, fallen at Naltchik; Ludovic Ifraim, fallen at Rostov"—and new names were added every day.

In October, 1943, they had news that Lieutenant George Teodorescu of the 74th Infantry regiment was reported missing in the Stalingrad encirclement. Then the old woman wept—as she had not wept for either of her sons, nor for her husband. Emilia locked herself in the bedroom, pulled down the blinds, and did not come out for two days. Dan had been orphaned. How could a single woman with so much to do look after him? Luckily he was able to stay with Sabin; the latter's wife Anuta, who suffered from heart disease and had been pensioned, was able to look after both boys.

During the night Emilia entered the room where her mother slept on a hard wooden bed with a trayful of fruits painted on the bedstead and said to her in imploring tones: "Mother, let's sell the land and move to town. I've got a feeling that George's dead."

At that the old woman seemed to regain her former strength; she raised herself up on one elbow: "Are you out of your mind to talk such nonsense?" she cried. "Sell the land? Old and weak as I am, I'll plough, sow, and mow it myself, rather than let you sell it. Milia, Milia, where would we be without the land?"

That summer, after the two boys had come home on holiday, Mitru was sent to the front. He had been exempted until then because of his tobacco plantation, but Cloambes, who was otherwise known as Ladoi, had tricked him into selling it to him in order to keep his own son at home.

In August peace was signed. There was joy in the house; if George were alive, he would come home. That was how it had been in 1919—all the prisoners that were lucky enough to survive had come home.

But on the thirteenth of September the Germans and Hungarians again invaded the land. People loaded their belongings into carts and set off eastward into the path of the advancing Russians, for it had been rumored that the Germans took with them all males between the ages of fifteen and fifty. Emilia was at Arad, where she had gone to try to find out something about what had happened to George by inquiring at the military command there. The old woman would not hear of leaving.

"Go, if you will, my dears. How could I leave the house to the soldiers?"

"But Mother, for God's sake," pleaded Anuta, "How can you stay behind alone, an old woman like you?"

"Don't worry about me. I'll have my hatchet ready behind the door. I'm afraid of nobody on this earth. If they kill me, it's time anyway. You get along and don't waste time worrying about me."

The two boys hid the grain in a corner of the attic, then they loaded what they could onto a cart belonging to Turculet, the station-master. Ana accompanied them to the gate, then shot the bolt and locked herself in the house after making sure that the hatchet was handy. About three o'clock in the afternoon the last frontier guards withdrew. A few of them knocked on the door and she served them with bread and milk.

"Don't give up," she told them. "Come back again!"

Then she went back into the house to await the arrival of the enemy. Towards evening the Hungarians entered the village. A few cavalrymen, headed by an officer, passed down the village street; Sofron, bowing down to the ground, welcomed them at the village hall with the traditional offering of bread and salt, and supplied the information they wanted. Billets were now sought in the semi-deserted village; about a hundred men and five officers were billeted at the school. When they began to hammer on the gate Ana crossed herself, wrapped her shawl about her, and went out to meet them.

"Where are the masters of the house? Where's the schoolmaster?" an officer demanded.

"They've gone, sir," she replied in Hungarian.

"Have they run away from us?"

"That's their business."

"And who are you?"

"Just an old woman."

That night the officers had a rollicking party. The men slept on straw in the classrooms, after killing all the hens and chickens. One of them, who looked fortyish, began to talk with the old woman. He was depressed, had left four children at home, and had no news of them.

"Our people say we'll be in Bucharest in a month, but I don't believe it. The Russians are advancing, and there's little chance of stopping them."

"Yes," agreed Ana, "they're good fighters."

"Blast this war."

By now the officers were drunk; they slashed the bedclothes with their swords, broke the windows, tore George's books. A day later they were gone. Heavy-hearted, Ana did what she could to restore the house to order. What would Emilia say at sight of the mess and the destruction?

Three days later her daughter was back, with Dan and a crowd of peasants. The Germans and Hungarians had caught them at Gurba and forced them to turn back. Anuta was beside herself with grief; Andrei had got separated from them and was gone, Heaven knew where.

"Never mind, he'll escape all right," the old woman said, trying to cheer her up, although she sensed that her words had no effect. Such is a mother's heart—it knows no respite from anxiety. Later her daughter would realize that all things in this world are foreordained and it's no use struggling; as Fate determines, so things come to pass, and you can't change it.

One day she stood on the threshold, staring through narrowed lids at the littered yard. Suddenly she heard a stifled cry and saw Anuta collapse. Icy fear gripped the old woman; she ran over to Anuta, knelt down beside her, and felt her heart. It had ceased to beat. For a few moments Ana knelt there as in a stupor, incapable even of uttering a groan, then the blood rushed to her head, and she raised her arms towards the blue sky. "My God," she thought, "why do you afflict us like this?"

Summoning up all her waning strength, she managed to lift the body in her arms and carry it into the house; she held a mirror against the bluish lips, but no moisture gathered. Dan, his hands clasped, wept silently.

"Go look for your Uncle Tulea and bring him here," ordered the old woman. "I don't know what we're to do. There isn't a priest in the village."

Tulea hammered together a coffin from some old boards he found in the attic. He also dug the grave in the cemetery. With great difficulty they found a cart to which they harnessed a cow. The old woman, Dan, and Tulea walked behind it down the deserted street in the light of a wan autumn sun.

They lowered the coffin into the grave with the help of a rope, then Tulea took his shovel to fill in the earth, but the old woman stopped him.

"Wait, we're not heathens!" And in her quavering, tremulous voice she began to chant: "With the souls of the righteous that have given up the ghost, Lord, please suffer the soul of Thy servant to rest in bright places, in green valleys, whence all worry and sadness hath fled. . . ."

Resting on his shovel, Tulea gave the answers: "Amen" and "To her eternal memory." Then they filled up the grave, Tulea with his shovel, the old woman and Dan with their bare hands. They returned home in silence. That evening the old woman said to her grandson: "Man's greatest punishment, Danut, is life. The hell of which the saints speak is on earth, and nowhere else. Nowhere else but on earth."

• • •

All that was over and done with. The refugees had returned to their homes, the war was over, and they had received a letter from George that he was alive and a volunteer with the Russians, and that he was returning home.

It was a long, severe winter. Huddled by the fire, the old woman listened to the wind howling across the plain, to the groaning and creaking of the well post, to the snow sliding off the roof and thudding into the yard. She slept very little; most of the time she was talking to her dead.

One day there was singing in the eaves.

Then she went out into the yard. It was still cold, but the wind was warmer, milder.

A fortnight later she touched a willow twig, and felt the silky catkins. The sun was good and warm. From time to time she could not feel it; then she knew it had been covered by a cloud. She knew, but she could not see.

They got a letter from George that he had been wounded at Debreczen and was coming home.

As with all wars, all sorts of odd rumors were going around; everybody was keen to live, to take it out on someone, no matter who, for all the sufferings that had been endured. The men were like women, talking incessantly. The times had scared them; the war had sapped their vitality. Some were saying that it would be the same here as with the Russians; that is, collective farms—that everybody would eat in soup-kitchens, a ladleful each, and that in the morning they would be herded out to work to the sound of a bugle, like cattle.

Well, if there was any truth in what was said—it had been the same in Hungary after the other war—then the ploughmen would know what to do; you could be certain of that.

Woe to the people who wanted to spoil the order of things! But the old woman knew there were no such people, that they had no power to do so; it was just talk, born of men's bitterness.

She hadn't walked outside the yard for a long time; she felt weak. But in the spirit she could roam as far as she wanted down the main street until beyond the cross at the other end of the village, where the holdings bordered on each other.

The old woman knew exactly to whom every strip of land belonged, just as if each owner were standing on his holding; each strip of land had its name, as if it were alive.

With the advent of spring, and the wind blowing, you could feel a surge of new strength, so that you wanted to work from sunrise until sunset, to have a hearty noonday meal, though not too heavy, so as not to get sleepy, and to bend again over the plough, your eyes fixed on the black, sticky, glossy lumps of earth that are turned over and that belong to you, each of them; handed down long ago by the early inhabitants of Lunca, and belonging to you for all time.

Dumitru Radu Popescu

(b. 1933)

A collection of short stories, *The Flight* (1958), brought to notice a prose writer who blended dramatic situations and lyrical narrative. The milieu he preferred was the village and its inhabitants, today and in the past. The novel *Week Days* (1959), built with obvious skill so as to relate occurrences during one week in a village today, depicts the new way of life and work in opposition to traditional customs and hidden conservatism. The short stories included in the volumes *The Parasol* (1962) and *The Girl from the South* (1964) deal with more comprehensive themes, proof of the growth of Dumitru Radu Popescu's talent. This has been once more corroborated by *Oltenians' Summer* (1964) for which he drew on every-day occurrences and in whose heroes the virtues of socialist morality are embodied. With a peculiar bent for extreme situations, Popescu dwells on psychological processes, alternates the narrative with images created by fantasy, and illustrates more comprehensively the universe of his characters. In D. R. Popescu's prose writings the epic blends with an inner breath of poetry. With him, human nature finds expression in simple gestures that are yet all the more suggestive.

Alone

Two dry acacias, hollow and branchless, stood bending towards each other as though they wanted to clasp one another and die together. The rains and the winds, the sunshine and the storms had stripped them of their bark, leaving them for a time to shine white on moonlit nights. Then they turned purplish-blue like corpses, and now they were looking like two charred monsters. Where they stood, near the truck gardens of the inhabitants of the village of Ponoare, in the same line as the row of tall young poplars, the two acacias seemed not even to exist. The eye could distinguish them only after admiring every poplar separately. Maybe it was because they were not in the way that the people of Ponoare did not cut them down and burn them. Every spring, people were surprised to see green leaves on them. It was a long time since they had grown any shoots. The roots they had dug deep into the earth could hardly collect the sap without which they could not live. Some of the villagers said that when their grandparents were living, shady acacia woods used to grow on the spot where the poplars stand now. The water of the Danube rose repeatedly in spring and autumn and flooded the surrounding land. The marshes of Ponoare became wider. As acacias thrive on sandy soil and as dampness withers and destroys them, all that was left of the woods of yesterday were the two trunks alone, left as a memory—the two trunks looking like two charred monsters.

As evening descended upon the gardens like a warm bluish shower, the people of Ponoare watered their gardens, gathering the tomatoes they would eat the next day when at work in the fields, and digging up the potatoes they would take to market. The moon threw a silver shimmering light on the leaves of the poplars which quivered lightly in the still air. The whole plain, stretching from the end of the gardens, far away to where the shining waters of the Danube slowly glide towards the sea, rang with the loud cries of a lad perched high up on a poplar. Ligia, the boy's stepsister, stood leaning against the same poplar, singing without paying attention to his shrill yowling. As a matter of fact, Mircea did not mean to mimic her. He wanted to sing with her, but his voice betrayed the imperfect ear that could not remember a tune. Mircea knew the words and was persuaded that he could sing too:

Do not stand about
So late into the night
When the stars shine bright
Ion, my lad

"Be quiet, little Potbelly, be quiet! Let the girl sing."

Between the two acacias, seated on two upturned buckets, Ilinca and Filimon were chatting. The boy's voice irritated them. With the palm of his hand Filimon was driving away the mosquitoes that were trying to sting his bald head. He had left his hat behind at the other end of the garden two hours ago, when the sun still made the mosquitoes hide among the reeds. He lit the butt of a cigarette in the vain hope that the smoke would drive away the insects that would not let him alone. His wife Ilinca was, like himself, over sixty; she had her hands clasped in her lap and was fuming because Mircea would not obey her.

"Are you deaf? Hold your tongue. Can't you hear me?"

"I can't," the boy replied impudently, annoyed at the old woman's nagging.

"Be quiet! This is not your mother's house, nor your father's land to make you sing with joy."

The boy would not be silent. Out of spite he howled louder still:

Do not stand about
So late into the night
When the stars shine bright
Ion, you fool!

"Filimon, tell Tudose to shut his brat up, or he won't sleep under the same roof with us tonight. Tell him to let the girl sing. Maybe she's sad. Why should that little Potbelly mimic her?"

Tudose and Leonora had watered the cucumbers and the tomatoes and had started digging up some potatoes which Filimon was to take to market the next day. Hearing his mother-in-law refer to his son in so nasty a manner, Tudose struck the ground so savagely with his spade that with two blows he dug up all the potatoes on one root. Leonora bit her lips and said nothing about his cutting the potatoes in two. He was throwing up lumps of earth every which way, potatoes and their stalks as well.

Come away and do not linger;
Your love is lost in slumber.
The gate is locked,
The door is closed,
Ion, my lad!

Ligia was singing with a sadness unusual for a girl of sixteen. All day long she had been alone, isolated from the other girls, who were all younger than she, and she had sung softly, softly and sadly. Now the sadness of the day had become too poignant and the girl suddenly found herself singing louder than she had ever sung before in her family's hearing. She had always been ashamed and frightened to speak her thoughts or to sing what she liked, especially in front of the old people. She was glad that Mircea was singing in his own way too and that it annoyed her grandmother. Her grandmother's irritation gave her great pleasure. If Mircea were to stop singing, she would stop too; on no account did she want her grandmother to listen to her singing and be pleased. She did not trust her joy, nor the words of praise she was in the habit of giving her when she had obeyed one of her orders.

"Aren't you going to be quiet, you Potbelly brat?"

Ilinca called Mircea a potbellied brat when he did not obey her. Sometimes she wanted to thrash him, but the boy would run away and hide wherever he could. Although only ten, Mircea could look after his own skin as well as a grownup. Before coming to Ponoare he had had two stepmothers who had both been in the habit of venting their anger on him by pulling his ears or by slapping whatever part of him was handy. Leonora was his third stepmother; he had got no thrashing from her, but on the other hand, Ilinca had made his ears smart several times. Mircea was of middle height and well-proportioned, except that his belly stuck out more than usual. In retaliation, every time Mircea heard her reference to his anatomical oddity, he called her, under his breath, of course, "Gitlan's one-eyed shrew" —Ilinca had a glass eye.

"Filimon, tell Tudose to shut that brat of his up, once and for all. . . ."

"Hold your tongue, Mircea," said Tudose getting on with his work.

The boy was silent. Fed up with being ordered about, Mircea had made up his mind to do only what his father asked him. The whole village might shout at him to pick up a straw and he would not, because he thought that they could easily do it themselves.

"Sing, Ligia. Why have you stopped? Go on singing—you've got a voice like a nightingale, really you have. When I hear you singing I seem to see myself at sixteen, pretty and all dressed up. . . . Then I had a voice like a nightingale, like you. You can ask Filimon. . . . Sing, Ligia! Really it does my heart good to hear you sing."

The girl did not comply with her grandmother's request. She walked past her, playing with a sprig of basil, and stopped by the side of her mother who was on her knees gathering up potatoes in a bag. "Potbelly is to blame. He has annoyed the girl with his howling," thought Ilinca. "That's what it is to have a stranger in the house. You tell him to do one thing and he does another. Would to God he'd fall from the top of the poplar and break his neck! That would teach him to do what I tell him another time."

"Get down from the tree! What are you doing up there, perching like a crow?"

"I'm waiting to see the moon."

"Can't you see it from here? I'm one-eyed and can see it. Look, Filimon, hear how cheeky Potbelly is to me."

"One-eyed shrew, one-eyed shrew, one-eyed shrew!" Mircea said over and over again to himself.

A warm wind was blowing from the Danube, making the poplar leaves quiver in the silvery moonlight. The two hollow acacias stood perfectly still, like two charred monsters. Tudose's hoe had come out of its handle and had stuck in the ground. He was trying hard to get it back in its proper place by striking it with the edge of an axe he had borrowed from a neighboring garden. The sound of the metal on metal, now shrill, now leaden, depending on whether Tudose struck hard or gently, reminded Leonora of the sound of a cracked bell. Alternately dull and shrill, the sound deafened and irritated to the point where she stopped her ears with her fingertips to keep out the evil sound. It was the same sound that Leonora had heard a fortnight before, when the church bells tolled, especially the small bell, the cracked one. That time, too, she was in the garden, but alone. She had had a premonition of some unusual and unspeakably sad event. And when she got to the village she heard that Lenuta Berindeanu had poisoned herself with soda and died. Two days before, she had met Lenuta near the village, coming by cart from Severin. They had not spoken very much, but from her voice Leonora had guessed that Lenuta was distraught because of some deep sorrow. The same evening the mystery was cleared up. Deserted by her first husband who had had an affair with a young shop girl, Lenuta had been deserted by her second husband too, a very handsome bank clerk whom she had married after a year's courtship. The bank clerk had run away with the wife of an ex-officer, leaving Lenuta a note to say that he no longer loved her and begging her not to make a scene, but to pack her things and leave his house. Lenuta had come to her parents, in Ponoare, without telling them anything, except that she was getting to like the job she had at the central post office better and better. In a moment of despair, she had killed herself to escape from the gossip and the disgrace of having twice been deserted by her husbands. Leonora had not forgiven her this; she herself had been deserted by five husbands and had never thought of suicide. The truth is they had deserted her because of her parents, but every time Leonora hoped she would find a husband who would please both her and her parents. Tudose was her sixth husband, but he too was not to her parents' liking. Ilinca and Filimon had said the others were lazy, drunkards, vagabonds, but of Tudose they said he did not come of a good family and was not rich enough.

"If you take much longer filling the bag with potatoes, it'll soon be morning and we'll still be here. Tudose, you've been hitting that hoe enough now. You're messing about with it as though you wanted to make a new one out of it. . . ."

Leonora looked bitterly at her mother. The old people were still sitting under the two acacias, motionless. That evening they had not used the hoe once and had not thrown one single potato into the bag. They did not go home lest people should say they did not work at all. They sat on the buckets and shouted at Mircea to climb down from the tree, or blamed them for not lifting the potatoes quickly enough.

"Ligia, why don't you sing? Look at her, Filimon, and see how she keeps silent and won't obey me, as if I were a stranger. . . . Dear me, dear me, what a world I live in, so rude and so stupid."

"Tudose, haven't you got a cigarette? If you have, give me one. Bring me my hat too; those brutes of mosquitoes are biting me."

The son-in-law brought him his hat and handed him his cigarette case to choose one for himself. When Tudose walked away, Ilinca whispered to her husband:

"How slowly the fellow moves! Instead of being glad that you ask him for something, he moves like a snail as if he didn't really want to. A lazy dog. He's bone-lazy, Filimon, and he's got no land and does not even come of a good family. I wonder what Leonora saw in him!"

"His bicycle," laughed the old man. "She must have liked to see how quickly the mechanic can ride his bike. We've never had a smith or a mechanic in the Gitlan family. Now we've got one. Everything is topsy-turvy nowadays. Your own flesh and blood no longer obeys you. Your relations no longer listen to you, let alone strangers. Get down, you brat, get down off that tree, don't you hear?"

"I won't. There's dew, and I'll get my feet wet."

"Well, don't then, stay up there and hang yourself with your belt from the top of the poplar. If you were my child, I'd roll you about in the dew and knock that nonsense out of your head, but one day I'll catch you. Tudose!" Filimon called out to his son-in-law, "tell your son to get down off that tree. Why won't he obey me? Does he think he knows better than an old man? If I want him to get down from the poplar, why doesn't he obey? Why doesn't he do what I want him to?"

"I won't do what you want. I will not, I will not, and that's that! What business is it of yours if I want to stay up the tree?"

"Mircea, get down and hold your tongue!"

The boy obeyed at once. When he walked past the old people, he heard the "one-eyed shrew" tell the old man to break off an acacia shoot and whip his legs with it to teach him to obey his elders.

Fortunately, the acacias had not borne shoots for a long time.

To get the children away from the badgering of the old people, Tudose had told them to go and pick cucumbers and tomatoes. Left alone with Leonora he said to her in a low and determined voice:

"We can't go on like this, Leonora. Your mother calls my child names and thrashes him; your father treats me as if I were his servant. If it weren't for you, heaven knows what I'd do to them. This week I'll get my things together and leave."

"No, please. They won't go on trying to pick quarrels all the time."

"I'll leave, really I will; I always do what I say."

"If you do, you'll leave me alone. . . ."

"Stay with them; they're your parents. Call them now; the bag's full."

Tudose hoisted the bag onto his bicycle and started for home. The children followed him, one counting the tomatoes, the other the cucumbers. When Ilinca saw them, she called them to go back and fetch the buckets on which she and the old man had sat. The children pretended not to have heard.

"Ligia, dear, come with Potbelly and take the buckets. See, Filimon, they won't obey me, damn their impudence!"

"Go on, mother; I'll carry the buckets," said Leonora.

Then, remembering what Tudose had said to her, she felt a cold shudder pass through her. Five husbands had deserted her because of her parents; for nights on end she had wept; for months she had been ashamed to look people in the face. Should she be deserted the sixth time, then. . . . Tears came into her eyes. A name haunted her insistently. She whispered it, scarcely audibly: "Lenuta, Lenuta."

Before dawn, when the village was still asleep, it was Tudose's habit to get up from beside his wife and cycle to the garden to bring back weeds for the pigs. When he got back, he used to find Leonora in the kitchen boiling the milk. The children were shivering around the fire, sleepily. Sometimes they took both of them to the fields; at other times only one. When the old people woke up there was nobody at home. And they woke late enough, for the pigs didn't squeal with hunger and the ducks had had their fill. When they had had their meal, they would sit down facing one another on two small stools, look at the sky, and talk about the weather. Then they would reckon how much the prices of vegetables and fruit had gone down, the price of an egg, and that of a litre of wine. They would congratulate themselves that their neighbors could seldom sell anything while they sold something every day, either at the fairs or markets in the neighborhood, or even in the village.

That morning, when Tudose got back from the garden on his bicycle, he told Leonora that in the night someone had been stealing their potatoes. Filimon had returned soon enough from the fair at Craiesti and was very angry when he heard about the loss. Tudose could not understand why the people in Ponoare seemed quite indifferent when they heard that thieves had robbed Filimon Gitlan again. Did they hate his father-in-law? Maybe they did, but when a thief robs one's neighbor, the community should certainly be afraid of being robbed in turn. But the people in Ponoare did not take the trouble to try to find the thief, or even to be concerned. It was as though they felt that as not everybody in Ponoare had a garden it was natural that some people should try to satisfy their appetite by stealing tomatoes or potatoes from those who did.

"Aren't you going to hoe the corn at Cioaca?"

"Yes, father, right away," said Leonora.

"Don't take Ligia along with you. Let her go and graze the oxen;

the little one is always up to some mischief when he goes to the common, and in the evening he brings the animals home hungry."

"You go with the oxen; I want to go hoeing with mummy," said Ligia in a frightened voice.

"I think the way to Craiesti and back was enough for me. I think it's enough for me for today. If you won't go, Ligia, we'll hire a servant to go with the oxen, and that'll be the end of it."

"All right, I'll go," the girl agreed, to put a stop to the argument.

The old man stroked his bald head with the palm of his hand, a sign that his wish had been obeyed before he lost his temper. Tudose and Leonora started for Cioaca on foot. They had not left earlier because of the calf which had found the gate open and had run after its mother. It had taken quite a time to get it home from the pasture.

After they had gone, Filimon saw that there were mulberries lying thick and black on the ground under the tree near the shed, and realized that Ilinca would suggest that they gather them. He did not like the idea of dirtying his hands, or of standing for a couple of hours under the mulberry tree to pick up all the berries. He could not lie to his wife and tell her he was tired after having been to the fair, for she knew that he took the potatoes to an acquaintance in Valea Anilor, who dealt with a merchant in Severin. The merchant paid a few pennies less a pound, but in this way people did not see you selling, and you were spared the trouble of bargaining.

"Ligia, don't eat any cheese, d'you hear! Look, Filimon, she won't listen to me! I don't want misfortunes to come upon my family because this glutton of a girl won't fast on Fridays. Friday's a fast-day and one shouldn't eat cheese. You'll soon be getting married and God will punish you if you don't teach your children to fast. Don't you hear what I am saying? Stop eating cheese! Look, Filimon, how. . . . Now you're sulking. Be off with the oxen or evening will come before you get there."

Ilinca took the cheese and wrapped it up in a striped napkin. She waited until Ligia had gone out of the kitchen and hid the cheese away in the cupboard among the earthenware bowls. She wondered where and when the "potbellied brat" had disappeared: he had had no food that morning.

"Mircea, where are you? Filimon, where's Potbelly?"

"Let him go to blazes. He can't have drowned, can he?"

Coming from the orchard where she had filled a small bag with apples, Ligia did not tell them that Mircea was fast asleep in the sun on the hayrick. She got the oxen out of the cattle shed and drove them towards the gate. Ligia could not love her grandmother or her grandfather, although she had tried to. She did not like to see them merry and when they complained of something and were sad, she was glad. She knew she ought not to rejoice at their sorrow, but she could not help it.

"My goodness gracious! Filimon, come and see something you've never seen before in your life! You can't be quite right in the head, Ligia, to take so many apples. D'you want someone to steal them from you? Leave some at home," said the old woman, emptying the bag into her lap. "Two or three apples will be enough for you. Do you want to make gluttons of all the girls in the village? If they're hungry for apples, let them buy them, not get them for nothing."

The girl passed through the gate biting sadly into an apple.

The day promised to be dreadfully hot. In the scorching heat, although the night was not long gone, people were hoeing corn. Leonora alone, with her own and her husband's hoes on her shoulders, and carrying the basket of food in her other hand, was walking along the highroad, silently, feeling the scorching heat of the sun on her back. When she came to the well by the cross she saw that Tudose had forgotten the water keg and sent him back for it. A wagon loaded with sedge drove along the middle of the road and the driver bade her good morning. She answered mechanically, then gazed after him and recognized the brother of Avram, the last man who had deserted her.

She remembered the last evening when she had eaten fried fish with Avram, fish he had brought from the cooperative farm. They were very tired after the reaping, and he had forgotten that the day before he had told her they would separate. Ligia had eaten with them and told how a girl had fallen into the watering trough of the well in the yard of the cooperative farm and had got wet clear through; how they had dressed her in the old tattered rags they had taken off the scarecrow in the middle of the rice field. Ligia had laughed in recalling the incident and Leonora was glad to see her merrier than she had ever been before. Since Leonora had joined the farm with her land and Ligia's, the girl had made many friends. She sang with them in the evening on the way back to the village, laughed, and there was more color in her face. She was glad to work and to be relieved of the chore of grazing the oxen, and glad also that the lads no longer teased her by saying it was only children and old people who grazed oxen in summer on the common pasture and in the marshes. The girl no longer had to listen to her grandmother advising her to drink milk in the morning and not to take bread and tomatoes in the fields with her, because they would spoil her appetite for the evening meal. "Have a good square meal in the morning and you won't be hungry till night," were Filimon's words and Ilinca took them for gospel.

That evening, at supper, Ligia's funny story had made Leonora forget the day's fatigue; it had made her do something she had never done before. She had asked her mother to bring up a bottle of wine from the cellar and she had taken five glasses out of the cupboard and washed them. She wanted to rejoice at Ligia's joy and at the fact that Avram was laughing. She wanted to rejoice at the fact that he no longer thought of parting from her, that he had forgotten the trouble her old parents had caused him. She had filled the glasses with the wine brought by her mother, had risen to her feet to wish everyone an abundant crop, said something else about happiness, and then ordered:

"Now, let's drain our glasses!"

She put the glass to her mouth at the same time as Avram and Ligia and drained it. As she swallowed the wine she closed her eyes, shuddered, and a feeling of nausea came over her. Then she coughed a number of times helplessly. Ligia spat out the wine and Avram dashed the glass to the floor furiously.

"You miserly lot!" he said and left, never to return.

Ilinca had brought them vinegar and water. She had not meant to play a trick on them or to make a fool of them, but to be sparing with the good wine which she could sell.

The other men too had deserted her because of her parents. But Leonora and Tudose Ceta had been in love with each other in their youth, and he would not desert her, despite her parents. Tudose would not let them trample him underfoot: he would put up with as much as he thought fit, then compel them to behave decently. She had met him when she was Ligia's age, one Sunday, at the *hora.** They met again the following Sunday, danced, and talked to their hearts' content. Marriage was out of the question then, for he was poor while she was of a good family, the daughter of a well-to-do mayor. Two years ago, his wife, Mircea's mother, had died. He had remarried because he had to have someone to look after his child. He had been obliged to do it. This spring Leonora had met him at the fair one Tuesday and asked him how he was getting on. They had not forgotten each other. Then, in spite of the old people's hesitation, they had got married. "No, he won't leave . . ." she thought.

Leonora was thirty-five. At that time of life you do more thinking than loving. The youth of peasant women is over at twenty-six. From childhood on Leonora had always obeyed her parents implicitly. She

---

* Rumanian country round-dance.

had not had much happiness in her life. She fondly remembered the prize-giving days at school, her only joy, when the schoolmaster used to hang a garland round her neck as first prize. Although she had been a better pupil than her brothers at the primary school, Filimon had kept her at home while, after finishing high school, his two sons had studied medicine, and now one was a surgeon at Craiova and the other at Galati. It was a long time since the doctors had been at Ponoare: both they and their wives had quarreled with the old folks and now they wrote about once every two years. They forgot Leonora sooner than their parents and they didn't know how many husbands their sister had had or how hard she had worked that they might become doctors. Maybe they thought she was happy, particularly as she had got from each of them an acre of land.

"Half of my life is gone," thought Leonora, "the finest part is over. If only Ligia could enjoy things, at least . . ."

Since they had left the farm, the girl had only very seldom seen her friends. When Avram left, the old parents got her to leave the collective farm, as they had plenty of land themselves to be worked. Land! How strange the word "land" sounded! It seemed to stand for all the disagreements between people, all the sadness that might be joy. They wanted to separate Tudose from her because he did not possess acres of land.

"No, he won't leave . . . I still have half of my life before me and I want it to be happy . . . and I want to make Ligia happy . . . and Mircea too. . . . Why, the old folks will change; they can't go on being so hateful all their lives . . . Tudose won't leave me; he won't disgrace me. He knows that I've never been like them. . . ."

Hope made her utter those last words out loud. She stopped. She pushed back her kerchief, revealing her dark hair streaked with grey at the temples. She looked back. Tudose was not to be seen on the road. It was very warm.

The sun made the air boiling hot.

Filimon had hid a bottle of wine under his coat, the smith having given him the money for it the evening before, asking him to bring it to him in the morning. The old man opened the door of the sty to let the pigs out into the courtyard. He held his left hand close to his body so as to protect the bottle and keep Ilinca from seeing it. The pigs rushed towards the mulberry tree by the shed, pushing the door of the sty back so that it hit Filimon's knee. If he had not straightened his back in time and the door had come against him while he was bending down, the bottle would have broken and Ilinca would have quarreled with him for a whole week for having taken the wine on the sly.

Ilinca had picked up a big stick and was trying to defend the berries against the snouts of the grunting beasts. While one was running away after being hit on the back, another would come near her fearlessly and root up eight or ten berries at a time.

"They're ruining us, Filimon! We shan't even taste mulberry brandy this year. . . . Stop, you greedy brutes!"

They could hardly manage to get them out through the gate and into the road. Filimon had not been a great help. He heaved a sigh of relief when he saw the pigs trotting along the middle of the road towards the common pasture. He would not have to gather the mulberries and his wife had not noticed the bottle under his coat. When he had told her that he would drive the pigs first to the outskirts of the village, she had not liked it too well. Was she to gather the berries while he went for a walk? He had persuaded her that he'd soon be back and she had agreed to let him go.

Summer, spring, and autumn Filimon did not trouble much about food for his pigs, although he had a herd of them. While in recent years there had been fewer of them, still he had more than two or three neighbors taken together. Every morning Filimon drove them to the end of the village to let them lie in the mud and gather their food by themselves in the field. The weeds brought by Tudose stayed their hunger but did not satisfy them. When he was the mayor of the village, Gitlan had arranged for his pigs to come to the common without paying anything. For twenty years, spring, summer, and autumn, the villagers had seen his pigs on the outskirts of the village. As long as grass grew in the fields he did not feed them one single grain of maize from the barn. Some years his pigs numbered more than a hundred. Now Filimon was no longer the mayor, but he had not lost his habit of driving his swine to the fields every morning. He would strut proudly behind them, not greeting anybody, nor answering anybody's greeting. When he was the mayor he used to greet people; now he did not, saying it would be undignified for him to bow to his former servants.

"Filimon, don't be late!"

"I won't die there, no fear. I'll be back right away!"

When she saw he was about three hundred steps from the gate, Ilinca hurried to the shed and brought out a bottle of wine. She wrapped it up in her apron and when she was near the fence she called Varvara, her next door neighbor. The latter appeared immediately, took the bottle through the stakes, and gave the old woman five *lei*.

"Don't let them know I sold it to you and that it is from us!"

"How could they? Has anybody ever found out before?"

"Your guests haven't come this year."

"God forbid that we should have such guests, Varvara. They come and bring nothing . . . as if they hadn't a farthing in their pockets, as if they lived on grass the whole time. I have drudged like a slave all my life, from morning till night, and have gone without food to bring up my children and make great men of them. And what good are they to me now? The children are strangers to me now. They've married and have children of their own. . . . My daughter, the least said about her, the better. The way she's been looking at us lately, as though we hadn't looked after her, the apple of our eye! Hide that bottle under your apron and don't let anyone see you carrying it or suspect I've given it to you. That's how Leonora is . . . seems to have gone crazy. She disgraced us with that wretch who belonged to the collective farm; now she's disgraced our whole family with this smith, this mechanic, or whatever he is. . . . He is stinking lazy and poor. Yes, Varvara, stinking. . . . See you don't spill the wine and then say I didn't fill the bottle. You couldn't buy wine like that at five *lei,* no matter how hard you tried. I'm selling it cheap to you because you're my neighbor and I know you can hold your tongue, otherwise. . . ."

"And aren't the guests coming?"

"We're better off without the likes of them. Two mouths ruined me two years ago, in a single week. Especially that child . . . he ate so much, it frightened me. The way he stuffed himself! You'd have thought he'd never have enough. And dear me, what a lot he wasted! While they were here I killed two chickens and one hen. They had meat every day, like at a restaurant. One is better off without that sort of guests."

Two years before Ilinca had had the wife of Doctor Gitlan from Craiova and her son Ionel, as guests.

The thicker the mulberries lie on the ground, the quicker you gather them. A pity Filimon had left without shaking down the fruit. It's not wise to get the berries down with a pole; you risk crushing them. You climb right up to the top of the tree and shake the branches vigorously until all the ripe berries fall down. She did not want to call in a neighbor to help her; he might ask for something, a glass of wine or a hatful of apples.

"Mircea! Where are you? Are you deaf?"

Potbelly liked to climb to the top of the poplar; only yesterday evening she had begged him to come down and stop yelling, and now she had to beg him to say a word and come out of his hiding-place. If he showed himself, she'd give him a hiding; otherwise he'd refuse to climb the mulberry tree.

"Mircea! My pet, aren't you hungry?"

He might have gone with his father to hoe the corn, or maybe he had followed Ligia. He had had nothing to eat that morning and might have gone to one of his father's relations to ask for a bit of bread. . . .

"The little wretch, he disgraces our family!"

And Filimon was late; he must have stopped to chat with someone. The mulberries had to be shaken down; why miss a chance of gathering in one effort what usually took several.

"I'll try to climb the tree myself. It won't give way under me. . . ."

Ilinca brought the ladder from the stable loft and set it carefully against the mulberry tree. People had gone to their work and there was no one to see her. Even if anybody did see her it wouldn't matter very much. With her good eye she looked at every rung of the ladder before setting foot on it. When she no longer needed the ladder, she remembered with relief that the dog was on the leash and the pigs in the fields. What if one of the sows had rubbed against the ladder and made it fall down? If she had to stay in the tree all day long, it would be the last straw. What would people say of her? She'd get talked about and all the villages in the neighborhood would laugh at her. They might even make a song about her.

With both hands she grasped a branch and began to shake it as vigorously as she could. The berries fell like hailstones. The branch on which she had set her feet was thick and she could shake it only by jumping up and down on it. She did so several times as though she were dancing a very lively country dance. If only Mircea turned up so she could ask him to step almost to the end of the branch on which she was standing. Mircea was not heavy; the branch would not give way under him, and he could shake down so many more ripe berries.

"Mircea! My pet . . ."

Perhaps it was better not to call him. Suppose Potbelly took it into his head to throw down the ladder? That would be just like him. And then he'd laugh like mad.

Ilinca climbed higher still. She looked towards the road and saw nobody. She thrust seven or eight berries into her mouth at a time. They tasted extraordinarily sweet and soft. She had eaten rather too many of them since Filimon had left—she almost had a pain in her stomach after so many—but none had tasted so sweet as these. She thrust another seven into her mouth, just as sweet and soft as the others. She was thinking of Mircea with some apprehension. If Potbelly threw down the ladder and she got a bellyache, what could she do? Spoil your stomach with mulberries and it runs through you like it does with ducks. Whenever the pain starts you just have to stop and you daren't get up until it is over. What if the pain should start when she was still up in the tree and without a ladder! And the berries!

"I'd better hurry and shake them down. If Potbelly sees I'm up the tree, he's sure to play some dirty trick on me."

The berries came down like a shower of rain. Ilinca looked down to see how many there were. As she bent her head towards the ground her glass eye came out of its socket, glided down through the leaves, fell down and broke on a stone.

"Damn that Potbelly! Why couldn't he have stayed at home and shaken down the mulberries! He likes climbing up the poplar, the wretch!"

She felt a terrible hatred for Mircea. He alone was to blame for her glass eye being broken.

"What the devil possessed me to waste a lot of good money on that bit of glass? At least I should have worn it only on holidays."

She climbed down from the tree, collected the fragments of glass in the palm of her hand and mourned her great loss. "If only I had sold it to some younger woman. I won't last so very much longer. . . . Why should I be buried with a glass eye? To turn into a ghost?"

"I won't buy another one. Why should I waste money? After all, you can't see with a glass eye." Suddenly the thought that her sons might each give her a present of a glass eye occurred to her. She'd write them and if they did . . . well, then she'd have two glass eyes for sale!

"I wonder how much I'd get for them. If one is . . ."

While counting the mounting sums in her mind, she reached the garden. She felt gnawing pains in her stomach: the mulberries were working. She went near the hayrick and was about to squat when she heard someone cough and sneeze. . . .

"Is that you up there? Get down, and run into the courtyard!"

"My feet are sore."

Ilinca had to retreat. She went behind the hayshed and left Mircea alone. After a time she came back in a fury, caught the boy by a leg, and pulled him down from the hayrick.

"There! That'll teach you to climb the poplars! That'll teach you!" Every exclamation was punctuated with the sound of a slap.

The boy was hungry. In the morning when he started to eat and had three or four mouthfuls, Ilinca had said: "Where the devil have you room for all that? You've got a small stomach. It's true, you're potbellied, but your stomach's small. Where have you room for so much bread?"

He had left the table sulkily and had lain down in the sun on the hayrick. Falling asleep immediately, he had awakened only when he heard Ilinca enter the garden.

"Fancy sleeping on the straw and spoiling it, you lazybones. And you won't climb up the mulberry tree! And when I call you, you turn a deaf ear! There! That'll teach you not to be deaf another time!"

She was venting on him all the pentup anger caused by the recent events. Holding him by his right ear, she entered the courtyard with him and kept slapping him all the time. It was then that Tudose appeared at the gate from the road. He had come to fetch the water keg.

"Let him go!" he thundered, frightening Ilinca. "Why are you beating him? What has he done? Why don't you answer? Mircea, come to me. Stop crying. . . . Come. . . . We're going. . . ." And he went out into the road holding his boy by the hand.

After a while, when he was far away from the house, Ilinca burst out: "The cheek of him asking me why I was beating Potbelly. You'd have thought this was his father's courtyard. Bloody mechanic!"

* * *

"I've been told you mix water in your wine. . . ."

"Of course I do. It's a trick of the trade. You mix a little water in if you want to earn a copper. When you make horseshoe rails or horseshoes don't you ask for more iron than you really need?"

Filimon was sitting under the mulberry tree drinking wine with the village smith. It was Sunday morning and an hour when people had not had anything to eat yet. The smith had been drinking the whole night and had come for a pick-me-up that would make him sleep. Ilinca had come near the smith to tell him too how, the day before, Tudose had packed up his things and gone to his own village.

"He had such a lot of things that ten wagons could hardly hold them. Fine blankets he had too, and cows and oxen, and all kinds of things . . . and I cried my eyes out at losing such wealth and such a man. The mechanic told my daughter she could come along with him if she wanted; she would be welcome. He'd welcome her in his palace; he has a house like a pigsty. The mechanic would like her to leave her family for the sake of his ugly mug!"

"I heard he stole a lot of potatoes from you last night."

"He stole some last night and has stolen some before. He only had to get on his bicycle and he was at the garden in no time. He said he went for weeds, but he was carrying potatoes to his relations. We'll catch him at it yet and then the whole village will be laughing at him. Aren't I right, Filimon?"

"He's worked for them for nothing and now they're calling him a thief," thought Leonora. "They've always been like that and they won't change. All their lives Ilinca and Filimon have robbed each other and together have robbed others, either strangers or their own children and grandchildren. When someone accused them they always found a convenient scapegoat."

"And is Leonora not sorry that Tudose's gone?"

"She is glad to be rid of him. She's not so foolish as to be sorry. The world's full of men like him. The Gitlans never weep when they are rid of paupers. You can see my Leonora comes of good stock. She does not pine for a miserable wretch; she doesn't throw herself into a well or take soda like Lenuta Berindeanu. . . ."

Lenuta. . . . Lenuta. . . . In the garret, near the chimney, there is a bottle of soda. If the old people knew that yesterday Leonora had spoken to Marina, the sister of Ligia's father, and told her she was going to live in town for a couple of years! If they knew it, they'd come and hug her, and kiss her and ask to be forgiven for what they did to her. But they go on talking indifferently, not knowing she is leaning against the corner of the house and taking a last glance at the courtyard. The mulberry tree seems taller than ever, its leaves look greener, and the sky bluer. From the garden comes the sound of apples falling to the ground and she seems to feel their sweet taste in her mouth. Ligia is biting into an apple and she too does not realize that by the time she reaches the common pasture with the oxen she will no longer have anyone to say "mother" to. If, at least, *she* could be happy! If she at least could get married somewhere far away, far away from her grandparents. . . . If she could forget them, forget the days when instead of going to a dance she had to take the oxen grazing! If she could forget that she, Leonora. . . . The sun is not very far from the earth! The apples are falling in the gardens and the wagons are driving past on the road at full speed, exactly as they passed yesterday and the day before yesterday, and as they will pass tomorrow and the day after tomorrow. The life of people, the life of trees, and the life of birds change . . . only her life has always been the same. If your parents give you life why don't they let you live it? Why do they bring you up to be a servant to them? Rather be born blind, better never to be born at all . . .

Do not stand about
So late into the night
When the stars shine bright
Ion, my lad!

Why is Ligia singing? What can her heart be yearning for?

"Shut up, Ligia, damn you! It's only Tudose's potbellied brat who howls like that! You're cawing like a crow! Let folks hear what they've got to say to one another and don't deafen them with your nonsense," said Ilinca coming out of the kitchen and making for the gate. She had ten eggs hidden in her blouse. She had lied to Filimon so that he might not suspect she was hurrying to bring the eggs to the young schoolmistress who had paid for them two days before.

"Stop your singing, Ligia! Leonora, send her with the oxen! Don't stand there leaning against the house. Go do the cooking and leave off thinking. It doesn't do for you to think too much. Lenuta Berindeanu drank soda because she thought too much. Don't stand there idle! Go and put the pots on the fire. Don't wait for me to return from the village and do the cooking. You're young, and when I was your age. . . ."

On Sundays it is the old folk who go with the oxen to the fields instead of the grandchildren. It is a very old custom to let young people go and dance the *hora* and have a good time. All the week the lads and lasses work, thinking of the past Sunday's *hora* and of next Sunday's. When they meet on the road, at noon, or especially in the evening, the lads talk about the girls, while the girls ask one another which is the most handsome lad, which of them is the best dancer, the hardest working, or the most amusing. Their opinions differ greatly. One of the girls thinks that none of the lads in the village is as hard-working and as amusing as her neighbor; another thinks quite the other way.

It is five weeks since Ligia has been to the *hora*. Her grandfather will not take the oxen grazing because he does not want to have the village laughing at him, and on Sundays her grandmother will not hear of going with the oxen, any more than she would on other days. On Sunday Ilinca goes to the *hora* wearing a tight-fitting peasant skirt and with her face made up. With her good eye she watches to see which families are planning marriages so as to increase their wealth. In the evening she will not let Ligia stop on the road to talk to girls or lads of her age. She takes her grandchild by the hand, brings her into the house, and tells her to go to bed for she must be up early the next morning to go reaping, picking plums, hoeing, or grazing the oxen again. Why should Ligia, a granddaughter of the Gitlans, stand on the road in the evening? Paupers are paupers because they don't sleep enough and stay chattering late. People of good family always go to bed at sunset and get up in the morning feeling rested, ready for work. Why should Ligia stand and talk to who knows what pauper and be a disgrace to the Gitlan family?

"Where's mummy, grandfather?"

"How can I tell? She must be somewhere; she can't have gone and drowned herself."

* * *

"Where's mummy, grandfather? I want to give her a ripe apple; look, this one. . . . She's very fond of apples and this one is ripe and sweet and smells so good. . . ."

Filimon did not answer her. He saw the smith to the gate, then came back under the mulberry tree and drank the wine the latter had left in the bottle. Ilinca had returned from her visit to the schoolmistress to whom she had sold the eggs on the quiet.

From the garret came the sound of a bottle breaking. A sudden cry made Ligia stop just as she was going to open the gate and leave with the oxen. A few seconds later, the door of the house was flung wide open and Leonora, without a kerchief, her hair dishevelled, hanging loose on her shoulders, looking as if she were drunk, called to her: "Ligia! Come here! Come!"

She had climbed up to the garret to throw away the bottle of soda and get rid of the temptation. She had to live, to bring up her daughter, get her married, and not leave her a servant to her old parents. Why should Ligia not go to the *hora* on Sundays? Why should she not stand on the road in the evening and talk and sing? Why should she have to go and graze the oxen without having had a bite of food? If her parents had ruined her life, why should they ruin Ligia's? To get rid of her problems she had been foolish enough to think of the soda hidden in the garret. Did the Gitlan family ever care that she, Leonora, had never been happy and that the village had been gossiping about her for more than fifteen years? Suddenly she realized there were other ways of breaking free of her parents. Just then she heard Ligia asking for her.

"Ligia, leave the oxen; you're going to the *hora* today."

"And who the devil's going with the oxen?" asked Ilinca sharply.

"Whoever wants to. . . . I'm going away with the girl. I'm not going to stay with you any longer."

"And where are you going? To the cemetery? You're not going anywhere," said Filimon. "You were born in this house and you'll die here! He hasn't bewitched you, has he?"

"Whether he has or he hasn't doesn't matter. I'm going to him. And I'm taking the girl with me."

"Have you gone mad? Oh, Lord, that it should have come to this! Are you going to leave your own courtyard, your own house, your comfortable bed? You're drunk, Leonora, or you've taken leave of your senses and don't know what you're saying. Where are you going? Are you going to him like this, without a bite of food? Wait, Leonora; wait a little. Let's talk. How can you go away like that?"

"If you go to live with the mechanic, you won't get one patch of land from me!"

"I don't need it. I won't starve. I'm healthy and I can still work. I haven't forgotten how."

"Are you going to that thief, Leonora? Is that who you're going to? I saw him in the village on his bicycle. He must have been stealing our potatoes again. . . . Don't go, Leonora; you'll disgrace our family! Look, Filimon, she won't listen to me!"

And Ilinca started to cry, saying that all her life she had drudged like a slave to bring up her children and now, in her old age, no one was thankful to her. Leonora would not listen to her and went out holding Ligia by the hand.

"Leonora, don't go; don't leave us here . . . damn your eyes, you fool! Leonora, you'll disgrace our family! Oh, Lord, why didn't she do like Lenuta Berindeanu? It would have been better if she'd taken soda and gone to the devil, rather than leave us and go away. . . ."

Towards evening, Filimon walked to Valea Anilor to meet the fellow from Severin to whom he had given the potatoes on Friday, and who was to pay him tonight. Left alone, Ilinca had a good meal, drank two glasses of wine and, feeling sure that this night too Tudose would try to steal potatoes from their garden, she had called Varvara to the fence and asked her to come with her to watch for the thief, catch him, and let the whole village know. The neighbor, a kind-hearted woman, did not refuse to accompany her. The latter even proposed they should take her two sons along with them, one of eighteen and another of twenty, and so catch the thief more easily. On the way to the garden they called the smith and asked him too to come and help. On Sunday night, after supper, people are willing to go anywhere, because they know they won't be asked to do any work. The smith took his wife along with him. Ilinca kept saying she had seen Tudose in Ponoare in the morning and it was likely he would try to steal potatoes this night too, as the next morning there was a fair at Craiesti.

"I think Leonora must have put him up to it; you can't trust even the children you've borne and brought up. She must have put him up to it before!"

They all hid among some tall corn that grew on one side of the garden, towards the village. The ground was warm and so was the air. There was no wind and the leaves of the poplars shone, moving only very rarely. In the light of the moon the two hollow, branchless acacias looked like two charred monsters. Their trunks shone in the moonlight. The poplars seemed to be made of silver, the acacias seemed charred.

"Filimon was saying that Tudose's son used to steal the eggs from the nest-box."

"Who . . . Potbelly?"

"He stole them and drank them like the magpies do. So Filimon was telling me this morning," said the smith.

"Yes, yes, Potbelly stole the eggs!"

"He said your courtyard was full of hens but you had no eggs at all."

"If that magpie of Mircea drank them . . . at meals he used to sulk for the least thing you said to him and would not eat. Of course he could afford not to eat if he'd had his fill of eggs. That's why he used to sing, or rather to howl. He climbed up into the poplar and howled the way dogs howl at the moon! He howled because he had a fine voice with all the eggs he stole and drank. . . ."

"Hush!" said the smith. "There he is! He's coming from the common pasture. Look how he's trying to hide. . . ."

The thief was coming towards them by leaps and bounds.

"See how he jumps! Anyone would think he was twenty," said Varvara in a very low voice.

They let the thief get right in the middle of the potatoes and begin his work. There was a dead silence. All seemed to be holding their breath. Varvara's sons whooped as they ran towards him. The smith's wife was left behind. The chirping of the crickets in the pasture seemed to scratch the stillness of the night.

"He's left his bicycle in the village so as not to leave any trace we might recognize . . . or perhaps he left it in the pasture," thought Ilinca. Then, unable to control herself any longer, she nudged those who were near her and cried out: "Catch the thief! Catch the thief!"

The thief was about two hundred meters away. Leaping over the stalks of the cucumbers and tomato plants, the small group ran towards him. The night was as clear as day. You could see the thief's face.

"Catch him! Damn him, bloody thief that he is! Catch him! Stop! Stop!"

Varvara's sons had overtaken the thief and thrown him down. Ilinca drew nearer, with her fist full of earth.

"Let me put out his eyes!"

Varvara's sons lifted the thief to his feet and Ilinca heard him say: "What the devil's come over you, woman?"

"Oh . . . well . . . I thought . . . we wanted to catch Tudose. . . ."

"Then why have you fallen upon me? Let go my hands, do you hear?" he said to Varvara's sons. "Can't a man come to his own garden without being set on? I was going to Valea Anilor," Filimon said as though addressing only the smith, "to see a friend of mine and

I didn't want to go empty-handed. I came here to get a few potatoes. I prefer to give them to friends rather than let the village steal them from me."

"True," agreed the smith. Then, taking his wife with him, he walked away towards the village together with Varvara and her sons.

The old people stayed on in the garden; they wanted to talk. They leaned against the two hollow acacias and gazed at the moon and at the poplars. The night seemed to be made of silver. The air was hot and so was the ground. From somewhere, from among the potatoes, came the growling of a dog.

"Ilinca, it's our dog Vidra. Don't you see her?"

"I don't see her, but I can hear her. . . . Vidra, come here; good dog, come to your mother; come here."

The dog started but ran away from them. She was yelping as though they'd flung stones at her. Ilinca had not seen her in their courtyard since the morning when she had thrown a stone at her. What was she doing in the field? Maybe she was looking for Ligia.

"I wonder what Ligia's doing."

"What could she be doing? She's singing to the moon with Pot-belly while Leonora and Tudose are dancing with joy. . . . The paupers!"

The poplars looked like huge silver spears. In the silvery night only the acacias had the appearance of charred monsters.

Vasile Rebreanu

(b. 1934)

The collection of sketches *In Broad Daylight* (1959), including prose poems as well as the short stories "Before Sunrise" and "Bitter Land" reveal the poetical attributes of Vasile Rebreanu's writing. His sketches depict the horror of the atrocities perpetrated by the Nazis during World War II, often conveyed through the prism of abused, ravaged childhood, whose charm is set in contrast to the horror of war. In his novel *The House,* (1962), a rendering of village life, Rebreanu passed successfully to an ample epic structure. In the collection of short stories *Autumn Morning* he resumes the narrative themes from his first volume but uses a new technique, that of suggestion. Various aspects of life in the countryside today are also depicted: they reflect the inner struggle preceding the choice of a new path.

The Earth's Grass

Hearing his master's footsteps, the horse neighed briefly and grazed on. Ana got up and went to her father in silence. She crossed the glade and her slender face was illuminated for a moment, spotlighting her many big freckles. Her thin, short, and reddish pigtails, sticking out from under her gray kerchief, also took on an unnatural glimmer. For a moment her whole being seemed to be a frail apparition of light. Once in the shadow it regained its lustreless appearance. From the forest, the machine guns could still be heard. The thud of bigger guns could be heard in the distance.

Adam Buga unbound the horse and set out, rope in hand. The horse came after; the little girl beside him.

Reaching the edge of the forest, the man stopped and scrutinized the field for a long time: nobody was in sight. "They won't catch me," he said to himself. He perched the girl on the horse's glossy back. He looked again about the field, then jumped on himself. The horse, under the impact of Adam's body, staggered, moving his hoofs. Adam Buga touched it with his feet, and the horse started off, trotting lightly.

The field was almost empty. Autumn was shedding its golden light on dry corn lands. "They won't catch me. I'm going by the back of the garden. I'll leave the horse there; then I'll take the food and come back to the forest. No, they won't catch me. . . ."

"Tac-tac" . . . the sound of the hoofs was heard leaving behind the dust . . . and the forest. The rusty forest. . . .

Over them a squadron of planes flew away with a deafening noise. Ana shrunk instinctively, grasping the black mane in which she had thrust her fingers more firmly. "She is afraid," the man thought, and in order to drive away her fright, he began talking to the girl in the playful way they reserved for each other.

"Don't be afraid, my lassie."

"I am not afraid, daddy. I am not a 'lassie.' "

"Then what are you?"

"I'm your doe."

"Well, does are afraid, aren't they?"

"Then I'm the earth's grass, too."

"Really?" the father made a sham show of surprise. "The earth's grass, and what else?"

"The night stars, too; that's what I am," the little girl said proudly. "And a cornfield, too!"

They were reaching the village. "I'll leave the horse at the back of the garden," Adam said to himself again. "If they should come, they won't see it. I'll manage to steal away, somehow. I'll steal out and run away."

"And what else am I, dad?" the little girl broke the train of his thoughts.

"What else are you? . . . hm, hm. . . . What more could you be? Gold, lassie."

"And what else?"

"And the sun, lass."

"And what else am I?"

"Don't know," pretended Adam.

"How is it that you don't know, daddy?"

"You are the field's dew, too, Ana."

Ana chuckled and wanted to turn around. She lost her balance and slipped off. Adam caught hold of her and put her back on the horse, holding her tightly by the arm. He looked for a while at her short, thin, reddish pigtails, her thin neck, and slender face full of freckles. "They say this girl isn't a beauty," he thought. "And the sun might be blamed for it."

Beauty or no beauty he loved the girl beyond words. . . .

Adam Buga had not fathered a child until very late in life. He had given up hope when, all of a sudden, his wife told him she was pregnant. She had died the fifth day after the birth.

Adam brought up the girl as best he knew and could. She had even been nursed by a gipsy woman, Safta, who had just given birth to a child. People could hardly believe that "Kind Adam" had a child, and that it would live. This had been Adam's nickname since his young days. People had gone on calling him so. . . .

"If we run into the Germans," Ana shuddered, drawing closer to Adam, while he was tying the horse to the fence at the back of the garden.

"Well, look about carefully, lassie, and if we see any traces of them we'll keep away from the yard."

Small groups of the Fascist army quartered in the neighboring village, beyond the Somes, had been searching every court for the past few days. They were requisitioning horses, grabbing people, and sending them to dig trenches, somewhere, far away, very far from the rear. Adam Buga had run away to the woods, like everybody else. Holding Ana by the hand he was making carefully for the courtyard. "Here," he said to himself, casting a hurried look at the haystack at the back of the stall, "this is where the weapons are hidden. They might have come home. . . ."

Two, yes, precisely two weeks ago, Horthy's Fascist armies had been stationed in the village. There were many soldiers from Transylvania. Two had been billeted to him, and they had become friends. The night before their departure they had asked for civilian clothes and had run away. They had left him their equipment, weapons, grenades, the lot. Adam had concealed them.

"They might've gone rusty," he thought as he opened the gate and entered the courtyard. A strained silence had settled over the whole village, over the place. Reaching the front of the house, he unlocked the door and went in. The cool shadow and a smell of earth and camomile assailed him pleasantly. Ana got her hand free from Adam's grip and flung herself with a chuckle on the bed. She loosed her kerchief, and stretching her arms, shut her eyes for a moment; then, with a sigh of relief, opened them again. Inside, the room was cool and very cozy.

Ana had pined for home, for the smell, the silence, and the shade reigning here. Adam looked at her, then put his straw hat on the bench and went out. He entered the larder, and stopped for a long time to look at it as if he no longer recognized it. He saw the harnesses hanging in a corner; over them some dirty linen, a few wheat flour sacks on the floor, and, beside them, the wine barrel. "I must build a cellar. This will hardly do for the wine." He climbed up to the garret. From here he could hear fairly well what was going on in the street: he heard children shouting and a shot followed instantly by a frightened bark. He cut the bacon and climbed down. He passed through the larder, by the hens cackling in the entrance hall.

"They need feeding." In the room, with eyes almost shut, Ana turned to him. "Are you sleepy?"

The girl nodded. The father placed the bacon on the table and went to Ana. He sat down on the bed.

"How is the earth's grass?"

"?"

"Is the doe going to sleep?"

"Yes."

"The sun too?"

"Yes. And the moon . . . and the spring winds, and the mountain gold, dad."

"And what else?"

"The glowworms which can be seen at night."

"So you're a glowworm too, are you?"

"Yes."

"And what else?"

"And a water spring, dad."

"What else?"

"Our summer apple tree in the garden. . . ."

"And what else?"

"A swallow, and the mountains, and the forest. . . ."

The girl went to sleep, and the man got up. He went on tiptoe to the garden. He made for the street. As he looked out the door, he saw three men in gray coats coming out of Gorea Simii's house. It was the Nazis searching the houses for horses and people. He saw their clean-shaven faces, their epaulets—all of them were officers, but he could not distinguish their rank. One wore glasses. Adam turned back quickly. He entered the house. He hesitated on the threshold for a moment. He thought of waking up the girl but hesitated. He thought: "If I wake her up suddenly, she will be frightened. She will cry and might even scream."

"And if I take her? If we run by the courtyard they are sure to catch us. I can steal out more easily alone. They're as good as here. They may come in any moment. And then the Nazis will catch us. . . . But what happens if I leave her here? They can't take a child. And, after all, I'll return as quickly as possible. I shan't leave her alone for a long time. And it will not be very long before evening sets in. I'll come back, I'll come back. . . ."

The decision made, he started off alone. He rushed to the courtyard, then to the garden. At the back of the garden was the horse. He reached it. He mounted and galloped to the forest.

He stopped at the edge of the forest. He got off, pulled up a bunch of grass, and slowly wiped down the heated animal with his big hand. He went amidst the trees, and hobbled the horse again. The silence of the forest overwhelmed him, and he sat down, his back leaning against a tree. He looked at the horse, and, as he stood thus, memories of the past came flooding back to him. . . .

Oh, the forests, the forests! How long had it been? He was thirty years old then. His face was thin and his body slim and hard. He felt fit cutting fir trees. Always unshaven, he rarely smiled so that his companions kept saying: "This man's teeth can be seen only when eating."

A month later, they had received their first payment. It was less than they were supposed to get. No matter; they would make it up the next month. But the second month they received even less. And the third month they received nothing at all. They learned then that the man who had hired them, a stranger who presumably was the head of the company, had made off with their money, their money, their hard-earned money that meant so much to all the hungry ones at home.

They had received the disastrous news in stunned silence. It was summer. Adam remembered it all as vividly as if it were yesterday, and saw the eagles circling high above.

He had said nothing. He only looked to the challenging flight of the birds high up. A small black bird appeared from somewhere: a hen hawk. It also tried to revolve over the forests. The eagles came tumbling down, and fell upon the hen hawk. Shortly after, they returned, and began to revolve again in circles, growing wider and wider.

The men had decided to go after the thief. They started off. Night was setting in, and the forest shook with the wind. There were ten of them. They went through the forest, and stopped only at midnight. They lighted fires. One of them said:

"If we catch him, we'll knock the life out of him."

Nobody made any comment.

They set off further. On the way, somebody said:

"We'll gouge out his eyes."

Then, a few hours later, somebody else spoke up:

"We'll chop off his hand. You hold him; I'll place his hand on my shoulder, and cut it off with the knife."

"We'll do the same with his feet. Chop them off slowly."

They had wandered through the forest, for a day, then for another one, and one more. Somebody considered:

"We'll first tear out his nails."

"We'll cut every finger off."

"We'll kill him," somebody shouted in a frenzy.

One day more, then another day, then another. Until then everybody had spoken. Now they were silent, ashamed, helpless.

"Let's return."

"We can't find him. . . . Let's go back."

Then "Kind Adam" spoke up:

"We must find that man. I've an old rusty knife. . . . We'll chop him up. Slowly. For a whole day. We'll put him to torture. Every bit of him should perish. . . ."

* * *

As these memories crossed Adam's mind while he lingered in the forest, waiting and looking at his horse, he remembered the girl, and his heart sank. Night was setting in. Stars glittered in the sky. The wind blew and brought the smell of the earth's grass decked with dew. He unbound the horse, mounted it, and headed for home. The wind, the wind in the field—and the stars, the stars, the stars high above.

He saw the apple tree in the garden, then a glowworm. What's going on? Why is the house lighted? Whose voices are these? Warily, like a cat, he got nearer. Carefully. The step of a cat. Why should the sand rasp under his bare feet? Why are the men in the house shouting? If only the girl were all right. They couldn't possibly have harmed a child. . . . They're laughing. And they don't speak Rumanian? He can see them clearly now. He inches forward. The step of a cat. He sees the bacon and the wine on the table. There is no mistaking they've found the wine . . . the wine. And the bread. The bread too. Oh, they're laughing, so vehemently. The one with spectacles laughs loudest. . . .

He came nearer. He stumbled over something, like a coat, like a body. Ana's body. He felt her: blood. Her blood was still warm. Here, near the house. He looked for her head; no hair was left. They had burned her small, thin, reddish pigtails. . . .

* * *

First, they had searched the stables: they had found nothing. They had entered the house, found the wine in the larder, and the sleeping child in the room.

To see a child waking up with burning hair was so very fascinating! Just like a show! A first-class show!

That is how the performance had begun. A ghastly performance.

* * *

The next day a new group of people in gray coats came to requisition horses and people.

The bodies of three Nazi officers were found in that house.

Fanus Neagu

(b. 1935)

Belonging to the youngest generation of Rumanian writers, Fanus Neagu describes in his works the landscape typical of the marshes in the Danube delta near the town of Braila. He is particularly attracted by the folklore of these places and is considered as a successor to Panait Istrati. As a matter of fact, Fanus Neagu is much like his predecessor because of their common inspiration: the vast Baragan plain as far as the Braila swamps, a region inhabited by self-willed people, rash in carrying out their intention, impetuous in love as well as in anger, steeled by long suffering, but determined not to be humiliated, ready to fight for their dignity. After publishing three volumes of short stories, *It Was Snowing in the Baragan* (1959), *The Afternoon Sleep* (1960), and *Beyond the Sandy Grounds* (1962), Fanus Neagu is now writing a novel, promising excerpts having already appeared in various literary magazines.

Excerpt from *It Was Snowing in the Baragan*

Chivu Capalau got up late that Shrove Tuesday in 1949. His sleep had been as heavy as lead; the night before he had sat down to drink with the village chanter and had got fuddled. The chanter had come round to tell him that Father Ragalie was planning to get Capalau out of the parish council, because of the rumor that had come to his ears that Onica, Capalau's younger son, was carrying on with Vica, the wife of his brother Babalete. Worse than heathens, they were!

As soon as he got up, Chivu Capalau drank another mug of wine—like cures like—and called for his boys to give them a piece of his mind, but there was no one about. As he was pulling on his high boots, he thought that after all there was some truth in the gossip; Babalete, a half-wit since birth, had only been able to get a wife from a village some 25 miles from Suligatu. Vica would never have taken him—as would none of the girls of the neighboring villages—had she not had a child out of wedlock. Last spring, she had been alone in the fields ploughing when a young kulak, who was now in jail, had raped her. Her father had forced her to accept Capalau's elder son, had beaten her till she agreed to the match. Capalau had brought her in a sledge to her new family one night, just after Epiphany. One week after her arrival her child had died; ever since she refused to share her bed with Babalete, forcing him to sleep on the floor, near the stove. She was not lawfully wedded to Babalete. Capalau wanted to keep her unwedded for a month or so, to see how she behaved and how she worked; if he was satisfied he would arrange for the wedding.

"No wonder the wench is so hot-tempered," muttered Capalau to himself that Shrove Tuesday, as he walked out onto the porch staring at the raging blizzard that had started before midnight. The wattle fence around the orchard had blown over, falling on top of the dog's kennel standing close to the corncrib. The barn, the stable, and the sheep pen could hardly be seen, swaddled as they were in their white swathes by the wind.

His face muffled in the collar of his sheepskin jerkin, Capalau waded through the snowdrift in front of the door, sinking into it as if it were a mound of chaff, and walked across to the kitchen, where Nadoleanca, his wife—in her greasy gravy-stained calico dress, her feet thrust into a pair of old hobnailed army boots—was busy preparing the feast for Lenten Eve to which his godchildren and their kin were to come.

Capalau was sponsoring weddings and christenings every year. A wedding or baptism was not much of an expense for the godfather; whatever he laid out on the wedding day was more than recovered later on. There was an old custom in Suligatu Village that on every more important holiday the godchildren were to call on their godfather, bringing him a present: ten brace of fowl and three of turkey every year, not to mention the rugs and tablecloths covering the consecrated wheatcake that was presented on Shrove Tuesday, Easter, and Christmas Day.

Besides, Capalau was a man of substance and would not refuse anyone if asked to be godfather.

"High time you got up," his wife told him when he appeared in the kitchen doorway. "I want you to kill that turkey. I'm going to fetch it. The water's boiling on the range. I'm ready to pluck the bird, but there's no one about to cut its head off."

Nadoleanca bent down to put a piece of wood into the fire. She was old, short and fat; her complexion, dark and sallow. A wart the size of a bean hung from the tip of her nose.

"Where are your sons?" inquired Capalau. "I expect they're loitering in the village and won't be back before the feast tonight! To be sure," he went on, snorting, "when there's work to be done they need urging, but when it comes to boozing they're the first to sit down at the head of the table and won't budge."

It was as clear as daylight that Capalau was set upon picking a quarrel. "That's what he's like the morning after," Nadoleanca told herself, waiting resignedly—as she had done all her life whenever her husband was in a bad mood—for the shower of oaths invariably poured over her drooping shoulders on such occasions.

"Don't you hear?" bawled Capalau. "Where are the boys?"

"Onica," replied Nadoleanca, "has gone to the brook to crack a hole in the ice and drop his net in. . . . Maybe he'll catch some fry. Babalete's in the yard chopping a log."

"Why don't you tell him to cut off the head of your turkey?"

"He doesn't want to. Says he's sorry for the poor bird."

"Sorry? I'll show him who to be sorry for. I suppose it's because he's sorry for him that he lets Onica carry on with Vica."

Nadoleanca turned pale. So that was the reason for Capalau's ill-temper today. She was terrified at the thought that Capalau would soon set eyes upon Onica, whom she loved more than anything else in the world. Without uttering a word, she hastily wrapped her woolen shawl around her shoulders and walked out into the snowstorm to return with the turkey in her arms. They had been fattening it with grains and hot corn-mush for the last three weeks.

Capalau seized the bird, stretched its neck across the threshold and, wielding his axe with gusto, struck out with zest. The blood gushed forth, splashing the door and the wall.

"Call Vica and tell her to scrape the blood away," said Capalau. "And take care the feathers don't get scattered; you'll need them to fill the pillowcases."

When he bent down he had suddenly felt the blood rush to his head. He was dizzy. His razor-nicked lower lip, hanging limply, trembled like an old man's.

Vica was not at home either. She had left with Onica to help him at the brook. Capalau tugged nervously at his moustache. He was a tall, bony man with sunken cheeks and deepset, green eyes.

"So she's gone to help Onica, has she?" he grimaced. "Why doesn't she help Babalete? You sheep's-head, don't you see the slut runs after Onica wherever he goes? I picked her out of the gutter and now she's making us the laughingstock of the village. I've a good mind to pack her up and send her back to her father—as a present for Shrove Tuesday!"

Nadoleanca never uttered a word. Capalau was obviously trying to make her say something in Onica's or Vica's defence, which would serve as a pretext whereby he would vent all his pent-up rage upon her. He suspected Nadoleanca of having a soft spot for Vica, because Onica had fallen in love with the young woman. When he saw she wouldn't say anything, he looked for a spoon and greedily spooned up the broth that had been left over from yesterday's dinner.

Just then Babalete strode in with some firewood. His ears, each as large as a burdock leaf, were too big for his fur cap. He had stayed out in the cold so long that their tips had frozen, which made him shake his head all the time like an unharnessed horse straining to get rid of its halter. He was a tall man, much taller than his father, broad-shouldered and hefty, with a large mouth and brawny hands that reached down to his knees.

"D'you know where your wife is?" Capalau asked him. "Do you or don't you?"

Babalete did not reply. He sat down on a stool and lifted up the sole of one of his boots that he had notched with his axe.

"Torn," he grunted in a deep voice, as he twisted his foot around. "I hit it with my axe and split it."

"You're a fool!" Capalau told him. "You're no good at anything. You're a sop; that's what you are! Go to the brook—that's where your woman is—grab her by the neck and shove her head into the icy-hole. And don't let go before she turns into an icicle!"

Wanting to appease Capalau, Nadoleanca caught Babalete by the arm and pushed him gently out of the kitchen.

"Get along with that log . . . I need some more wood."

"Naturally," Capalau flared up, "send him out into the blizzard, chuck him out! Why not, he's only an idiot! Let him freeze to death; it's only Babalete!"

His real name was Nita, but they called him Babalete, even at home; it was the nickname the village had given him.

After a while, his hunger stilled and the effects of his drinking bout dispelled, Capalau stepped out into the courtyard to look after the sheep. He poured some corn into a wooden trough for them, and stroked the bellies of the ewes that were due to lamb soon, reckoning the number of days they still had before their term. From the platform of the toolshed he took an acacia hayfork, nine feet long, with which he tried to prop up the orchard fence the wind had blown down.

All this time he was thinking of Onica and Vica. He kept casting sidelong glances towards the lime-kiln and the large gate that turned on an iron wheel; he was waiting for them to return from the river.

Capalau was fond of believing that the people in the village respected him for being virtuous. This, he was convinced, was the gift God in his grace had bestowed upon him at his birth. To make him appear before the village stripped of his virtue, like a corncob passed through the shucking-machine, as Father Ragalie was trying to do, was like pushing him over the edge of a precipice. And why? Just because Onica had got entangled with Vica, the woman he had picked for Babalete and whom he had purposely chosen because she had had a child out of wedlock, to be sure of her being submissive and never protesting against whatever work she was ordered to do? "No," Capalau told himself, "today they'll see that they've chosen foul herbs to help them in their love." He had closed his eyes to many of this young woman's whims: he had let her sing in the choir of the village club; people shouldn't say he was against the new system. On Sundays he also let her go with the neighbors to the lectures given by the schoolteachers or by the engineers who came down from the town. That would have to stop now; he would have to put his household in order.

While he was brooding over his wrongs, Vica, hoar-frosted by the snowstorm, hurried into the courtyard, the fishing-net in one hand and the pick-axe in the other. She edged her way past the well and its ice-coated walls and vanished through the kitchen door. Capalau did not drop his work at once; he would wait before taking Vica to task. Let her warm her numbed limbs first.

When she entered the kitchen, Vica flung her arms around the stove and then went up to Nadoleanca, asking her to unfasten the belt she had strapped round her sheepskin coat.

"Whew," she cried shivering, "There's a devilish icy wind in the valley at the brook that knocks you over. If it hadn't been for Onica, I should never've been able to cross that ford. I'd have got stuck there like a log."

"Where is he now?" asked Nadoleanca in alarm.

"Who? Onica? He's gone to the common behind the mill to 'toss the dogs.' We've not been able to catch anything, not as much as the tail of a fish."

"Thank God he hasn't come," sighed Nadoleanca, relieved. "His father's waiting to beat him to a pulp." As she spoke, the old woman kept scraping the frosted windowpane to look into the courtyard. "And don't let Chivu see you," she went on. "He's in a wild temper. Go and lock yourself in your room; he has sworn to knock the soul out of you. Hurry up before he finds out you're back."

"All right; I'll get out of the way," replied Vica, and, before Nadoleanca had time to avoid her, Vica had put her hands on her cheeks and, gazing tenderly into her eyes with a look of love and gratitude, she gave her a smacking kiss and rushed to the door.

It was too late. Capalau was already in the doorway and, when she attempted to steal past, he caught her and flung her onto the bed.

"What's come over you," cried Vica. "Have you gone mad?" She jumped to her feet, quivering with fury. Her blue, slanting eyes, ablaze with the blood seething in her veins, flashed daggers at him. Her cheeks were crimsoned by the frost, and a wisp of fair hair that had got stuck to her brow escaped from under the woolen shawl she had wrapped around her shoulders and tied behind her back. She was not afraid of Capalau. She had suffered too many blows from her father to be scared by a man who raised a threatening fist. Besides, she had never respected Capalau. She had been perfectly aware from the very first day that, as long as she stayed in Capalau's household, she would be nothing more than a beast of burden.

"Mad! You tell me I'm mad?" muttered Capalau. "You shameless slut! Why do you carry on with Onica and make Babalete sleep night after night on the floor near the stove? Well, today I'll judge you the way Jesus Christ was judged!"

"Not so loud, Chivu," ventured Nadoleanca in a beseeching voice. "The neighbors will hear you. Oh, God Almighty, there's never a day in this house without a row."

"The neighbors will hear me, will they?" Capalau snapped back. "Are you ashamed of the neighbors? Well then, get out and drive them away if there's anyone behind the fence!" And he pushed his wife out of the room with such force that the old woman tumbled over the threshold and fell down outside.

Vica gasped. She moved a step forward and shouted into his face: "Come on, judge me if you dare. It's a fine partnership. I and your Babalete. I brought the oxen and he the plough. You couldn't find a bigger fool than me!"

"Listen to this shameless hussy; the things she dares to say!" replied Capalau, raising his arms and rolling his eyes as if calling on the walls, the smoke-stained ceiling, and the sky above it to bear witness against Vica.

All of a sudden, shoving her elbow into his ribs, Vica pushed him aside and dashed out. She reached the house and locked herself up in her room. Her boldness and presence of mind amazed Capalau so much that for a moment he remained with his hands half-raised in the air, his eyes staring, his mouth agape. A thing like that had never happened in his house before. "I'll kill her," he roared and rushed after her, but at the door he stumbled against Nadoleanca, who was crouching near the threshold like a blackbird knocked down by the wind. He forgot about Vica and bore down upon his wife. He caught her by the shoulders and banged her head against the wall, so that her teeth almost dropped out of her mouth.

"Pack up her belongings and throw her out," he shouted. "I don't want her in my house! I don't want to see her anymore."

Frightened to death, the old woman kept nodding that she would do so. She could not say a word; her tongue was like a piece of wood stuck in her mouth. Fear seemed to have made her smaller than she actually was.

Capalau let her go; he returned to the kitchen, picked up a mug and went down into the cellar to fetch some wine. He needed a draught to calm his nerves. Down there, he found Babalete lying on the floor, sucking the cock of one of the wine barrels. Capalau flung himself astride his chest and beat him until he got tired of it.

Onica was on the common at the back of the mill, unaware of what was happening at home.

In Suligatu, as well as in many other villages of the Baragan plain, it was the custom to "toss the dogs" on the last day before Lent (after 1949 people gave it up, regarding it as inhuman and unworthy of them), and at night bonfires were kindled on the hilltops, and the young lads yodeled the "Olelie" calls, naming the girls that were still unmarried and telling the world their faults and foibles. Sometimes married women suspected of having cuckolded their husbands were not spared either. This year, the mayor, who in his young days had been a shepherd at a kulak's sheepfold where he had learned to love dogs, had posted the following notice at the crossroads of the village in February:

" 'Tossing the dogs' is a barbaric custom that is unbefitting. Whoever will henceforward practice it, shall be fined 25 (twenty-five) lei. The money will be paid into the fund for the construction of the new village club."

On reading the notice, Onica and his friend Danila Bis, who had never missed a show of this kind in their life, scraped up the money and paid their fine, so that nobody should spoil their sport. Onica had had half a mind not to pay, but Bis had forced him to. "Listen," said Bis, "are you a man or aren't you? Fork out the money and pay up!" And during the following week the two of them lured seven dogs with hot corn-mush, and locked them up in a ramshackle shed standing not far from the place where they were to be tortured to the delight of the gaping crowd.

Just before noon, when Onica turned the corner of the fence that separated the mill yard from the chanter's apricot garden, there were about ten lads stamping around and laughing near the drooping acacia tree that stood in the middle of the common. A bevy of brats, blue with cold, kept milling around them, alert not to miss anything. Although the wind was toying with the snow—scattering it about, blowing it into tall drifts, and sprinkling it lavishly over the people—the crowd included eight women who were sheltering behind the fence. Beside them, squatting on his haunches, was an old gaffer, puffing at his pipe, chatting with the twelve-year-old girl of the assistant registrar, who had dragged her black-nosed little dog along on a leash. She wanted him to be punished, for he had broken all the toys her father had brought her from Braila.

After taking off their sheepskin jerkins, Onica and Bis picked out a thick branch of the old acacia tree—some sixteen feet from the ground—around which they threw the rope. Then they told one of the boys in the crowd to take a dog out of the nearby shed. Bis caught hold of the dog, tied the rope twice round its body and handed Onica one end of the rope, which the latter had to hold tight and pull only when he was told. The crowd had gathered about them in a circle; Bis yelled loudly, and Onica pulled the rope up and down, until the dog, howling for dear life, was swaying high up above the crowd, shrivelled up with pain. They tossed it, swinging it to and fro several times, then suddenly dropped it into the snow. Bis was an old hand at hauling them up fast or slow, making them spin or arch their tortured body. On reaching the branch over which the rope glided, some of the dogs would try like mad to bite it. These dogs were lowered at once and released; henceforward no stranger would dare to go into the courtyard of the owners of these dogs. For the dogs that only kept yelping, the cure was different: by a quick movement of their arms Onica and Bis would undo the rope that was tied round their belly with a slip knot and the dogs would drop with such a crash that they started hiccuping when they hit the ground.

Bis had two mongrels of his own that he tossed every year and flung to the ground as hard as he could, but without avail; they could not be made to bark at anybody.

"There's nothing to be done with them," he would say, "they want to die this way."

The blizzard was growing stronger. Racing down from the heights, the wind tumbled over the wooden gallery of the mill and over the church belfry that rose nearby, and then rushed crazily into the fields, spreading its white banner as far as the other end of the Baragan. On reaching the river bank with its row of poplars, whose branches were interlaced like the mesh of a fishing net, the wind would swell and soar up wildly to the skies.

The gaffer with his pipe, the children and the women had left the common, when Bis told the lads to join him and call on Ene Lelea who owed him three gallons of wine. Onica tarried a while to coil up the rope; then, having wrapped his scarf more tightly round his neck, he dashed off to catch up with his friends but, at the corner of the fence, his brother Babalete stopped him, clinging to his arm.

"What's the matter with you?" asked Onica. "Where the hell did you crack that mug of yours? Did you fall?"

"Father caught me by the wine cask."

"Oh, then it's all right. Where Father strikes a blow, sound flesh is bound to grow. Let's get going."

Babalete would not release the grip on his arm. He kept squeezing it as though he were trying to wrench it off his shoulder. Onica planted his feet firmly on the ground and tried to tear himself loose, but his brother was stronger.

"Vica," uttered Babalete. And he repeated: "Vica."

Onica remembered that Babalete had been watching him for some time, that he knew he was running after Vica. Fear seized him. He was one head shorter than Babalete. His frail, lanky body, his downy moustache, his brown eyes and beardless face showed clearly that he was only just twenty. He wanted to call Bis, but the latter was already far away, lost in the snowy spray that enveloped everything.

Babalete had not come with any evil intent. He was tugging at Onica's sleeve to make him go home, because Vica had told him to do so.

What happened was this:

When he had tired of beating him, Capalau had sent Babalete into the courtyard to rub his face thoroughly with snow and return to the cellar. He felt sorry for him. "It's no use beating him," he thought. "It's not his fault that he's a nitwit! Should I kill him because he's a fool? It's Onica who needs a proper hiding!" The more he drank, the more aggrieved he grew for his son, reproaching Babalete for allowing his brother to hoodwink him. Why did he let that wench twist him around her fingers? Because he was a fool? True, he was a fool! There was no doubt about that, but if he would get hold of Vica, fling her on the ground and flog her with the harness straps where the flesh is tenderest, there'd be no more monkey tricks, nor would she call him a fool! They all grew virtuous and dutiful when you gave them such a hiding that they could only sleep on their belly for a month or so. . . . As for Onica, Babalete needn't worry, that was his, the old man's affair. He'd put a stop to his roaming, and marry him to a good farmer's daughter. . . . "I'll get you married lawfully and I'll tie a stone to his neck too." When he had drunk his third mug of wine, Capalau wished to know when Babalete had last embraced his wife.

"Quite some time now. When she first came to our place; I've no papers."

On hearing that, Capalau dragged Babalete out and led him to Vica's room. But she refused to open the door.

"I can't," she replied. "I'm changing my clothes; I'm undressed."

"Babalete will help you; don't forget you're his wife. It's for him that I brought you here," shouted Capalau.

"I'm not his wedded wife."

"Ha, ha," laughed Capalau, winking an eye at Babalete, "You're on probation, I know. Let's see how good you are on the job first; we'll give you a marriage certificate after. Come on now, open the door and take your husband into your warm bed."

"Lay him out on the straw, your Babalete; or shove him into the bitch's kennel. That's the right place for him."

Drunk as he was, Capalau turned purple-blue with rage and started kicking at the door.

"I'll teach you to speak decently, you bitch! I'll teach you, impudent slut, how to behave! I'll show you who's master in this house!"

"You can bang on the door till doomsday," Vica shouted defiantly. "You may even bash the door with the axe if you like, but I won't let you in."

Capalau was boiling with rage. He was about to fetch the axe, but changed his mind. He wasn't that far gone; this was a new door that had cost him a lot of money. No, he couldn't break it!

"Never mind," he said, "you'll come out again. You won't escape me, no fear." He told Babalete to keep watch on the doorstep. "Stay here till she comes out," he told him. "And when she tries to slip out, take hold of her and break her bones; and beat the guts out of her, the lousy hussy!" And, wild with rage, his nerves strained to the point of snapping, Capalau rushed out into the snowstorm to cool his anger and clear his mind.

Vica was conscious of the power she had over Babalete; she knew that a glance of hers made his blood freeze or boil in his veins. When Capalau had gone, she cracked the door open and, raising a finger to her lips, said to Babalete:

"Go fetch Onica. He's on the common by the mill. Tell him to come here. Come on, get going," and she pushed him out through the front door, so that the old man should not see him.

When they reached home, Onica made Babalete walk in by the big gate, whilst he ran through the little garden to the veranda and thence into the hall.

The violent snowstorm had played havoc in their yard. After flinging down the orchard's wattle fence, it had wrenched off the top of the pile of millet. Tufts of straw from the ravaged stack were flying about the yard like sparks from a burning roof. Capalau was fuming, and on catching sight of Babalete he shouted to him to fetch the stone roller they used for threshing the barley and throw it on top of the stack on which he had laid a log. Babalete, who had not forgotten the beating in the cellar, hurried to the tool shed and, with his stout arms, picked up the roller that was as heavy as a millstone.

Onica thought it wise not to be seen by his father just then. Foul-tempered as the old man was, he would not have been surprised to have Capalau pick up the iron hayfork and pitch into him. He had had hurled at him anything that Capalau chanced to lay hands on many a time. There was no love lost between father and sons. Babalete was not worth a glance; Onica was treated like a servant.

Capalau was one of the richest men in the village, having acquired much property. During the drought of 1946 he had made a lot of money buying up livestock in the mountain villages and selling them at a huge profit in town, at Braila. He'd bought land and hired servants. And when the new system had obliged him to pay the men decently, he had sacked them. Now his sons had to do all the work.

The tilling of the land was Onica's responsibility; it was he who did the ploughing, sowing, and harvesting. Capalau would rarely go into the fields. When he was not away for his purchases, he would saunter through the village, his hands clasped behind his back, sniffing right and left like a fox, or rather snorting so noisily that everyone called him Snorer. "Snorer is taking the air. He's driven his slave to the fields and now he's counting the stray strawblades along the alleys," the villagers would say.

Onica, reckoning he'd better do some odd job to explain his absence later on, propped the ladder against the hayloft and climbed up with a shovel to clear away the snow that had drifted through the cracks of the roof. He had quite forgotten Vica.

She had heard him go up to the loft. Why had he not come to her room? "He's scared," she told herself. "He's afraid of his father. Onica is no more than a servant in this house." She wanted to show him a letter she had been carrying in her blouse for several days, a letter from her cousin who was working at a building site at Braila. This is what she wrote:

"My dear, distressed cousin. I hope my lines will find you in good health. Mother was here yesterday and told me that Uncle has given you away to a fellow you don't care for, that you've left the village and that your child is dead. Poor girl, you must have suffered a terrible lot. But I find it's you who are to blame, for you could have come here and I would have helped you to find a place. I'm a waitress at the canteen of this building site, but I don't have to put up with what went on at restaurants in the old days. When a customer used to call you from a table, you had to run to do his bidding and not mind his pinching you. At this canteen we are four girls, neatly dressed; we are civil to everybody and no one ever addresses us harshly. We are paid well and if we do our work properly we get a bonus. So, dear cousin, what I say is, if things become too difficult for you, come over here and I'll help you. I spoke about you to the secretary of our Union of Working Youth branch and he said that if you come he'll lend you a helping hand too.

"I close now, with loving kisses. Your cousin, Silica."

"I'd better go up to Onica," muttered Vica as she opened the door and cast a searching glance down the porch. As there was no one about, she climbed up the ladder to the loft.

"What are you doing here?" cried Onica in alarm. "Someone may come and catch us. Go back to your room," he entreated her. "Father's in a hellish temper."

Vica nodded and sat down on a sack of beans. It was warm in the loft, cobwebs were swaying lazily in the dust-laden air, and there was a faintly sweet odor of mould. She watched Onica shovelling the snow down into the yard, while she picked out some dried raisins from the bunches of grapes that had been hung up in the autumn to be preserved for winter, and kept nibbling at them. When she had finished these, she thrust her arm into a sack from which she took a fistful of bitter-tasting seeds that she began to eat quietly. She moved about noiselessly in the shadow, her eyes downcast, now and again throwing a furtive glance at the lad.

Onica paused once to take a rest and listened to the wind whistling through the roof like a birch rod whirled over one's head. He gazed at Vica, who was sitting with her back to him, annoyed at her apparent indifference. He dropped the shovel and tiptoed up to her. Flinging his arms around her, he thrust her head back and pressed her full lips to his. Suddenly he started. Below, Nadoleanca was quarreling with Capalau for not having brought her the straw she needed to burn in the oven; the dough for the bread was leavened, ready to run out of the trough. Onica made a move to draw back, but Vica held him tightly by the coat, pressing him to her.

"Your mother told me they're going to get you married. After I sent Babalete to fetch you she came to my room and told me that's what the old man has decided. I am to remain with Babalete and you with whom chance may choose."

"Nonsense," said Onica, "They just wanted to scare you." But he was trembling, his voice shaking. It was plain he was afraid.

"It isn't nonsense, Onica. If that's what the old man has decided, we can't do anything about it. But I won't stay with Babalete. It was for your sake I suffered everything I had to endure in this house. I'm going to leave."

"Why?" muttered Onica. "I'm still here."

"No," said Vica, "it can't go on like this. I'm leaving. After all I've slaved long enough here. In this place everyone's your father's servant. And I don't want to be a servant any more."

Onica was at a loss what to answer. He held her close, gently caressing her. Vica was right. In their house Capalau was the master, and everybody else cringed before him and blindly carried out his commands. He for one had never dared to stand up to the old man, to face him bravely. As he grew older he felt his hate growing in him. He had never known a kind word or joy from his father.

"I know," said Vica, as if she had read his thoughts, "when it comes to facing your father you shrink to the size of a beetle." That was the truth. Onica could take no offence. He moved up closer to her and kissed her again. In her lips, in her body he felt resistance, the struggle that was rending her. He heard her beating heart cry out to him, a call to which he had no answer, no soothing whisper of comfort. He preferred to say nothing and drove all thoughts away.

When he climbed down and walked out into the yard he ran into Babalete, who, with a grin, was waiting for him and who fatuously asked whether Vica would still force him to sleep on the floor and whether . . .

"Go to the devil!" snapped Onica, turning his face to the wind, to cool his fever.

From the kitchen, Capalau caught sight of them through the window and stepped out on the porch.

"Where have you been?" he inquired. "Fleecing dogs?"

He had only his flannel vest on, and his words were uttered calmly, with a slow, broad drawl. His composure made Onica more nervous. Had he been greeted with oaths and raised fists, he could have hoped to get off with a few cuffs. As things stood, there was not the shadow of a doubt that his fate was sealed. "Whether you like it, Onica, or not," he thought, endeavoring to treat the matter lightly since he saw no way out, "you're in for it this time."

"I've been up in the loft," he replied. "I threw down the snow that had drifted in."

"Did you? All right. . . . By the way, tonight I'm sending the matchmakers to Lache Trufasu's daughter. Tomorrow we'll call on them and may even bring her home with us."

Onica crumpled a dry flower between his fingers, a flower that had probably been entangled in Vica's hair. When he realized what he was doing, he flung the crushed petals to the wind and rushed off to lie down in the hayloft. He didn't want to see anyone nor talk to anyone. What he had heard kept whirling in his brain, beating a quick tattoo, as persistent and trying as the hammering on a sounding-board: "Matchmakers, matchmakers."

As the afternoon wore into evening, the snowstorm died down and the frost set in. Tiny stars glittering through the dim mist were green, rather than yellow, tints in the cloudless sky.

Unrelenting in his resolve to marry Onica off, Capalau had crossed the road with a bottle of brandy in his coat pocket, to talk the matter over with Neculai Giuga. The latter was Lache Trufasu's godson and, as was the custom in those parts, would be at the Lenten Eve feast with his godfather. Capalau wanted to ask him to broach the matter of the marriage that very night, so that the next day, with their minds clear, he, Capalau, and Trufasu could meet to clinch the deal. He returned home, slightly tipsy, thrusting his sharp-pointed stick forcefully into the ground to keep him from slipping on the ice. He looked very pleased with what he had arranged. Neighbor Neculai Giuga had wholeheartedly agreed to act as go-between. He thought Lache Trufasu's daughter and Capalau's son would make an ideal couple. The lad, obedient and hardworking, was the son of a well-to-do family; the girl was not unbecoming, either. She had quite a good dowry and, to judge by her mother, would not bear too many children: one or two, at the utmost; not like other women who had a brat every year.

While the old man was away, Onica had tried to avoid Vica. He could not bear her reproachful eyes. "Why do you say nothing?" her eyes kept saying: "Are you afraid he'll beat you? He's a fiend; that's what your father is!" But Onica feigned not to see or understand.

When Capalau returned, he ordered Vica and Babalete to be off to Babalete's godfather at once, with presents and a wheatcake. "Stay there for an hour or two and then come back; the big feast will be here, at our place."

While Vica and Babalete went to their room to dress, Capalau called Onica to show him the flute that had a crack near the mouth hole.

"If you hear of anyone killing a calf," he told him, "let me know; I'll get a piece of gut to wrap the flute in. When the gut is dry, the flute is as good as new, if not better. Hey," he called out to Nadoleanca, "see you turn the tomcat out of the house, or he'll poke his nose into all the platters of meat and jelly." And turning back to Onica: "Don't forget, lad, if you happen to hear of a calf being slaughtered . . ."

"I heard all right; I'm not deaf," sighed the lad, his eyes fixed on the ground.

"Now then, no cheek from you," the old man warned him, "none of your lip, or there'll be trouble again. And we've hardly patched things up."

A long whistle was heard from the road, and Onica slipped out. Vica stalked into the kitchen, followed by Babalete who was dressed in a suit of black drugget cloth, a carnation stuck in his breast pocket; he kept tapping it with two fingers, his lips curled into an idiotic grin. Vica had come to fetch the basket with the freshly baked wheatcake—it was as large as a cartwheel—and the tablecloth they were to offer to Dumitru Caraiman, who had agreed to sponsor their wedding. Vica was wearing a dress of cherry-colored cloth, tight in the waist, with puffed sleeves. She had also put on her sheepskin jerkin, over which she had wrapped her shawl.

"Look at her, all swaddled up!" Nadoleanca exclaimed. "Why you've put on all the clothes you've got."

"It's cold," replied Vica.

"Now then, get going," said Capalau, "have a good time and don't forget what I said. And you, Babalete," rapping the boy's temple, "don't you start kissing the hands of my goddaughter when you leave or I'll twist your neck till your mouth reaches your nape."

At the gate, Vica and Babalete met Onica and Danila Bis.

"Good evening, Babalete," Bis called out. "Are you going to call on Caraiman? Good for you! Drink the old miser's cellar dry!" he cried, drawing aside to let them pass.

Onica seized Vica's hand, squeezing it tightly as if to crush her fingers, watching her with delight as she grimaced with pain.

"Have a good time, Onica," Vica said, "and good luck."

"Good luck to you."

"What a handsome wench this Vica is!" said Bis after a while. "She's really beautiful! If that poor wretch Babalete had only an ounce of brains in that skull of his, he'd break your bones for you."

"Shut up," Onica retorted angrily. "Have you nothing else to do?"

"No, I haven't; you're keeping me out here in the cold and I should be at the other end of the village by now. Tonight you'll hear me yodel the like of which has never been heard before."

"Have you got your speaking-trumpet?"

"One of the boys is bringing it."

"Well, then let's be off," suggested Onica.

Stodgy and tough, his hands thrust deep into his pocket, Bis turned his cat-like eyes on Onica.

"I say, Onica, what about having a drink first?"

"All right," said Onica, "come into the veranda; I don't want father to see you." He led Bis into the glass-enclosed porch, where they kept their artichokes, potatoes, onions and tufts of peppers that had been collected after the first hoarfrost, the loom, and several other articles. Then he went into the kitchen to fetch a mug to fill with wine.

Nadoleanca followed him into the cellar. She felt uneasy.

"Oh, my boy, please be careful," she started lamenting. "Don't do anything hasty; if you do, that will be the end of me. I've been torturing myself ever since I was born. I had hoped that in my old age at least, I'd lead a quieter life, and have a few moments of happiness. . . ."

After the wine, Onica and Bis set off across the vineyards and soon reached the hill from the top of which they were to do their yodeling. Five other young peasants were waiting for them around a fire that was fed with dry acacia twigs. The group had been larger, but had split into two teams. According to custom, one team had to pitch its camp on the hillock above the vegetable gardens and reply to the cries of the men on this hilltop. It took the second team half an hour to get to the other side, and their passage through the village was accompanied by loud yells.

Not far from the hilltop two shadows were dimly visible.

"I say," asked Bis, "who are those people there? Did you see them?"

"Yes. It's Marin Citu and his brother."

"Oh, what a fine couple they are!" exclaimed Bis merrily.

Every year, on Lenten Eve, Marin Citu, who had three unmarried daughters, and his brother would stick to the heels of the village lads, trying to prevent them from deriding his daughters. All he managed to do was to make himself the target of their fun.

A red flame rose from the other side of the village. That was the signal that the second team had reached the appointed spot.

Danila Bis, who was unsurpassed in this sort of feat, tossed off a draught from the bottle he carried in his pocket and, taking up the alphorn-shaped trumpet that one of the boys held out to him, tested his voice, yodeling into it:

Olelie, most lovely pearls
Here's the roll of the unwedded girls . . .

Down in the village, the people gathered at the tables, left their meat and drink and stepped out to listen. The men, warmed by drink and more thickly dressed than the women, ventured into the village alleys, to exchange a word with their neighbors, offering or asking for a cigarette and splitting with laughter at the young lads' quips. They were glad the boys had fine weather for their sport. After the storm, the cries of the young men on the hills rang out clearly in the frosty air, echoing far beyond the village.

The women, old and young, were on the porches and kept giggling. Nobody stayed indoors; nobody would miss the occasion, for merrymaking of this kind took place only once a year. Some of the women, whose conscience was not as clear as they would have liked it to be, felt their shirts burning against their skin and the perspiration breaking out everywhere; they were praying that they would escape attention.

On the hill, Bis was chanting in a sonorous voice the names listed on the roll that he had drawn up with his friends in the morning at Ene Lelea's, each with a glass of wine before him:

Olelie lie, o,
Everyone would like to know,

In her face exactly what
Ghisa's daughter hasn't got?

From the other hilltop, beyond the vegetable gardens, another lad replied promptly, shouting into a horn like the one Bis had:

What Ghisa's daughter hasn't got?
A nose for certain, she has not.

At home, Oana, Ghisa's daughter, buried her nose, no larger than a button, in her tear-drenched pillow.

The yodeling never lasted more than an hour. In the end, some furious and outraged husband or father would chase the lads away.

While Bis was chanting, Onica sprawled on the ground near the fire, unconscious of the cold, gazing into the flames. His thoughts were with Vica. Her sad expression after Capalau's return from visiting Neculai Giuga kept haunting and torturing him. Melancholy and sad, the woman had appeared more beautiful than ever. Shifting his gaze across the moonlit, silvery fields, shrouded in the smoky gray mist woven by the frost, he saw Vica's image again before his eyes. In his fancy he saw her slowly striding along the edge of the vineyards, her blue eyes lost in their violet shadows. "Why don't you say something?" those eyes kept inquiring. "Why don't you say something?" To escape this haunting vision, he lay on his back and peered at a tiny yellow star that looked no larger than a poppy seed. Imperceptibly, the star assumed Vica's features and, catching his eye, flashed the same words at him from its height: "Why don't you say something?"

Onica jumped to his feet and seized Bis's arm.

"Let go," said Bis. "I want to honor the manager of the cooperative store with an Olelie that he will not forget as long as he lives. They caught him the other day selling some kerchiefs at a higher price than he was entitled to charge. He's in for it."

"Call Lache Trufasu's daughter."

"Are you mad?" asked Bis, tearing himself free. "Do you want Trufasu to trample you under his feet? She's an honest girl."

"Give me the trumpet if you're afraid, and I'll call her."

"Onica," Bis shouted at him, "are you crazy?"

"Call her!"

"No," replied Bis obstinately, "I won't. I'll call another girl." And he raised the funnel to his mouth.

Olelie lie, Vica is her name.
Who doesn't know the pretty girl's game?
The grass in the fields,
And the yellow daffodils,

The path that runs up right over the hills—
All know the fine wench and her merry "coo"
And her brother-in-law with whom she carries on too.
I can swear it is true and am sure so can you
But her husband knows nothing,
He's peaceful and cool.
Don't tell him the secret. God bless him, the fool!

Capalau and Nadoleanca with all their guests had come out on the veranda as soon as the fires had started glowing on the two hilltops and they kept roaring with laughter every time Bis raised the trumpet to his mouth. But when they heard the last call they stared at one another in utter dismay, unable to believe their ears. Nadoleanca burst into tears and her relatives rushed her indoors, cursing the one that had besmirched an honest family. Her sobs were like a gust of icy wind that roused them from their drowsiness. Their dismay was followed by a feeling of rage. Capalau rushed up to the fence and, wrenching out a paling, called one of his godsons to take the iron hayfork and run towards the end of the village. The snowdrifts they had to wade through formed an endless row, like dunes in a desert. Capalau, who was certain that Onica had had a hand in this, kept shouting all the while: "I'll kill him; I brought him into the world, and it's me who'll bury him," and called to his godson to hurry.

But when they arrived at the hilltop, Onica and Bis were no longer there; they had fled into the village. After "calling" Vica, Bis had apologized to Onica:

"I did this on purpose, because you are a milksop. You've been telling me over and over again that you love her, but you do nothing to take her out of your father's house. Now, you've no choice; you have to take her and run away with her, or else Capalau will lay your head on the block."

"Where can I go?"

"Where? You are a sop! Go to Braila; there's a building site there. Others from our village have gone there already. Leave as you are. Leave right away," and Bis pushed Onica along the road leading out of the village.

Edging their way along the back alleys, wary not to rouse the dogs, the two reached Dumitru Caraiman's house, which was lit up as if for a wedding. On the porch, under the awning, they saw Babalete, who was bareheaded and kept shouting and waving his hands, while Caraiman tried to calm him and get him to come indoors.

From under the acacia trees where they stood concealed Onica and Bis watched the house closely. And when old Caraiman, feeling the pinch of the cold, went in to warm himself, Bis quickly crept up to the fence and called Caraiman's wife.

"What's happened here? Why is Babalete making such a row? What's happened?"

"His wife's run away, the poor devil! He's lost Vica and seems to have lost his mind too. She came with him up to the gate and told him: 'Here you are; take this wheatcake and give it to Caraiman and may he eat it in good health. I,' she said, 'I'm leaving. I've had enough. I'm fed up with all of you, up to my eyes.' And he, the ass, let her go."

"There's nothing you can do about it, mother," said Bis. "Things like that will happen. Good night!" And he crossed the road to give Onica the news. The latter, in his hiding place near the acacia trees, however, had heard every word the woman had uttered and had set out alone for the railway station.

"He is a fool," muttered Bis, gazing at the receding figure. "I must go and harness the horses to the sledge, or he'll never catch the train."

George Calinescu

(1899-1965)

George Calinescu is one of the outstanding personalities of contemporary Rumanian culture. He engaged in extensive activity as critic, literary historian, prose writer, poet, and publicist. His works of literary history and criticism (*Life of Mihail Eminescu* [1932], *Life of Ion Creanga* [1938], *The Works of Mihail Eminescu,* [5 vols., 1934-1936], *History of Rumanian Literature from its Origin to this Day* [1941], the monographs *Grigore Alexandrescu* [1962] and *Nicolae Filimon* [1959], and various studies on world literature) are all remarkable for their scholarly approach, subtle analysis, and original artistic expression. G. Calinescu made his debut as a prose writer with his novel, lyrical in character, *The Wedding Book* (1933), followed by *Otilia's Enigma* (1938), *Poor Ioanide* (1954), and *The Black Chest* (1960). His writings include *Three Short Stories* (1949) as well as a volume of verse, *In Praise of Things* (1963). Noteworthy examples of his activity as a publicist and literary chronicler are his virulent *Chronicle of a Misanthrope,* written for the democratic press during the interwar period, and the *Chronicle of an Optimist* inspired by the new realities in Rumania, published in the columns of the literary review *Contemporanul* as a response to the former. He also wrote two volumes of travel sketches, *Kiev, Moscow, Leningrad* (1949) and *I've visited New China* (1955), as well as numerous studies in special reviews.

Excerpt from *The Black Chest*

(George Calinescu's *The Black Chest*—a continuation of his novel *Poor Ioanide*—presents a vast fresco of Rumanian society extending over the last three or four decades. The earlier novel surveys the events that occurred in Rumania during the interwar period: the royal dictatorship, the instauration of fascism, the rebellion of the Iron Guard, the pogroms and plunders perpetrated on this occasion, and finally the second World War with the Hitlerite forces in Rumania, the disintegration of the ruling classes, and the defeat of the Germany army. *The Black Chest* explores the deep structural changes wrought in Rumanian society after the second World War. George Calinescu evokes the instauration of the people's power, the work of reconstruction carried out by the new regime in Rumania, the resistance to or the integration in productive work of some elements of the former ruling classes, the building up of the socialist society. In particular the author insists upon the cultural revolution, the changing, and frequently contradictory, mentality of the intelligentsia, the wise policy of the government towards them, and the climate of spiritual renascence and creative effervescence initiated and fostered by the new social system.

The central character in both novels—through whose eyes the entire psychological and social process is analyzed—is the architect Ioanide, an intellectual whose general outlook is undergoing a fundamental evolution.

This excerpt recounts the story of the family of Count Jablonski, a Polish nobleman who fled to Rumania when his country was invaded by the German army. Introduced by a Rumanian aristocrat, a relative by marriage, Jablonsky is first appointed bookkeeper to Antoine Hangerliu's estate. When the latter loses his fortune, Jablonsky becomes a salesman, then a railway station porter, and ends up by accepting any odd job, asking only to be able to support his family, and above all, his daughter, a seventeen-year old girl who is struggling to become a ballerina at the Bucharest Opera House.)

Tadeu Jablonsky first met Lydia, his present wife, in his early school-days, at a children's ball given by an aristocratic family in Warsaw. Lydia was a girl of eleven and Tadeu a boy of thirteen. At that age Jablonsky was a tall, pale, young stripling whose hair—like Liszt's—hung down in long tresses. Frail as he was, no one would have then dreamed that he would ever become the athlete of later years.

The affection that had arisen between them could hardly be called love; it was certainly not a soul-stirring passion but rather the reflection of some vague notions of love that the children had overheard from their elders or conjured up from books. What they did know, however, was that when two young people were in love with each other they became husband and wife. So, as soon as they grew older they solemnly pledged themselves to get married. As their parents were on friendly terms, and as Jablonsky belonged to one of the best families in the city and had every prospect of making a brilliant military career, the parents of both children amused themselves by referring to them as "our fiancés." When Jablonsky came of age he asked his parents the favor of marrying Lydia. Jablonsky's father, a colonel, who was particularly eager to meet his son's wishes, hastened to request authorization from the military authorities.

It was then that an unexpected obstacle arose. An uncle of Lydia's, her mother's brother-in-law, a physician of high repute—who viewed this marriage with displeasure (certain people claimed that it was because he himself would have liked to marry Lydia)—had persuaded the girl's parents that young Jablonsky was inevitably doomed to consumption, all the more likely as numerous members of his family had died from this disease. There was some truth in this statement too. Jablonsky's mother had a weak chest and she would certainly never have reached her present age had it not been for the exceptional medical care she was given and for the large part of the year she spent in the south of Italy. Two of her brothers had passed away at the ages of seventeen and nineteen respectively, and one of Tadeu's brothers had died in a sanatorium in Switzerland. What's more, in this respect the family had even gained literary fame, because of a great Polish poet who, at the beginning of the century, had written a poem singing the love and deeds of a maiden who had died in the prime of life, a prey to tuberculosis, and this maiden had been a member of the Bilinsky family to which Lydia's mother belonged.

The doctor's genuine or feigned concern led Lydia's parents to oppose the union, under the polite pretext that the girl was not ready for marriage. Lydia herself was not persuaded that the doctor's statement was entirely ungrounded, but, romantically-minded, she was ready to marry Jablonsky and thus fulfil her sacred pledge, even if he was ill, and even if it meant sacrificing her life to nurse him to his last days. Tadeu and Lydia resolved to get married without their parents' consent, with the connivance of a liberal-minded aunt of Lydia's who had offered to put up the lovers at her country manor. Before carrying out their threat, Tadeu wrote a letter to his father, begging him not to oppose their marriage and to forgive him if, by marrying without due authorization, he was jeopardizing his military career.

Jablonsky, the father, ran instantly to General Lubomirsky (the commander of the brigade to which Colonel Lenkowicz, the girl's father, belonged), requesting him to use his authority to persuade the colonel to reconsider his decision, in the interest of the children and to avoid endangering young Jablonsky's career. The general summoned the colonel, and with assurance of utmost esteem, broached the subject: of course he did not wish to interfere in the colonel's private affairs, which a father alone has the sovereign right to decide, but, just as friendly advice and without any obligation on the part of the colonel, he wished to make it known to him that the young man, who was an officer in his regiment, had—at his own request—been examined by several physicians and found perfectly healthy. This was confirmed by the regimental doctor together with Professor Novotny, the world-famous specialist in lung diseases, who had certified that there was not the slightest symptom of t.b., hence no risk of contamination and that, considering the wealthy circumstances of the young man, it was out of the question for him ever to catch this disease, a malady that was rampant only among indigent families. He showed him the doctor's certificate, which Jablonsky had asked for in view of the marriage; he, General Lubomirsky, would never have mentioned it, of course, had the matter not come up now and, after all, in his capacity of spiritual father of all the officers in his regiment, he had taken the liberty of committing this indiscretion. Thereupon the general took some photographs out of his wallet and handed them to Colonel Lenkowicz.

"I too have children and I know what a father's responsibility and care mean."

They looked through the snapshots together, admiring the photos of the general's daughter and two sons of various ages, and they exchanged their common worries and affections.

"This is Leopold," said the general, pointing to the elder of the boys. "He is a student. He suffered from a severe inflammation of the lungs, following a cold he had caught ice skating. Look at him now; he's the picture of health and as strong as a stallion."

Colonel Lenkowicz gave in and the young couple were surprised to receive a telegram before committing their act of defiance, a telegram reading as follows: "Agree to marriage. Put off wedding till our arrival." The ceremony was held at the country manor, in a restricted family circle, with only one or two neighbors and townspeople attending. Towards midnight young Jablonsky offered Lydia his arm—Lydia was wearing an airy blue tulle dress, which she had donned after she had taken off her bride's dress—and after bowing to the guests left the house. All the guests escorted them up to the drive in front of the castle from which the park stretched away. A little hunting lodge that lay at the far end of the park, next to the firwood forest, had been reserved and fitted out for them. There they could stay quietly for several weeks without needing to call at the manor house.

Since the alleys of the park grew darker as they advanced, turning into dense groves of birch and oak trees, six footmen carrying lanterns—each consisting of a candle covered with a globe—were placed at every turning to light the path. This had been General Lubomirsky's idea; it was he too who had brought the orchestra out on the drive and had ordered it to play selections from Mozart's *Marriage of Figaro*. Followed by the ever fainter strains of the music gradually melting into the rustle of the leaves of the age-old trees, the bridal couple walked along, guided by the flickering flames of the candlelight that sent their shadows rolling forward to shrink instantly after, as if a crowd of people had suddenly raced ahead of the convoy. Every time a louder rustle came from the bush, Lydia, with a slight shiver, would tighten her grip upon Jablonsky's arm. The trees here joined branches and the air was damp and cool.

Jablonsky clasped Lydia's hand in his palms and found it burning, but when he mentioned it to her, Lydia replied that it was just the excitement and fatigue and that she would get over it presently. When they reached the pavilion and were then left to themselves a natural feeling of embarrassment came over them. They realized that they would have to exchange their formal style of address for a more familiar tone. Jablonsky moved closer, kissed Lydia's hand, then brushing her cheek with his lips, raised her lightly in his arms, wishing to place her on a sofa in the living room where a fire was burning in the fireplace. While in his arms, Lydia suddenly choked, stifling a slight spasm, which recurred when the young husband put her down. Jablonsky gave her a little water to drink, which, rather cold, caused Lydia to break into a fit of coughing.

"Don't worry. I'll be all right," said Lydia to Jablonsky in answer to the worried look that had come into his eyes as he felt his young bride's feverish cheeks. "Let me just regain my breath."

She then coughed to clear her throat, and a trickle of blood gathered in one corner of her lips. Feeling it, she wiped it away with her handkerchief which, when she saw it stained with blood, she dropped to the floor in alarm. More bleeding followed, which frightened Jablonsky into a panic. Utterly at a loss as to what to do, he shouted for the housekeeper, an old woman who had been entrusted to take care of them. She arrived still drowsy with sleep; she had fallen asleep after waiting hours for the bridal couple to arrive. Her medical ministrations consisted of tying a handkerchief soaked in cold water round Lydia's head and in fetching a white porcelain basin in which the blood looked even more terrifying. Jablonsky dashed out, and followed by one of the old woman's sons, who carried a lantern, raced back to the castle. The dance was in full swing and General Lubomirsky, in particular, cut a dashing figure, dancing the mazurka to the accompaniment of Chopin's music. There was no doctor among the wedding guests. Horses were then hastily harnessed to a carriage to fetch a doctor from the neighboring village.

When he was brought to the hunting lodge the doctor, a moustached old gentleman, found Lydia lying on the sofa with the hemorrhage practically stopped. He explained that the cold wet handkerchief that the sick woman had instinctively moved from her head to her chest had done her good. He ordered ice bags or compresses with ice-cold water to be laid on her chest and that the patient should even swallow little pieces of ice. As no ice was available, for the block in the ice bucket that had chilled the champagne had long since melted, it was decided that the cold water from a nearby mountain spring would serve the same purpose. Lydia was also told to drink mouthfuls of salt water from time to time. That was all the country practitioner knew, and there were no coagulating medicines at hand. He wired to town for a doctor, but it was only on the third day that the family physician arrived. He examined Lydia carefully and found that she had tuberculosis in a rather advanced stage, with lesions in one of the lungs. Lydia appeared shattered, not so much by the disease itself, which seemed to impress her slightly, as by the idea that it was she who was consumptive and not her husband against whom her family had raised objections on this very ground. She considered his divorcing her perfectly justified and waited, with resigned grief and shame, for her unfortunate marriage to come to an end. Jablonsky wouldn't even think of such a thing and kept assuring her she would soon recover. When after a short while she felt a little stronger, Lydia was carried to town, examined by a number of physicians, and then placed in a sanatorium. Jablonsky, unfailing in his devotion, visited her twice a day, brought her books to read and gay and optimistic friends to entertain her. One of the younger doctors of the sanatorium showed her photographic plates to prove to Lydia that his had been the gravest case of consumption ever known but that now, thanks to rational care and competent treatment, he had been forced, as he graciously put it, to get well and even to become a dreaded sportsman, the terror of all tennis tournaments. Whenever Jablonsky came across a former consumptive among his acquaintances, he would bring him along and introduce him to Lydia to comfort her and restore her hopes. Jablonsky took Lydia to Switzerland, where she spent a number of months in a sanatorium, then traveled on with her to the Côte d'Azur as a devoted and austere nurse, never even hinting about his marital rights. Gradually Lydia's health improved, her illness became chronic and non-progressive, allowing her to live a normal life with certain restrictions. The relations between husband and wife became what they should have been; the doctors, however, forbade Lydia to have children, a situation that grieved Jablonsky, particularly when his parents died and he was left the sole descendant of the family. Lydia, who had not failed to sense his grief, one day said to her husband: "If, Tadeu, in your desire to have children you approach another woman, I should never reproach you for it, after all the affection and devotion you have showered upon me."

Jablonsky waved aside the mere mention of such a solution. Yet, after several years, when he was in his late thirties, he met a ballet dancer at the opera, a woman of Rumanian origin, who bore him a little girl they named Cucly. For a number of years, Jablonsky was reluctant to inform Lydia of the existence of the girl though he was convinced she knew about it, for more times than one she had bought toys and children's clothes, which, with a tender and encouraging look, she had presented to Jablonsky to give to a policeman's child he claimed to be looking after. Cucly grew up in the atmosphere of a corps-de-ballet and at the age of six was even cast to act the part of an elf. The ballerina, who was anxious to leave the country, as rumors of war were growing more alarming, asked Jablonsky what to do with the girl, who restricted her travels and career. It was like a bolt out of the blue, when Lydia one day said to her husband with her usual tenderness:

"Tadeu, why don't you bring the little girl home? We'll adopt her. Hotels are not the proper environment for a child to be brought up in."

Jablonsky was at first dumbfounded, then gradually realized that Lydia knew everything about it and had even talked to the ballet dancer. He kissed Lydia's hand, but out of a sense of modesty refrained from commenting on her proposal that day. Cucly moved into the Jablonsky's sumptuous house and found in Lydia the most generous and understanding foster mother. To the child, however, Lydia's involuntary rigid appearance, the sedentary life spent on sofas and chaise longues which her frailty forced her to adopt, was unusual, and often caused her to be shy. Cucly was of an excitable nature; she kept kicking her legs in the air whenever she heard the beat of a dance tune and would turn somersaults and do all kinds of exercises to keep her body supple. In brief, she continued the existence she had led in the midst of the ballet-corps. She was not attracted to luxury either; often after dinner, where she had turned her nose up at the food she had just nibbled at, she would take a piece of bread and go out and munch it alone as she lounged about in the garden. Her opulent life was short-lived, however; for with the German invasion of Poland, Jablonsky took refuge in Rumania with his wife and Cucly.

"This is my story, Sir," concluded the porter, ex-count Jablonsky, fastening a rubber band round one of his legs. "I'm off to get a gas cylinder."

That same day, Cucly, walking into the large drawing room, suddenly asked the architect, who was convalescing in bed after his operation, "Would you like me to dance for you, Mr. Ioanide?"

"Why, I should be delighted," replied the architect.

Cucly, who had come equipped with a bag, like a professional, pulled out two dancing slippers and an immense ball of white foam, which proved to be a tulle skirt (without the classical tutu and tights), for a fantasy ballet turn. She flung herself into an armchair, kicked her shoes off and put on her pointed dancing shoes. Then, walking over to the fireplace, where her figure outlined across the room appeared to Ioanide a pure and sublimated form, she pulled her dress off over her head without the slightest embarrassment and remained in a thin white bathing costume that slightly compressed her breasts and barely covered her hips. Her kneecaps were large, the muscles of her legs sinewy and supple, her stomach so scooped that the pelvic bones were precisely outlined. On the whole it was the articulation of her body that stood out more clearly, the flesh appearing rather like a network of twisted chords strung to be set in motion. Every part of her body taken separately was uncomely; the entire picture, however, was rendered fascinating by its union of irregular gracefulness. Cucly pulled on her airy kilt that looked like a lampshade, and fastened the hooks behind. Then she picked out a record, putting it on the player. It was the waltz from Gounod's *Faust*, the *Walpurgisnacht*.

Cucly stood waiting. With one leg resting on a single rigid toe, she was like a bird ready to soar to the skies, and at the first bar of the waltz she leaped forward upon a wave of air, stretching her arms wide and tossing her hair back. She floated for a moment and then alighted on the points of her toes, slightly touching the parquet floor as though the air—become miraculously ponderous, dense and elastic as water—prevented her from dropping to the ground, allowing her only to touch the floor with the tips of her toes, swelling the umbrella of her tulle skirt. She danced the waltz, gliding down the whole length of the room, stopping for a pirouette when the impression of a whirl had to be underlined, waving her arms wide, and then concluded her movements with deep curtseys and bows to the right and left. The insignificant littly Cucly, in her flight, became an air-maiden, metamorphosed into a wondrous bird escaped from her cage. What moved Ioanide in particular was the unexpected expression that not only came over her countenance but over her entire body during the dance. Cucly spoke with her arms and legs, revealing the elasticity of the air and picturing unseen geometrical figures; she turned musical values into movements disclosing her consummate power of expression. Her face was rounded and aflame, her unreddened lips became voluptuous and moist, her head fell coyly or defiantly over one shoulder then over the other, her arms and legs plunged into the air, roused to a tempest. Cucly, who in her daily talk uttered nothing but shallow commonplaces, proved in dancing to possess a spirited body that responded to Ioanide's architectural concepts and was able to analyze and render the most delicate shades of feeling. Cucly was talking to Ioanide in her own language, a language in which she was able to convey her comprehension of his dreams of reaching the skies, filling empty space with buildings like jeux d'eaux, proving that everything stems from music and geometry, transcribing in choreographic volutes the deep essence of life. When the waltz was over and the phonograph clicked off, Cucly, who had glided up to Ioanide's bed, sank to the floor in utter prostration, her skirt spread around her like a bell of foam.

"Do you like my dancing?" she asked with eager curiosity.

"You are a second Fanny Elssler!" the architect replied.

Flushed with excitement, Cucly rose to her feet and walked again to the far end of the drawing room.

"I shall dance for you to a Campanella by Paganini. I love to interpret all music, even if it is not written for a ballet."

She started the record. The music that Cucly had chosen without turning the record over was a violin piece of virtuosity, with numerous pizzicatos, measures played saltato with vibrating and forceful flourishes of the bow. Cucly trod with minute steps on the point of her toes according to the quantitative value of every note, gracefully raising her leg at a rallentando and leaping buoyantly into the air on the long bars, simulating through gestures the notations on the stave, thus tracing an airy picture of the musical text. When she advanced gingerly on tiptoe, Cucly became a vertical line, then, as cautiously as an acrobat on a tight rope, she kept her balance with her arms raised to avoid an obstacle in her slippery path. When she depicted arched bridges over the parquet, she would spread her arms sideways, as if she were floating on liquid, rise or sink quickly or slowly to the musical passage piano or forte. The point of her toe, in particular, marked every movement of the bow, pricking the parquet floor when the violinist played with the tip of his bow, and unfolding her whole compass when the bow glided all its length down to its heel. Thus did Cucly interpret the Campanella with her legs, ending on her knees beside Ioanide's bedstead.

The architect gazed at her searchingly. Her platinum blonde hair, with its scattered red highlights, was not combed, but spread irregularly like the bushy coarse mane of an adolescent who had not had a haircut for some time. Her eyes—it was only now that he noticed them—were blue, like his own, and her cheeks were stained with red dabs that seemed splashes from a painter's brush. Her rougeless lips were slightly chapped, crude in their voluptuousness. There was a gap between her front teeth. Her physiognomy was roughly that of an impulsive, playful imp, devoid of the customary restraints, a face remarkably ingenuous in its innocent savagery. Prompted by the simple need of expressing his inner feeling, Ioanide stretched out his left arm and ran his hand through the girl's ruffled hair. Her eyes sparkling with emotion, Cucly caught hold of the architect's hand, which was resting closed upon the blanket, and raising his heavy fist between her tiny palms, kissed it with fiery passion. Taken by surprise, Ioanide hastily withdrew both hands.

"Whom do you plan to marry?" he asked another day just to make conversation, "a fellow artist from the stage world or a man outside your profession? I often wonder what the dreams of a ballerina are."

"I don't intend marrying anyone," said Cucly. "I have decided not to marry at all."

"Why is that?"

"Because I don't want to."

"Do you hate men? A ballerina-nun sounds highly interesting. A chaste dancer would be quite a sensation."

"Not at all. I don't hate men. Who ever told you that?" Ioanide noticed the familiar tone that had slipped into her sentence. "I told you I don't want to get married. I want to be a free woman, free to dance, and free to love whomever I like and as long as I like."

"No one prevents you from marrying the man you love."

"Yes, but suppose he's married."

"Well, that's another matter. So then you love a man who is not free."

"I didn't say so, but it may happen."

The ballerina's gaze wandered.

"Do you know what the man I'd love must be like?" said Cucly one day to Ioanide, as she was sitting on the edge of his bed. "He must not be young, but must be a great man, powerful, famous, with white hair . . . a man I should be afraid of."

"Well, in that case," said Ioanide jokingly, "that rules me out. My hair is not white enough."

"Not at all, certainly not!" Cucly hastened to contradict, vexed by the distorted conclusion. "Lord, what a stupid ignorant fool I am! I never manage to say things right! I'd better dance something for you."

This time, as she had no tulle skirt on, Cucly danced Liszt's transcription of Schubert's Valsecapriccio in A major in her simple print dress and barefoot, with a simulated partner who floated in the air a few inches above the floor. She spun crazily all around the room, her dress billowing over her thin sinewy thighs, until she dropped, breathless, on the edge of Ioanide's bed.

"The man I'd love," she cried panting, "should have to be like you."

His first reaction was an instinctive recoil at her unexpected familiarity. He had however little time to reflect, for on his lips he felt a long and fiery pressure: Cucly was kissing him. The gesture had been so unexpected that Ioanide raised his right arm and put it around the girl's waist.

"Duckie!" exclaimed Cucly in a whisper, voicing her gratification with the architect's response.

But Ioanide, recovering his self-control, could not refrain from reacting to the inanity of the word "Duckie." The first idea that flashed across his mind was that Cucly was a girl of the loosest morals. When, however, Cucly raised her eyes full of candor and respect, he instantly revised his opinion.

From that day on, when she was alone with the architect, Cucly called him in turn "Mister" or by his Christian name, crossing uncertainly the boundary between ceremony and familiarity, sprinkled with that irksome appellation of "Duckie." In other people's presence, however, her tone was formal and respectful.

"Cucly," asked Ioanide, still at a loss to make her out, "Have you known any man up to now? Tell me the truth."

"I've nothing to hide! I know all kinds of men. I live amongst people. I'm no hermit."

"I don't mean that. What I mean is whether you ever kissed other men the way you kissed me."

Cucly surveyed Ioanide with her clear blue eyes.

"No, Duckie, how could I?"

"But you were able to do it with me."

"But then, you . . . I love!"

Cucly uttered these words like a woman with great experience in love affairs; and yet Ioanide felt she was not aware of the true value of the words but simply enjoyed uttering passionate declarations.

"Why do you keep on saying 'Duckie' all the time?"

"That's how the boys and girls talk at the ballet-corps."

Cucly would occasionally kiss Ioanide's hand like a respectful daughter, and then suddenly she would wrap her arms around his neck and smother him with kisses.

"If you wish to love me," she said to the architect, "I'll come whenever you choose, and I'll be no trouble to you. I've always dreamt of being the mistress of a man like you."

"Let's be serious," said Ioanide. "I see that in your artist's world, you have a rather bold way of expressing yourself."

"We express what we feel. But maybe, Sir, you don't love me!"

"I don't know whether I love you or not; or rather, I don't quite know whether I should."

"Why shouldn't you?"

"Because you are too young and I too old, and because your father would be grieved if this were to happen.

"Father would have no objection."

"How do you know?"

"Because he loves me and because I told him."

Ioanide stared at her in alarm.

"You told him what?"

"That I like you!"

"What an expression! What can you like in me?"

"I told him I loved you."

"And what did he say to that?"

"He stroked my hair."

A feeling of embarrassment came over Ioanide when he came face to face with Jablonsky again.

"Your daughter Cucly," he forced himself to say innocently, "is an exceptionally gifted dancer and charming in her naivete."

"Her education is very incomplete," remarked the porter gravely, "but she's got a pure heart, and she's capable of great feelings."

The tone of Jablonsky's words betrayed no suspicion of the intimacy between the architect and Cucly; and soon after he passed on to another subject.

"Sir," said Cucly a few days later, in a tone of utmost deference, "please don't be angry with me. I know I am a bit crazy, and I do all kinds of foolish things."

"Butterflies are crazy too, Cucly. A little folly is the privilege of all great artists. As a matter of fact it is not folly, it is an unusual excitement, a shift or a shunt in the electricity."

Cucly gazed at Ioanide with the extraordinary candor that her blue eyes so strongly expressed. Sophisticated words always roused in her a feeling of religious humility.

"How beautifully you speak! How clearly you understand everything! I am never able to find the right words. For me it's easier to say things by dancing."

And whistling a tune Cucly jumped off the bed and began to spin around in pirouettes in the large drawing room. Just then Mini, Ioanide's secretary, came in. She looked at the young girl with her accustomed calm and mild air and seemed pleasantly surprised at the sight of the young Jablonsky girl dancing.

"I hear you've been dancing. Won't you dance for me too?"

Ioanide cast an inquiring glance at Mini's smiling face. But Mini then sat down in an armchair, eagerly waiting for Cucly to put the record on and begin to dance. Cucly knew that Mini was fond of Handel's music so she picked out at random one of the composer's airs, an *andante quasi adagio* from a violin concerto. After a few moments of hesitation, during which she searched for a choreographic idea, Cucly began to move with lingering, floating steps, swaying and revolving on the tips of her toes with such slowness as to express the amplitude of every long note, ending with the grave finale which she performed with deep curtseys, slow genuflections, and wide arc-like openings of the arms.

When the dance came to an end Mini congratulated her. "You're like a butterfly!" she said, unknowingly repeating the architect's simile.

During the dance Ioanide had watched the two young women and had weighed their charms. He was unable to decide whose was the greater. Cucly dancing was a sublime physical phenomenon, like the spirited play of a fountain or the flashing flight of a swallow skimming the surface of a pool. She reflected, as a total image, a moment of art, an intense, complete, overwhelming expression of a sentiment. Seen thus, Cucly was unique. Mini, on the other hand, in her contemplation, was the picture of an angel radiating felicity and gentleness, a being real and yet so fragile that one feared to approach her lest she should vanish into the mist. When Cucly sank into an armchair facing Mini, the comparison between the two was even more striking. Cucly, with her hair ruffled, her parched lips, with beads of perspiration on her brow, continued to be, in herself, an original creature; and yet Mini with her calm and self-control easily carried the palm. The sensitivity printed in the lines of her puckered brow and the tremor of her face was borne out even more vividly in the sparkling intelligence of her eyes. Her words, too, reflected without effort the realities she perceived.

"Miss Cucly," she said "does not dance: she floats. I had the feeling that I was seeing Handel's music unfold before my very eyes."

Of course Mini's utterances were not exceptionally original and yet one realized she was true to herself and capable of grasping the emotions of others. Ioanide felt that she sensed all the struggle and contradictions present in his soul and that, whatever he would do, she would not judge the gesture as such, but as an integral part of the manifestations of the complex personality of the man she admired. If the architect were, for instance, to kiss her, he was confident that Mini would not be shocked nor would find the gesture shameless, but—with the tolerant understanding for a man from whom she admitted everything—she would mildly push him lightly away, as if he were a child and would playfully remind him: "No, Sir, you must not make any violent movements; remember what the doctor said."

Mini would never dream of calling him "Duckie."

Now that the dance was over, Cucly sat listlessly and uneasily in her chair, like a medusa cast on the sands. Her legs with their large kneecaps and sinewy muscles were ungraceful and her feet, crooked in high-heeled shoes, looked ungainly. Her creative *élan* was gone and the girl sat crouched in her armchair, sulky and embarrassed. Mini sensed her frame of mind and sought to restore the excitement of the dancer. "You'll soon be building that new great theater hall, Mr. Ioanide, and Miss Cucly will then find the proper abode to live her airy existence."

* * *

For a long while after, Ioanide lay musing, picturing Cucly in her two guises: dancing and sitting next to Mini. He dreamed of her as a large butterfly, flying with her tulle wings over his bed and swooping down to kiss his lips. He would stretch out his hands to clasp her in his arms, but her wings would drop off—a tangled bundle of rags—and before his eyes would rise the other Cucly, the sad little girl, with dishevelled hair, with freckles on her face and parched lips.

The next day, when Cucly came to see him, he caught her roughly by the hair, and gazing deep into her blue eyes, he drew her to him and pressed his mouth on her lips that were almost blood red, cracked by the wind.

"Count Jablonsky," cried Ioanide, when the porter entered the drawing room a short while after—and alluding to the transfusion but with the memory of the kiss fresh in his mind—"Polish blood now runs in my veins too."